Folens

GCSE Applied Science

DOUBLE AWARD

Colin Bell • David Brodie • Byron Dawson • Ann Tiernan

Editor: **Joanne Mitchell**

About the authors

Colin Bell is a former Deputy Head of a comprehensive school. Previously he had been Head of Biology in grammar and comprehensive schools. Colin now works as a freelance author. He has long experience working with various awarding bodies as a Senior Examiner for GCSE in the UK and internationally.

David Brodie has been Head of Science in a Midlands comprehensive school, a Senior Examiner and Moderator, and has worked for the Nuffield Foundation as editor of GCSE and GNVQ publications as well as for the British Association for the Advancement of Science. He is author of a wide range of educational resources across the whole range of the science curriculum.

Byron Dawson is a former Head of Science and is now an Assistant Head Teacher with responsibility for the curriculum in an 11–18 secondary school. He also works as a freelance author, and has written science textbooks for several publishers. Byron is also a Senior Examiner, with responsibilities for the assessment of GCSE Science and overseas 'A' level Biology examinations.

Ann Tiernan was a Head of Science in an 11–18 secondary school for many years. She now works as a freelance author, producing texts and Internet-based learning materials for use at key stages 3 and 4. She also works for awarding bodies as a Senior Examiner, managing the assessment of chemistry and science at GCSE and 'A' level both in the UK and abroad.

About the course

Welcome to GCSE in Applied Science (Double Award)

In this course you will be learning about science at work and in the world around you.

This course is made up of **three** units. These are:

Unit	Title	Type of Assessment
1	Developing Scientific Skills	Portfolio
2	Science for the Needs of Society	Externally tested
3	Science at Work	Portfolio

In your student book, *Theme 1 Introducing scientific skills* shows you how to work safely in science. It also introduces you to carrying out practical tasks.

Working through the topics within each theme will help you to gain the knowledge, skills and understanding you need for the course. It will also help you to prepare for your assessments, including your test for Unit 2.

Your teacher will be giving you practical work to do. Some of these practical activities will help you to understand the topics in your student book. They will also help you to develop practical skills that you will need for your assignments (practical assessments).

You will collect the assignments for assessment for Unit 1 and Unit 3 in a portfolio. You will have this work marked and graded by your teacher.

Throughout this book there are case studies telling you about science at work and in the world around you.

Theme 6 Science in the workplace gives you information about working in science that will be helpful for you to look at before doing the assignment on Science at Work for Unit 3.

We hope that you will enjoy using *Folens GCSE in Applied Science* and that it will help you to have an interest in science. We also hope you will be successful in your GCSE in Applied Science (Double Award).

Contents

Contents

How to use this book

The book is divided into Themes. These are shown in the contents.

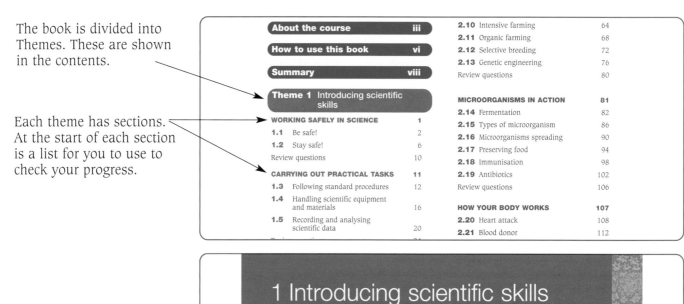

Each theme has sections. At the start of each section is a list for you to use to check your progress.

At the start of each section you will see a list of topics and where to find them.

This shows which assignments and practicals are linked to this section.

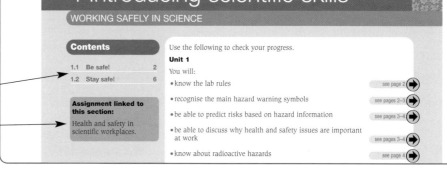

1 Introducing scientific skills

WORKING SAFELY IN SCIENCE

Contents

1.1 Be safe!   2
1.2 Stay safe!   6

Assignment linked to this section:

Health and safety in scientific workplaces.

Use the following to check your progress.

Unit 1

You will:

- know the lab rules — see page 2
- recognise the main hazard warning symbols — see pages 2–5
- be able to predict risks based on hazard information — see pages 3–4
- be able to discuss why health and safety issues are important at work — see pages 3–4
- know about radioactive hazards — see page 4

Key words are shown in **bold type** and some have word check boxes to tell you what they mean.

Extra material for those working at a higher level is shown with a tint of yellow behind it.

Answering these questions will check your understanding of what you have read.

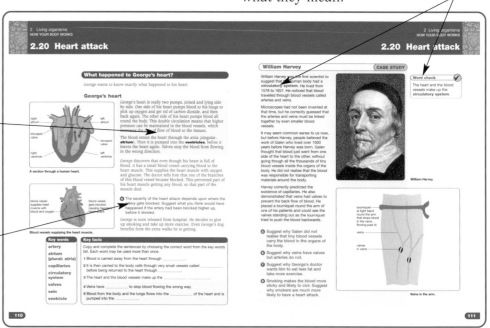

How to use this book

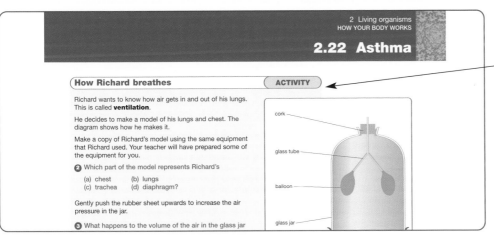

Doing the activities will help you to develop knowledge, skills and understanding.

2 Living organisms
HOW YOUR BODY WORKS

2.22 Asthma

How Richard breathes   ACTIVITY

Richard wants to know how air gets in and out of his lungs. This is called **ventilation**.

He decides to make a model of his lungs and chest. The diagram shows how he makes it.

Make a copy of Richard's model using the same equipment that Richard used. Your teacher will have prepared some of the equipment for you.

2 Which part of the model represents Richard's

(a) chest   (b) lungs
(c) trachea   (d) diaphragm?

Gently push the rubber sheet upwards to increase the air pressure in the jar.

3 What happens to the volume of the air in the glass jar

cork
glass tube
balloon
glass jar

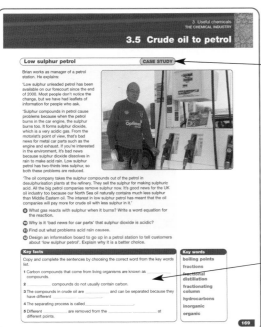

Case studies show people working in science or science being used in everyday life.

3 Useful chemicals
THE CHEMICAL INDUSTRY

3.5 Crude oil to petrol

Low sulphur petrol   CASE STUDY

Brian works as manager of a petrol station. He explains:

'Low sulphur unleaded petrol has been available on our forecourt since the end of 2000. Most people don't notice the change, but we have had leaflets of information for people who ask.

'Sulphur compounds in petrol cause problems because when the petrol burns in the car engine, the sulphur burns too. It forms sulphur dioxide, which is a very acidic gas. From the motorist's point of view, that's bad news for metal car parts such as the engine and exhaust. If you're interested in the environment, it's bad news because sulphur dioxide dissolves in rain to make acid rain. Low sulphur petrol has two-thirds less sulphur, so both these problems are reduced.

'The oil company takes the sulphur compounds out of the petrol in desulphurisation plants at the refinery. They sell the sulphur for making sulphuric acid. All the big petrol companies remove sulphur now. It's good news for the UK oil industry too because our North Sea oil naturally contains much less sulphur than Middle Eastern oil. The interest in low sulphur petrol has meant that the oil companies will pay more for crude oil with less sulphur in it.'

8 What gas reacts with sulphur when it burns? Write a word equation for the reaction.

9 Why is it 'bad news for car parts' that sulphur dioxide is acidic?

10 Find out what problems acid rain causes.

11 Design an information board to go up in a petrol station to tell customers about 'low sulphur petrol'. Explain why it is a better choice.

Key facts

Copy and complete the sentences by choosing the correct word from the key words list.

1 Carbon compounds that come from living organisms are known as _____ compounds.

2 _____ compounds do not usually contain carbon.

3 The compounds in crude oil are _____ and can be separated because they have different _____.

4 The separating process is called _____.

5 Different _____ are removed from the _____ at different points.

Key words

boiling points
fractions
fractional distillation
fractionating column
hydrocarbons
inorganic
organic

169

Copying and completing the key facts boxes with key words will help your learning.

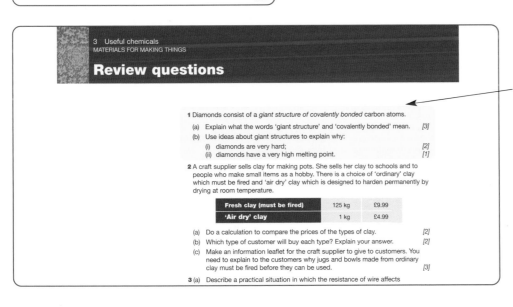

Answering these questions at the end of each section will help to prepare you for your course assessment. This includes your Unit 2 test.

3 Useful chemicals
MATERIALS FOR MAKING THINGS

Review questions

1 Diamonds consist of a *giant structure of covalently bonded* carbon atoms.

(a) Explain what the words 'giant structure' and 'covalently bonded' mean.   [3]

(b) Use ideas about giant structures to explain why:
(i) diamonds are very hard;   [2]
(ii) diamonds have a very high melting point.   [1]

2 A craft supplier sells clay for making pots. She sells her clay to schools and to people who make small items as a hobby. There is a choice of 'ordinary' clay which must be fired and 'air dry' clay which is designed to harden permanently by drying at room temperature.

| Fresh clay (must be fired) | 125 kg | £9.99 |
| 'Air dry' clay | 1 kg | £4.99 |

(a) Do a calculation to compare the prices of the types of clay.   [2]
(b) Which type of customer will buy each type? Explain your answer.   [2]
(c) Make an information leaflet for the craft supplier to give to customers. You need to explain to the customers why jugs and bowls made from ordinary clay must be fired before they can be used.   [3]

3 (a) Describe a practical situation in which the resistance of wire affects

Summary

Summary of where you are covering Units 1, 2 and 3 in this Student Book

Further coverage is provided in the assignments, practical activities, reference sheets and practice tests in the Teachers' Support Pack.

Topic		Unit 1	Unit 2	Unit 3	Topic		Unit 1	Unit 2	Unit 3
	Theme 1 *Introducing scientific skills*				3.3	Salt from rock salt		•	
1.1	Be safe!	•			3.4	Iron and steel		•	
1.2	Stay safe!	•			3.5	Crude oil to petrol		•	
1.3	Following standard procedures	•			3.6	Bulk and fine chemicals		•	•
1.4	Handling scientific equipment and materials	•			3.7	Making ammonia		•	•
1.5	Recording and analysing scientific data	•			3.8	Putting numbers into industry		•	•
	Theme 2 *Living organisms*				3.9	Mixtures everywhere		•	
2.1	Cells	•	•		3.10	Splitting the atom		•	
2.2	Diffusion	•	•		3.11	Making salts			•
2.3	Osmosis	•	•		3.12	Chemical analysis	•		
2.4	Characteristics		•		3.13	More about molecules		•	
2.5	Cells dividing		•		3.14	Energy and chemical change		•	
2.6	Inheritance		•		3.15	Bricks		•	
2.7	Photosynthesis	•	•	•	3.16	Polymers		•	
2.8	Exchange of gases	•	•	•	3.17	Electrical behaviour	•	•	
2.9	Minerals	•	•	•	3.18	Physical properties	•	•	
2.10	Intensive farming	•	•	•		**Theme 4** *Energy and devices*			
2.11	Organic farming		•	•	4.1	Fuels and generators		•	
2.12	Selective breeding		•		4.2	Looking inside the body		•	
2.13	Genetic engineering		•		4.3	Nuclear and renewables		•	
2.14	Fermentation	•	•	•	4.4	Lighting power		•	
2.15	Types of microorganism	•	•		4.5	Heating for profit		•	
2.16	Microorganisms spreading		•		4.6	Cooling systems		•	
2.17	Preserving food		•		4.7	Road safety		•	
2.18	Immunisation		•		4.8	Electronic life support			•
2.19	Antibiotics		•		4.9	Movement under control			•
2.20	Heart attack		•		4.10	Digital information			•
2.21	Blood donor		•		4.11	Lifting			•
2.22	Asthma		•		4.12	Gears			•
2.23	Aerobics		•	•		**Theme 5** *The Earth and universe*			
2.24	Oxygen debt		•	•	5.1	Our atmosphere		•	
2.25	Keeping warm	•	•		5.2	The Earth and the environment		•	
2.26	Diabetes		•		5.3	The Earth beneath our feet		•	
2.27	Cells and communication		•		5.4	Waves and communication		•	
2.28	Drugs and the body		•			**Theme 6** *Science in the workplace*			
	Theme 3 *Useful chemicals*				6.1	Working in science			•
3.1	Elements from the Earth		•						
3.2	Compounds from the Earth		•						

1 Introducing scientific skills

WORKING SAFELY IN SCIENCE

Assignment linked to this section:

Health and safety in scientific workplaces.

Use the following to check your progress.

Unit 1

You will:

- know the lab rules — see page 2

- recognise the main hazard warning symbols — see pages 2–3

- be able to predict risks based on hazard information — see pages 3–4

- be able to discuss why health and safety issues are important at work — see pages 3–4

- know about radioactive hazards — see page 4

- be able to plan to prevent accidents — see page 3

- know what to do if accidents happen in the lab — see pages 6–7

- be able to give basic first aid — see page 7

- know when it would be dangerous to give first aid — see pages 6–7

- know why it is useful to have a first aid qualification — see pages 6–7

- know the names of the organisations which give training in first aid and how to contact them — see pages 6–7

- know what to do if you hear a fire or smoke alarm — see page 8

- know what to do if you find a fire — see page 8

- know how fire doors function — see page 8

- know how to use the different kinds of fire extinguisher — see page 8

- know about the use of automatic sprinkler systems. — see page 8

1.1 Be safe!

Safety at work

**DANGER OF DEATH
ELECTRICITY
KEEP OUT**

You probably know people who work in hazardous places such as building sites or hospitals. By law, employers have to make workplaces as safe as possible. One way of doing this is to have safe working rules for people to work to. Signs remind us what we are supposed to do.

Workplaces are full of warning signs.

Lab rules

LAB SAFETY RULES

I Tie long hair back when using a Bunsen burner

2 Always

Safety poster.

Look at a copy of the safety rules for your own lab. Your rules probably contain advice about:

- behaving safely to prevent accidents
- safe use of hazardous equipment such as Bunsen burners
- when to use safety equipment such as goggles
- reporting accidents.

1 Look at the poster. Choose one of your own lab rules. Draw a similar cartoon to warn people what might happen if they ignore it.

2 Look at the photographs at the top of the page.

(a) Why do you think safety rules are often illustrated with simple pictures?

(b) Working as a group, design simple pictures to illustrate each of your own lab rules and display them around your lab.

3 Carry out a safety survey of your own lab. How are the furniture and flooring different to a normal classroom? What extra safety equipment is there? How many sinks, gas supplies and sockets are there? Where are the fire escape routes and fire extinguishers? Make a list of all the ways the lab has been adapted to make it safer for doing experiments.

1.1 Be safe!

Looking at risk   ACTIVITY

Working in science often involves a **hazard**. Science hazards are often shown by a hazard warning sign.

Word check

A **hazard** is a danger.

4 Work in groups. Research ONE of the hazard symbols each. Use books and Student Safety Sheets. For your hazard, find out:

- what harm your hazard can cause

- what you can do to keep safe when you are in contact with it

- what you should do in case of an accident.

Present your findings to the rest of the group. Make a table to summarise the class research on all the hazards.

5 Find out how hazardous chemicals are disposed of from your lab.

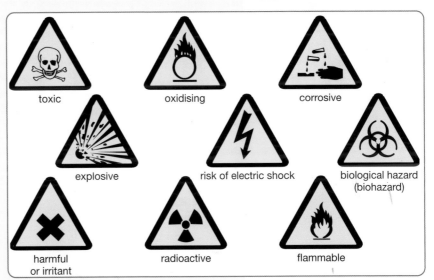

toxic   oxidising   corrosive

explosive   risk of electric shock   biological hazard (biohazard)

harmful or irritant   radioactive   flammable

Some hazard warning signs.

Hazards and risk assessments

How much **risk** is involved depends on the type of hazard and the person doing the work. For example, you probably have a sharp kitchen knife at home. The *hazard* is that it could cut someone very badly. How much *risk* there is depends on where it is kept and who can get hold of it, for example, a young child.

At work or during your course, a **risk assessment** will have to be carried out if you are using hazardous substances. For experiments, how much risk there is depends on:

- what you are going to do: for example, a flammable substance is only a high risk if you are using heat or flames in your experiment;

- the people involved: for example, some of the hazards you handle in your course must be kept out of the reach of younger students.

Look at these instructions for a chemistry experiment.

Put small amounts of the following metals into separate test tubes.
MAGNESIUM POWDER   ZINC POWDER   LEAD POWDER
Add DILUTE HYDROCHLORIC ACID to each test tube.

6 Look up the chemicals using Student Safety Sheets. Think about how to carry out this experiment as safely as possible. Copy and fill in the following table.

Material/ procedure	Hazard	What could go wrong	Safety precautions	In case of accident	Risk (high/ medium/low)

Word check

A **risk** is how likely it is that a hazard can cause harm.

Word check

Risk assessment is a statement of the risks and safety precautions for an experiment or procedure.

1.1 Be safe!

Health and safety at work

Health and safety checks are carried out in all workplaces.

You might feel that science labs are full of rules, but it's the same at work! Every workplace has a Health and Safety Representative who carries out checks to make sure that the buildings are safe, all the safety equipment is available, and that workers know the safety procedures.

Try to find out who is the Health and Safety Rep for your school or college. (It might be possible for them to come to talk to you.)

⑦ If you can arrange permission, interview your lab technician or someone from the Design and Technology department about their work.

(a) *Lab technician*: Find out about how the prep room is designed with safety in mind. What does he or she do to find out about the hazards? Write some questions in advance. Write a short report about 'Safety in the prep room'.

(b) *Design and Technology*: How are these risks different to science risks? What safety procedures are important here?

Working with radioactivity

A film badge for detecting radiation.

Some people have specific work hazards to deal with. Workers in nuclear power stations worry about risks from radioactivity. There is a maximum dose that is safe for a person to have each year.

Radioactive sources are always kept surrounded by lead, which absorbs the harmful rays. You may have been asked to wear a lead jacket if you have ever had an X-ray in hospital or at the dentist.

Some people work near radioactive sources all the time. They wear badges containing film that is sensitive to radioactivity (just as normal photo films are sensitive to light). The films are checked to make sure that the workers have not been exposed to too much radioactivity.

1.1 Be safe!

Transporting hazardous chemicals ⬤ CASE STUDY

Jack is a trainee firefighter. He explains:

'By law, any vehicle carrying hazardous chemicals has to show hazard warning signs. We know how to deal with a spill by looking at the label. The symbols are understood by fire services all over the world.

'The labels tell us what fire extinguishers to use, what protective clothing to wear, and whether we need to think about evacuating people from around the spill. Sometimes we can dilute the spillage, which means we can clear it up by washing it away with lots of water. Really nasty stuff has to be contained – we surround it with sandbags and pump it up into containers we can seal. The sealed waste gets buried in safe sites.'

Jack wears full body protective clothing to deal with a chemical spill.

Key to the symbols used in the hazard warning signs on vehicles

P	V	FULL	DILUTE
R			
S	V	BA	
T			
W	V	FULL	CONTAIN
X			
Y	V	BA	
Z			

Fire extinguisher

1 JETS 3 FOAM
2 FOG   4 DRY AGENT

V   Chemical may react violently.
BA   Breathing apparatus
FULL   Full body protection
E   CONSIDER EVACUATION

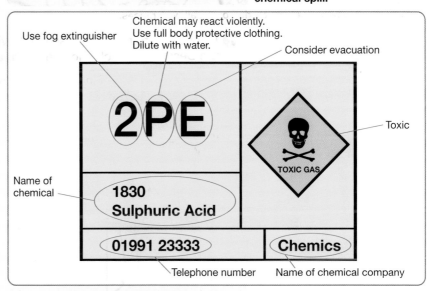

Use fog extinguisher

Chemical may react violently.
Use full body protective clothing.
Dilute with water.

Consider evacuation

Toxic

Name of chemical

1830
Sulphuric Acid

01991 23333

Chemics

Telephone number   Name of chemical company

8 What would the firefighters do if these chemicals were spilled?

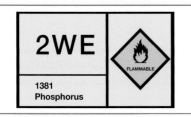

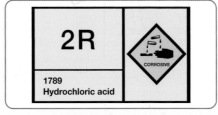

9 How does Jack say that 'really nasty' chemicals are disposed?
Find out how your school or college disposes of waste chemicals.

1.2 Stay safe!

First aid

Morris is a volunteer in the St John Ambulance Service. The service provides both first aid and high quality training. Your school will probably have at least one 'First Aider' who has been trained and passed examinations run by the St John Ambulance Service or the Red Cross. Training is rigorous. Morris has to retake his examination every three years in order to keep up to date with new developments. Imagine having to retake your GCSE examinations every three years, to keep them up to date.

1 Why do 'First Aiders' have to retake their examination every three years?

Common laboratory injuries

How many hazards can you spot in this lab?

Laboratories can be dangerous places. Don't worry: science teachers are safety conscious. This means there are not many accidents in science labs. We can make them even safer if we know what the risks are and what accidents are likely to happen.

These are some of the most common laboratory accidents:

- Burns: including heat burns from hot tripods, or scalds from boiling water in a beaker. Some chemicals such as strong acids or alkalis can burn the skin.

- Breathing in fumes or swallowing chemicals.

- Electric shock: most labs are now fitted with special devices that switch off the current to prevent serious injury.

- Cuts: handling glassware can lead to breakages. The sharp edges of the glass cut skin easily.

- Damage to the eyes: you probably get fed up with the number of times your teacher tells you to wear safety specs. Blindness lasts for the rest of your life.

It is possible that you have never seen an accident in a laboratory in all your years at school. This is because teachers follow the safety procedures carefully. But sometimes an accident does happen. When it does, you need to know what to do.

2 What are the most common accidents in a school laboratory?

1.2 Stay safe!

Giving first aid | ACTIVITY

Imagine there is an accident in the laboratory. Would you know what to do? Probably not – many people just panic. That is not only bad for the injured person, it could also be disastrous for the rest of the class. The first thing to remember is that you are probably not a qualified First Aider. It is no good trying to help if you do not know what you are doing. Get help from the teacher or technician as fast as it is safe.

Giving a first aid talk to the class

Look at the previous page. It has a list of the most common accidents that happen in school laboratories. They are burns, poisons and fumes, electric shock, cuts and damage to eyes.

Prepare a talk that you could give to the rest of the class.

You should start your talk with:

1. Why it is useful to have first aid qualifications.

2. The names of organisations, such as the St John Ambulance Service, that give training for first aid qualifications and how they can be contacted: www.sja.org.uk or www.redcross.org.

Take each injury in turn and explain how you would do each of the following:

1. Give basic first aid.

2. Decide when it would be dangerous to give first aid. Many people are electrocuted when they try to help someone who has had an electric shock. They forget to switch off the electricity first.

Giving a talk on first aid.

Tips to improve your talk

• Make notes on each of the above numbered points.

• Produce some overheads and use an overhead projector. Better still, use a video projector and a software package such as Microsoft Powerpoint.

• Keep it short – about ten minutes will do.

• Be prepared for questions afterwards.

3 Why should students know about basic first aid procedures in the laboratory?

1.2 Stay safe!

Fire prevention

Another aspect of laboratory safety is the prevention of fires. Very few fires occur in school labs. The vast majority of injuries caused by fires happen at home. Surprisingly, school is a safer place to be than at home.

Why are schools so safe?

1 **Fire practice.** Schools have a fire practice at least once every term. When the alarm bell sounds, students know that they stop work – put down equipment – and proceed quietly and in an orderly way down to the 'safety area', usually the school yard. A safety area is a collection point where everybody goes to in the event of a fire. A register is taken to make sure everyone has got out of the building safely.

4 Look at the wall of the laboratory. There should be a poster telling you what to do in the event of a fire. It will include a diagram of the safety area and how to get there. Make a copy of the poster to keep in your file.

2 **Finding a fire.** Schools are fitted with fire alarms. These are activated by breaking the glass in the small red emergency fire alarm boxes that are situated all around the school. In the event of fire, break the glass and proceed to the 'safety area'.

5 Unlike accidents, why may you not need to tell a member of staff that there is a fire?

3 **Fire doors.** Fire doors are thick heavy doors that prevent fire from spreading, but only if they are shut. It is sometimes tempting to leave them open. This will allow a fire to spread. They close automatically and should be allowed to do so at all times.

6 Why should fire doors not be propped open?

4 **Fire extinguishers and fire blankets.** School labs can have different kinds of fires. Each kind of fire should be dealt with by the appropriate fire extinguisher. Different types of extinguisher for putting out a fire include water, carbon dioxide, dry powder, foam or a fire blanket.

7 Under what conditions would you use each of these devices? (Look on the extinguisher label for information.)

8 Why would it not be a good idea to use a water extinguisher on a fire caused by an electrical fault?

5 **Sprinklers.** Automatic sprinkler systems are sometimes installed. The heat from the fire turns them on automatically.

A carbon dioxide fire extinguisher.

1.2 Stay safe!

Morris the First Aider CASE STUDY

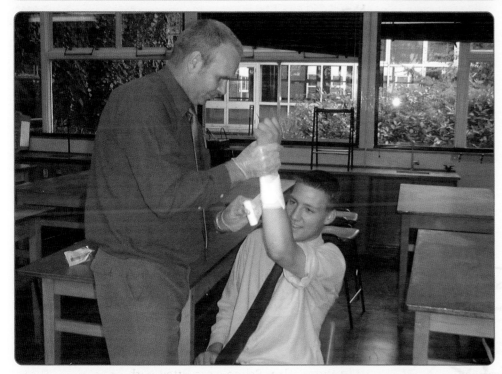

Morris gives first aid to a boy who has cut his arm.

Morris is a teacher in a large secondary school. He has been a First Aider for many years. He trains other people who want to get the St. John Ambulance First Aid Certificate. He sometimes has to carry out first aid. First aid is about doing your best and weighing up the risks. A golden rule is 'do no harm'. This also means 'do not harm yourself'. Morris would be no good to the casualty if he became injured as well. He must remain calm and handle his patient with confidence. There are guidelines that he must follow:

- assess a situation quickly; check safety for himself, the casualty, any bystanders, and summon appropriate help.

- identify as far as possible the injury or the illness affecting the casualty.

- give early, appropriate and adequate treatment in a sensible order of priority.

- arrange for the movement of the casualty to hospital, to the care of a doctor or home.

- remain with the casualty until handing them over to the care of an appropriate person.

- make and pass on a report and give further help if required.

9 Why should Morris not give first aid until he knows that it is safe for him to do so?

10 Can you think of TWO examples of cases in which a First Aider might be injured when giving first aid?

11 What should Morris do first when he gets to an accident?

12 Why must Morris remain calm and handle his patient with confidence?

Review questions

1 Ella has been offered a holiday job. She is going to use a sprayer to spray weeds. Her job involves:

  • mixing a tin of toxic weedkiller with water from a hose in a plastic backpack.

  • carrying the backpack across fields and fences.

  • spraying the weedkiller on the weeds.

The job is very well paid, but Ella is worried about the safety of the work.

(a)   The weedkiller is toxic. What risks are there in carrying out each stage of Ella's job?   [3]

(b)   What safety equipment do you think Ella should use?   [3]

(c)   What information should Ella ask the farmer before she accepts the job?   [2]

2 Morris is a St. John Ambulance First Aider. He is called to an accident in a school laboratory. Philip has cut his arm on some sharp broken glass.

(a)   Explain the procedure that Morris goes through when handling a first aid incident.   [6]

(b)   Describe the basic first aid that Morris should give.   [4]

(c)   Describe some other common injuries that can occur in a school laboratory.   [4]

(d)   Philip decided that he also wants to be a First Aider. Name two organisations that train First Aiders and research their website addresses.   [2]

1 Introducing scientific skills

CARRYING OUT PRACTICAL TASKS

Contents

Assignments and practical activities linked to this section:

All of them link to this section.

Use the following to check your progress.

Unit 1

You will:

- know how to read a standard procedure and carry it out see pages 12–15

- be able to carry out a Health and Safety check of your working area see pages 13–15

- be able to carry out a risk assessment see pages 13–15

- be able to follow instructions see pages 12–15

- be able to identify standard laboratory equipment see page 16

- be able to organise your work area and obtain the appropriate equipment see pages 16–18

- be able to calibrate instruments see page 17

- be able to make accurate observations and measurements using appropriate equipment including data logging equipment see pages 17–18

- be able to identify sources of error and improve the reliability of your experiments see pages 20–21

- be able to present data in a variety of forms see pages 20–23

- be able to carry out simple calculations see page 21

- be able to analyse and interpret results see page 23

- be able to evaluate investigations and suggest improvements. see page 23

1.3 Following standard procedures

Laura and Sacha go on work experience

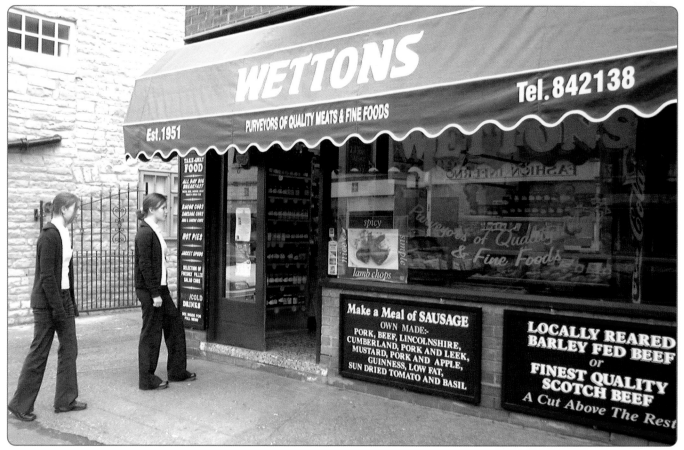

Laura and Sacha are about to start work experience. They are going to spend a fortnight working with Andy the butcher in his shop. They know that working in a butcher's shop has to be treated seriously. Cleanliness and handling meat correctly are very important. Andy does not want any of his customers to get food poisoning. Andy tells the girls that he has standard procedures in his shop. **Standard procedures** are instructions that everyone who works in the shop must follow.

Andy explains that the standard procedures that he uses in his shop were agreed by all his staff. They were written specifically for his shop so that any new staff who are employed will immediately know what to do and how to do it correctly. He tells them that all large companies use standard procedures, especially if they are doing research and carrying out practical experiments. This means that when other people see the results, they know exactly how the observations and measurements were made.

Andy tells the girls that there are standard procedures for each of the following in his shop:

- using dangerous equipment, such as the bacon slicer;
- handling raw uncooked meat;
- handling cooked meat;
- cleaning down work surfaces and equipment.

1.3 Following standard procedures

Standard procedures in the laboratory

When carrying out a standard procedure, these are the things that you should always do.

1 Read the instructions. Always read the instructions and make sure that you understand them. If there is anything that you do not understand, you should always ask. It is much safer to ask even simple questions, than to start work and make a serious mistake.

2 Carry out a Health and Safety check of the area. Never start work until it is safe to do so. When you are carrying out experiments at school, your teacher will always make sure that the laboratory is safe before you start. How often have you been told to put your bags underneath the table to prevent someone else from falling over?

3 Carry out a risk assessment. A risk assessment involves thinking about what could go wrong and what you would do if it did. Teachers have to carry out risk assessments every time you do a practical experiment. If the experiment involves using a Bunsen burner, they need to know where the mains gas tap is, and what to do if someone burns themselves.

4 Collect the materials and equipment that you need. When you do an experiment at school, you always get the equipment ready first and set out your work area. Halfway through the experiment is not the time to decide that you need something else. Good and safe experimental work involves good planning.

5 Follow the instructions one step at a time. Once you have read and understood the instructions, you should follow them one step at a time. Do not try to read them and then do everything from memory. You will possibly do something wrong or get things in the wrong order.

6 Make accurate observations or measurements. These should always be taken carefully and written down. You may think that you will remember them but you will soon forget. Make sure that you choose instruments that are appropriate and give the precision you need. It is no good choosing a 500 cm^3 measuring cylinder if you want to measure 0.5 cm^3 of water.

7 Identify sources of error and repeat the procedure if necessary. Even the most careful scientists make mistakes. However, good scientists can spot the things that will make the results less accurate than they should be. Then they try to make improvements to their experiment to get more accurate results next time. If you plot your results as a graph, look for points that are a long way from the line of best fit. These can sometimes reveal a source of error.

It is also a good idea to repeat experiments and calculate the mean (average) of your results. This will make your results much more reliable.

1.3 Following standard procedures

Standard procedures in Andy's butcher's shop

You must follow standard procedures when using the bacon slicer.

Using the bacon slicer

Andy asks Laura and Sacha to write a standard procedure for using the bacon slicer. This is what they write:

- Read the instructions for using the bacon slicer. They are stuck on the wall above the machine.

- Make sure that the area around the bacon slicer is clear and there is nothing on the floor that could make you trip and fall onto the machine. Make sure that you know where the first aid box is and never use the bacon slicer if you are alone in the shop.

- Make sure the bacon slicer is switched off when not in use and that the plug is removed from the wall. Ensure the blade is clean and the guard is in good working order.

- Make sure that the bacon is ready to hand and you have sufficient wrapping paper.

- You are now ready to start.
  Wash your hands. Place the bacon on the machine. Check the guard is closed. Switch on the machine. Start to cut the slices.

- Show the first slice to the customer to check that it is the correct thickness. The dial on the side of the machine can be set at the appropriate measurement.

Divide a sheet of A4 paper in half by drawing a vertical line down the middle, or use the template provided. Label the left-hand side 'Standard procedures' and make a list each of the procedures listed on page 13. Label the right-hand side 'Using a bacon slicer'. Look at Laura and Sacha's standard procedure and copy each statement by writing it next to the standard procedure list on the left-hand side.

The first one has been done for you.

Standard procedures	Using a bacon slicer
1 Read the instructions	They are on the wall above the machine.
2	....
3	....
....	....

1 Suggest how you could improve Laura and Sacha's standard procedure.

2 Why does Andy use standard procedures for his bacon slicer?

Weighing the bacon

Andy tells the students that they must then weigh the meat to work out how much to charge the customer. The girls want to know how Andy keeps his scales accurate. He tells them that they are regularly checked by a Weights and Measures Inspector. The inspector has a very accurate set of weights. He places them on Andy's scales. If the scales are wrong, they can be **calibrated** so that they read the weights more accurately.

1.3 Following standard procedures

Back in the school laboratory

Laura and Sacha realise that the knowledge they gained from their work experience should also be used when carrying out an experiment in the school laboratory. Their teacher explains to them that all scientists who work for companies need to use standard procedures to ensure they use exactly the same procedure each time. This means that when someone else sees the results, they know exactly how the observations and measurements were made.

Think of a recent experiment that you have carried out, in which you needed to measure something.

You are going to design a standard procedure for the experiment. Use the same headings that you used for the previous activity and write down next to each heading what you need to consider.

Look at the following points. They will help you to think about what you need to write down for your standard procedure.

Checklist for writing standard procedures
Have the material to hand for writing the instructions. This would be a good opportunity to practise your word processing skills.

- **Carry out a Health and Safety check of the area.** Describe any hazards such as loose materials on the floor or bags left in dangerous places.

- **Carry out a risk assessment.** For example, what could possibly go wrong with the experiment and what would you do if it did? What would you do if a fire broke out? Where is the first aid kit and can you contact help if you need it? What clothing and safety equipment do you need? Copy and complete the table below.

RISK ASSESSMENT

Name of person/s carrying out activity ....……......

Type of practical ....….........….............

Date to be carried out ....….......

Material/ procedure	Hazard	What could go wrong	Safety precautions	In case of accident	Risk (high/ medium/low)

- **List the equipment needed for the experiment.**

- **Write instructions.** Write an exact list of steps that the experimenter needs to follow.

- **Observations or measurements.** What exact observations or measurements should be carried out? What instruments should be used?

- **Identify sources of error.** How should the experiment be evaluated? What can be done, if necessary, to make it more reliable?

1.4 Handling scientific equipment and materials

The field trip

Students set off on a field trip.

Laura and Sacha are about to go on a school field trip to a local pond. Their task is to collect water to perform a chemical analysis back in the lab. They will also monitor how the surface temperature and the temperature at the bottom of the pond change during the day, from the cool of the morning to the hot midday sun, and into the afternoon.

Choosing the apparatus

Laura and Sacha wonder what sort of apparatus they need to take to perform both of these tasks.

Their teacher shows them a range of different apparatus.

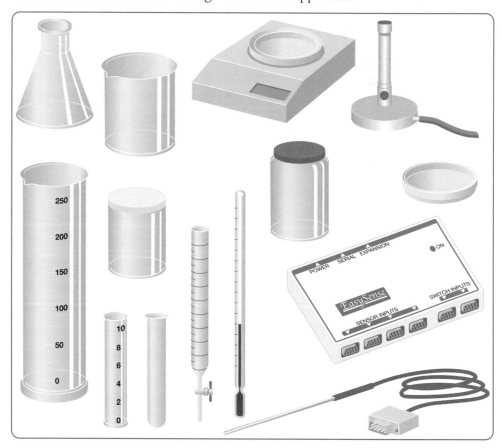

What do Laura and Sacha need to take with them?

❶ Look at the picture of different apparatus. Make a list of the apparatus Laura and Sacha should take with them.

1.4 Handling scientific equipment and materials

At the pond

It is decided that Laura will set up the apparatus for taking measurements of the surface temperature and Sacha will collect samples of pond water to analyse in the school laboratory.

Measuring the temperature

Laura has decided that she is going to use a temperature probe and data logger to take readings of the surface temperature. She sets the data logger to take the temperature of the surface water every 30 seconds.

2 (a) Do you think Laura has chosen a good time interval to take her readings?

(b) Suggest and explain what time interval you would have chosen.

The data logger with the temperature probe.

Sacha lowers the temperature probe into the pond.

Laura connects the temperature probe to the data logger and Sacha lowers the probe into the water. Laura notices that her first reading tells her that the temperature of the water is 60°C. Laura knows that this is much too warm and realises that she has not calibrated her instruments. Fortunately she has brought a 0–100°C thermometer with her. She takes the surface temperature of the water with her thermometer.

3 look at the thermometer. What is the surface temperature of the pond?

Laura takes the temperature probe out of the water and sets the data logger to read the same temperature as the thermometer reading of the pond water.

4 Explain why Laura should have left the probe in the water when calibrating her equipment.

Laura places the probe in the water and calibrates it properly this time. The temperature probe is placed just below the surface and the data logger starts to record the temperature at fixed intervals.

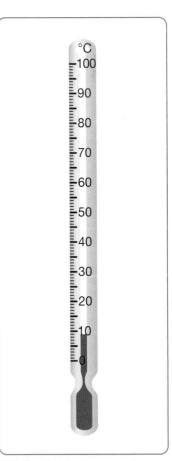

This is what Laura saw when she read the temperature on her thermometer.

1.4 Handling scientific equipment and materials

Collecting samples

Sacha decides to collect some pond water samples for analysis. She places 5 cm³ of pond water in ten different specimen tubes. All the samples are taken from the surface of the pond.

5 (a) Which measuring cylinder should Sacha use, a 250 cm³ or a 10 cm³, to measure the volumes? Explain your answer.

   (b) If a 5 cm³ graduated pipette had been available, would this alter your choice? Explain your answer.

Sacha took the sample from the surface water of the pond quite easily. However, she wonders how to take a sample of water from the bottom of the pond. Fortunately, the pond is only 50 cm deep.

6 Suggest how Sacha could use a screw-top jar to obtain a sample of water from the bottom of the pond.

7 What risk assessment should Laura and Sacha's teacher have carried out before the girls started working near the pond?

Back in the school lab

These are the graphs for the temperatures at the top and bottom of the pond that the girls printed out from their data logger.

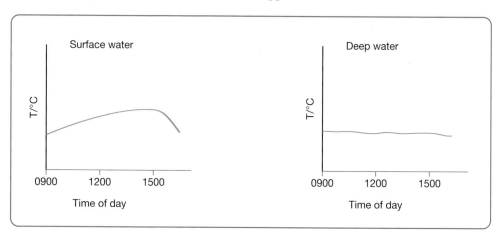

8 Which shows the greatest change in temperature, surface water or water at the bottom of the pond?

9 Suggest why the surface temperature of the water is greatest in the afternoon.

1.4 Handling scientific equipment and materials

The pathology lab CASE STUDY

Peter is in charge of a pathology laboratory in a large hospital. He has to make sure that everybody in the laboratory works safely and accurately.

see Blood donor, page 112

His first job in the morning is to list all the tests that need to be carried out and to organise the emergency ones first. He finds out how many blood samples must be tested that day. Most blood samples will be examined to determine their blood group as well as to count the numbers of red and white blood cells. Then he organises staff to do biopsy tests on tissue samples.

Another job is to measure the level of certain drugs in a blood sample when a drug overdose is suspected.

Emergencies interrupt Peter's work. Today, Peter's team have to examine some fluid from the spine of a patient suspected of having meningitis. They will centrifuge, stain and then examine it under a microscope.

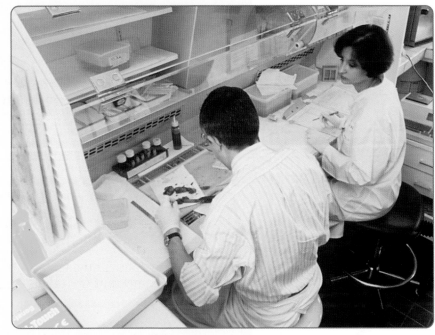

Peter and Ann test tissue samples.

Peter also has to make sure that everyone in the laboratory works safely. They have to be protected from any germs in the patients' samples and from any hazards from the chemicals used in the tests. Safety procedures include wearing protective clothes, using microbiological safety cabinets and doing different activities in separate areas. Everybody must also remember the basic health rules of not eating and drinking in the laboratory. Even when all the tests are complete, materials are autoclaved (sterilised by high-pressure steam) to ensure they pose no further risks.

see Preserving food, page 94

10 Explain why a patient's blood group must be known before surgery.

11 Find out how a centrifuge works and why it is useful.

12 Explain how autoclaving makes sure there are no further risks from samples.

13 Find out what is meant by 'biopsy tests'.

14 Look at the photograph of Peter and Ann working in the pathology laboratory.

    (a) Explain why they are wearing rubber gloves.

    (b) The floor is tiled. Explain why a tiled floor in a pathology laboratory is better than a carpeted floor.

    (c) Peter and Ann check each other's results. Suggest why they do this.

1.5 Recording and analysing scientific data

Hamid and William carry out an experiment

Hamid and William plan and carry out an experiment. They want to find out if students who have been given regular doses of vitamins by their parents are taller than students who have just had a normal diet. They decide that they will randomly choose a group of students in their year group. Both of them will do the investigation separately. At the end of the investigation, they will take a mean (average) of both their results.

Measuring and recording the data

Hamid and William decide to measure the height of the students in metres, correct to two decimal places. They design a form to record their data.

This is the equipment Hamid and William use to measure height.

RECORDING FORM

TO DETERMINE WHETHER VITAMIN SUPPLEMENTS AFFECT HEIGHT

Name ....

Height in metres correct to two decimal places ....

Male or female ....

Are vitamin supplements taken every day? ....

If the answer is yes, for how long have they been taken? ....

List of vitamins and doses taken ....

....

....

1.5 Recording and analysing scientific data

Hamid and William's standard procedure

The boys decide to use a standard procedure to take the measurements so that their results will be more reliable.

1 Randomly choose 100 students each from the year group.

2 Ask each student to remove their shoes.

3 Student stands with back straight against the wall.

4 Lower the bar until it rests on top of the student's head.

5 Take reading correct to two decimal places.

6 Ask each student to answer the questions for the recording form.

It takes a long time for Hamid and William to take the measurements and record all the data. This is what they found.

Name of student	Height (metres)	Takes/does not take vitamins
John	1.55	Yes
Mary	1.32	No
Reshma	1.48	Yes
Jo	1.72	No

Part of William's table.

❶ Suggest how Hamid and William could improve their standard procedure for the investigation.

They realise that the data in the table is not very clear or easy to understand. They need to display the data in a different format. First they need to count how many students are at each different height.

❷ Design a table that Hamid and William could use to store this information.

Carrying out numerical calculations

Hamid and William realise that they must convert their numbers into a percentage. Scientific experiments usually involve doing simple numerical calculations.

❸ Three out of fifty students had a height of 1.48 metres and took vitamins. What percentage of the students had a height of 1.48 metres and took vitamins?

(Hint: Divide the number of students by 50 and multiply by 100.)

1.5 Recording and analysing scientific data

Displaying results

Hamid and William want to display their results so that other people can understand them more easily.

Bar charts are used when data is divided into definite groups. Each bar shows the number of people in a group. Look at the bar chart on the right. It shows the number of people in each blood group. The bars do not have to be in any particular order.

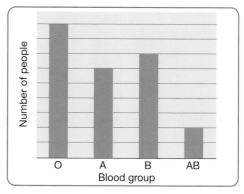

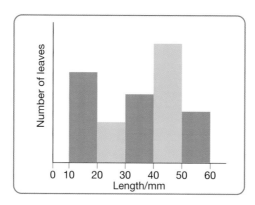

Histograms are used when the range of data is continuous with no definite gaps between where one measurement ends and another one starts. Look at the histogram on the left. It shows the length of leaves on a tree. Some leaves are short and some leaves are long. But there is a range of different lengths between these two extremes.

Pictograms use drawings to provide information. Each symbol represents a group of things, in this case ten frogs. The pictogram on the right shows the relative sizes of three different populations of frogs.

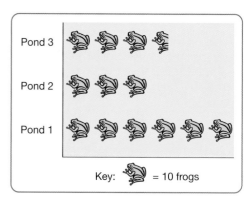

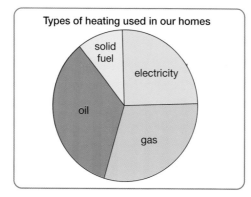

Pie charts are used to compare the relative sizes of different groups visually. It is a very good way to show how different sized groups compare with each other.

The angles for each sector of the pie chart are worked out like this:

$$\frac{\text{percentage of total}}{100} \times 360°$$

1.5 Recording and analysing scientific data

Graphs are used when there are two sets of data. If you were measuring the temperature of a beaker of water to show how quickly it cooled, you could show this on a graph. The time would be shown on the horizontal axis and the temperature on the vertical axis.

Time in this case is the independent variable. Temperature is called the dependent variable.

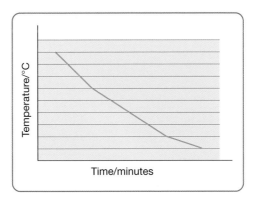

4 Suggest which of the methods you would use to display Hamid and William's results. Give a reason for your choice.

Analysing results

Hamid and William decided to display their results using bar charts.

These are the graphs that they drew.

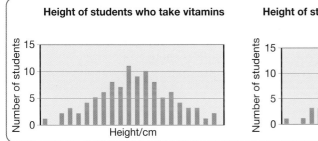

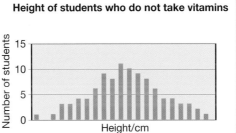

They knew that they should now analyse and interpret their results.

5 Compare the two charts. What conclusions can you come to from looking at their results?

Evaluation

To evaluate, they needed to look back at what they did in the experiment.

6 What do you think were the good points of the experiment?

7 What sources of inaccuracy could there be in the measurements they took?

Hamid and William realised that they could improve and extend their investigation to make it more accurate and reliable.

8 Look at the following list and explain how each point could be used to improve their experiment.

- Use a larger group of students.
- Choose students who took the same doses of the same vitamins.
- Use students of the same sex.

Review questions

1 Ranjit and Reshma have just started their GCSE in Applied Science. They are going out on work experience to a paint factory.

One of the jobs they have to do is mix paint of different colours.

(a) Describe the steps of a standard procedure that they would have to follow when asked to mix the paints. [7]

(b) Suggest why carrying out a standard procedure is necessary. [2]

2 Peter and Mary love sugar-coated sweets. Peter's favourite colour is the blue one. He wanted to know what food colour the manufacturers used to make the blue sweet.

Blue sweet	Colour A	Colour B	Colour C	Colour D

Mary did a chromatogram using the sweet and some food dyes.

(a) (i) Suggest why Mary included a chromatogram of a blue sweet. [2]

(ii) Suggest how Mary chose the dyes A, B, C and D. [1]

(b) Which of the food dyes do you think are used in the blue sweet? [2]

(c) Mary was not completely happy with her results. Suggest how she could make sure the results of the experiment were accurate. [2]

3 Raj carried out a survey. He wanted to know the frequency of different eye colours of students in his school.

This is what he found.

Eye colour		Number in a sample of 200
Pale blue		10
Blue grey		60
Grey green		50
Green		30
Pale brown		30
Dark brown		20

(a) Display the data that Raj obtained by using a:

(i) bar chart

(ii) pictogram

(iii) pie chart. [6]

(b) What percentage of Raj's sample had dark brown eyes? [1]

(c) Eye colours tend to blend from one colour to another. Suggest a procedure that Raj could have used to place each person's eyes in one of the above categories. [1]

2 Living organisms

THE WORKING CELL

Contents

Assignments and practical activities linked to this section:

Microscopy.

Using a light microscope

Osmosis in living tissue

Looking at chromosomes

Use the following to check your progress.

Unit 1

You will:

- understand how to make a temporary stained slide and use a light microscope to examine it
 see page 27

- present data in tables
 see pages 31, 35

- analyse and interpret results
 see pages 29, 31, 35

- evaluate investigations.
 see pages 29, 31

Unit 2

You will:

- identify useful products that can be made from living things
 see pages 26–29

- know that wool, silk, cotton, leather and many pharmaceutical products and dyes are obtained from living organisms
 see pages 26–29

- describe the cell as the common feature of all organisms and know similarities between plant and animal cells
 see pages 26–27

- explain how substances enter and leave cells by diffusion and osmosis
 see pages 30–37

- understand inherited characteristics and why you are unique
 see pages 38–41

- describe how cells divide by mitosis during growth
 see page 43

- describe how cells divide by meiosis to produce gametes
 see page 44

- know about monohybrid inheritance.
 see pages 46–49

Human cells from the lining of the cheek.

Plant cells containing chloroplasts.

2.1 Cells

Fibres of cotton, magnified 630 times.

Charlie the clothes designer

Charlie is a clothes designer, designing clothes for large retail stores. Part of her job involves knowing the properties of materials. This is to make sure they are strong enough for the designs she has in mind. She wants to be sure the clothes will not fall apart.

Some of the natural fibres Charlie uses, such as cotton, come from plants and others, such as leather, come from animals.

What are clothes fibres made of?

Wool is made of animal fibres similar to our hair. **Silk** is made from filaments produced by the silkworm moth. **Cotton** is made of plant fibres which are long, thin cells. **Leather** is made from animal skins, which are made of many layers of cells.

All living things are made of **chemical compounds** – proteins, carbohydrates (sugars and starch) and fats. The basic unit of all living things is the **cell**.

All cells have an outer thin **membrane**. This membrane controls what enters and leaves the cell. Inside the cell is the jelly-like **cytoplasm** where all the chemical reactions necessary for life take place.

The cytoplasm contains:

see Inheritance, page 46

- a nucleus, which carries inherited information in a code
- many mitochondria, where energy is released
- many ribosomes, where proteins such as enzymes are made
- one or more **vacuoles**, which contain a watery cell sap.

Mitochondria and ribosomes are very small and can only be seen clearly with a high-power electron microscope.

1 Which part of a cell controls what enters and leaves a cell?

2 Which part of a cell carries coded information?

3 Where in the cell do all the chemical reactions take place?

Plant cells are slightly different from animal cells. Since most plants do not move very much, their cells do not need to be flexible; but they do need to be strong. Therefore, plant cells have an outer **cell wall** made out of cellulose. Cellulose is a complex carbohydrate. Its chemical structure makes it very resistant and strong.

Plants can make their own food by a process called photosynthesis. To do this, plant cells contain special green structures called **chloroplasts**.

Plant cells also have large vacuoles filled with cell sap.

4 Write down THREE ways in which plant cells are different from animal cells.

5 Suggest why plant cells are different from animal cells.

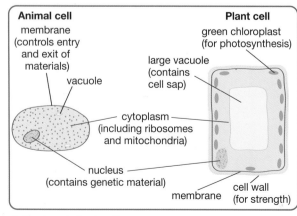

Animal and plant cells.

2.1 Cells

Looking at cells

ACTIVITY

Cells have a variety of shapes and sizes because they are specialised to carry out different jobs.

Onion cells are easy to look at. When you cut open an onion bulb, you see a number of layers. A thin strip of cells can be peeled off a layer and put on a glass slide. A stain such as Schultze's solution can be added to show the cell contents in different colours. Then a thin glass cover slip is carefully lowered on to the cells. It takes practice to avoid air bubbles. These cells do not contain chloroplasts.

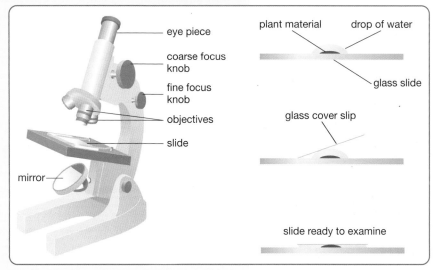

Looking at cells with a microscope.

6 Why don't cells from an onion bulb contain chloroplasts?

With practice, it is easy to tear off thin strips of cells from privet or geranium leaves. Some of the cells will contain chloroplasts.

You can look at **microorganisms** with a microscope. Yeast can be examined by placing a drop of yeast culture onto a glass slide and adding water. Yeast is used in brewing alcohol and making bread. Simple green plants called algae are easily found as green threads in garden ponds. Their cells are seen under a microscope.

Because of Health and Safety rules for handling animal tissues, it is better to look at prepared slides of animal cells. There is an amazing variety of animal cells. Nerve cells are long and thin to carry nerve impulses. Red blood cells are circular discs. Cells lining the windpipe have tiny hairs.

Some fungi can be viewed with a microscope. Using a high magnification, you can see that the body is not divided into individual cells. *Penicillium* is a fungus that is used to make the drug penicillin. Other **pharmaceutical products** are also obtained from living things.

7 Why do we use microscopes to look at cells?

8 Why do you think slides and coverslips are made of clear glass?

9 Why are stains sometimes added when examining cells?

10 Explain why you are not allowed to get some human blood and look at it under a microscope.

11 Imagine your school is having an open day for the local Junior School. Design and make an attractive display to show different types of plant and animal cells. You can use materials such as coloured wool or string, tissue paper, modelling clay, papier mâché around a balloon and threads linking the cell parts to their labels.

Word check

A **microorganism** is an organism which is so small we need a microscope to see it.

see Types of microorganism, page 86

Word check

Pharmaceutical products are drugs and other chemicals used in medicine.

2.1 Cells

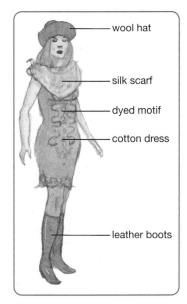

Plants and animals provide the raw materials for many of our clothes.

Some uses of plants and animals

Fabrics

In her clothes designs, Charlie prefers to use natural materials such as wool, silk, cotton and leather rather than nylon, rayon and polyester which are manufactured.

Wool and cotton are types of fibres, silk is made of filaments and leather is a thick tissue of many cells.

Charlie uses wool (from sheep) to make thick materials for warmth. The wool fibres are loosely spaced so wool is a good insulator.

⑫ Why does the structure of wool make it a good insulator?

Cotton fibres (from the cotton plant) are thin and tightly packed so cotton is a poor insulator. Cotton is therefore cool to wear.

Charlie sometimes uses expensive silk material. Silk filaments come from the cocoons of the silk moth. They are extremely fine and make very thin, cool material.

Leather is the skin of animals such as cows, deer and kangaroos. We use leather when we want a tough, waterproof covering.

Dyes

Plants such as onion, lichens and saffron contain many different coloured pigments. These are extracted to use as **dyes** to stain materials.

The ancient Britons used woad, an intense blue dye, to colour their bodies. Synthetic dyes made from coal tar are often used instead of these natural dyes, since they give a greater range of colours.

Key words

- cell
- cell wall
- chemical compound
- chloroplast
- cotton
- cytoplasm
- dye
- leather
- membrane
- pharmaceutical product
- silk
- vacuole
- wool

Key facts

Copy and complete the sentences by choosing the correct word from the key words list. Each word may be used more than once.

1 All living organisms are made of _____ _____.

2 The basic unit of living organisms is called a _____.

3 All cells have an outer _____ surrounding the jelly-like _____.

4 Plant cells are different from animal cells because they have a thick outer _____ _____ and large _____. Many also have _____.

5 Animals provide us with materials such as _____, _____ and _____.

6 Plants provide us with the material _____, as well as pigments for _____ and _____ _____ such as penicillin.

How Charlie's fabrics can be tested (CASE STUDY)

It is important to Charlie that the clothes she designs will be comfortable, look good and wear well. Because different materials have different properties, she needs to know how they will behave when they are made into clothes using her designs.

Scientists carry out research into the properties of different materials. Charlie can find out the properties of different materials from the results of these scientific tests.

One important property she is interested in is how far materials can be stretched yet still recover their original length. This is useful for clothes covering elbows and knees since it will prevent the clothes from going out of shape.

You may have done a similar experiment to the one that scientists do, to find out how materials stretch and how well they will recover.

A student attached thin strips of four different materials to a board. The strips were all the same length and width. He tied equal weights to each strip. The picture shows the results.

By increasing the weights, the student measured how far each strip would stretch before it became permanently stretched.

Testing fabrics.

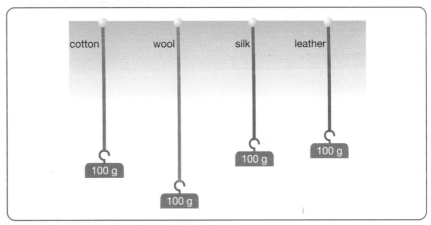

Testing how far fabrics stretch.

13 Explain how the student made sure the experiment was a fair test.

14 Which material stretched (a) the least, (b) the most, before stretching permanently?

15 Explain why wool stretched more than cotton, before stretching permanently.

16 Using the information from the experiment, explain why wool is an ideal material for sweaters.

17 Explain why leather is a suitable material for shoes.

18 Describe how the experiment can be used to test what effect rain has on the elasticity of different materials.

2.2 Diffusion

Luigi the chef

Luigi the chef.

Luigi is a chef and he likes to cook at home too. Unfortunately his family do not like the house to smell of cooking vegetables.

His wife buys a perfumed oil burner to make the house smell nice. The children want to know how the pleasant smell from the oil burner spreads around the whole of the kitchen.

The oil burner makes the room smell nice.

perfumed oil floating on water

candle

How does diffusion work?

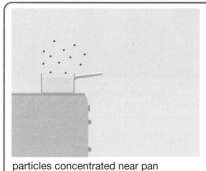

particles concentrated near pan

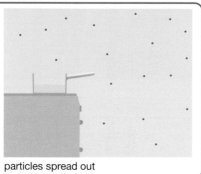

particles spread out

Movement of molecules.

The molecules in a liquid or gas move about in all directions all the time. This is called **random movement**. In time, the molecules of a liquid or gas will spread from where there are many molecules (**high concentration**) to where there are fewer molecules (**low concentration**).

The molecules end up spread evenly throughout the space available. This process is called **diffusion**.

The molecules given off from Luigi's cooking and from the oil burner spread to all parts of the house by diffusion.

Diffusion takes place faster in gases than in liquids because the molecules in gases are more spaced out.

Imagine a primary school where the girls come out of one door and the boys come out of a different door at break time. To start with, there are lots of girls gathered round one door and lots of boys round the other. Then they start to play, running about and changing direction all the time. By the end of break, there are boys and girls mixed up all over the playground. In the same sort of way, random movements of the molecules from Luigi's cooking cause the molecules to diffuse to all parts of the kitchen.

❶ Using ideas about perfume molecules, explain how the perfumed oil burner works.

❷ Explain why the burner works better when the candle is lit.

❸ Luigi's mother, who lives with them, is not happy about them using the burner. She thinks it is dangerous. Explain how it could be dangerous and describe ways of making it safer to use.

❹ Many supermarkets add attractive perfumes, such as that of baking bread, to the air conditioning. Suggest other places where diffusing perfume could be used.

2.2 Diffusion

Diffusion in liquids and gases ACTIVITY

The picture shows six numbered strips of red litmus paper attached by sticky tape to the inside of a bell jar. Red litmus paper is an indicator. It turns blue when an alkali is present.

A few drops of ammonia solution are placed in a dish on top of a beaker. Ammonia is an alkaline gas. The bell jar is placed over the dish of ammonia. In a few seconds some of the red litmus paper turns blue.

5 How has the ammonia reached the litmus paper?

6 Which strips of litmus paper will turn blue first?

7 Describe how the speed of diffusion could be measured using this experiment. Use:

$$\text{speed} = \frac{\text{distance/m}}{\text{time/s}}$$

Diffusion takes place in plants too

Four large laurel leaves are treated with petroleum jelly and then weighed. They are hung on a length of string as shown in the diagram and left for a day. They are reweighed. The table shows the results.

Leaf	Original weight/g	Final weight/g	Loss of weight/g
A	5.2	4.2	1.0
B	5.1	4.4	0.7
C	5.2	4.7	0.5
D	5.3	4.9	0.4

Leaves have tiny holes called stomata (singular: **stoma**) in their lower surfaces. These allow gases, such as carbon dioxide and oxygen, to enter and leave by diffusion.

Water inside the leaf can evaporate and diffuse out through these stomata. This loss of water is called **transpiration**.

Any weight that the leaves lose in the experiment is mainly due to the loss of water.

8 Which leaf, A, B, C or D, lost the least amount of water? Explain why.

9 Which leaf, A, B, C or D, lost the most water? Explain why.

10 Describe TWO possible sources of error which could occur in this experiment.

An experiment to show diffusion.

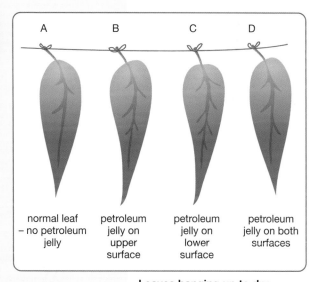

A	B	C	D
normal leaf – no petroleum jelly	petroleum jelly on upper surface	petroleum jelly on lower surface	petroleum jelly on both surfaces

Leaves hanging up to dry.

2.2 Diffusion

Diffusion is important to us

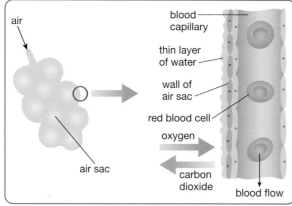

Gases enter and leave your blood by gaseous exchange in your lungs.

Oxygen is used by living cells to release energy from food. When you breathe, air containing about 20 per cent oxygen enters your lungs and passes down into millions of small air sacs. The lining of these air sacs is kept moist with a thin layer of water. Thin blood vessels surround the air sacs.

Since there is a higher concentration of oxygen in the air than in the blood, oxygen diffuses into the blood. At the same time, waste carbon dioxide diffuses out of the blood into the air sacs. Without using any energy, oxygen enters your blood and carbon dioxide leaves it by diffusion. This process is called **gaseous exchange**.

Diffusion also explains how digested food enters your blood.

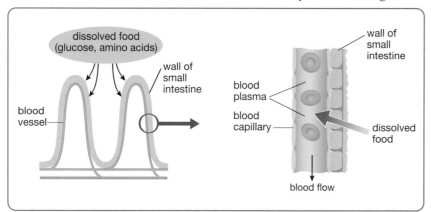

Food gets from your intestine into your blood stream by diffusion.

⑪ Put these statements about diffusion and digestion in the correct order.

A In the small intestine there is a high concentration of digested food.

B The very small food molecules therefore diffuse through the wall of the small intestine.

C The food molecules are carried away in the blood plasma.

D Food is digested by enzymes in the mouth, stomach and intestines.

E The blood arriving at the small intestine has a very low concentration of food molecules.

Key words

diffusion

gaseous exchange

high concentration

low concentration

random movement

stoma (plural: stomata)

transpiration

Key facts

Copy and complete the sentences by choosing the correct word from the key words list.

1 All molecules of a gas and liquid make _____ _____.

2 All the molecules spread out because they move from a _____ _____ to a _____ _____.

This movement is called _____.

3 Water vapour will diffuse from plant leaves by _____ through tiny holes called _____.

4 Diffusion is important in digestion and _____ _____.

2.2 Diffusion

Drying clothes

Luigi's café uses a lot of tablecloths. After washing them, Luigi hangs them out to dry.

He knows they will dry quickly when it is a good drying day.

What makes a good drying day for Luigi?

On a good drying day, there's a strong wind blowing and the sun is hot. The wind and the warmth make the water evaporate quickly. The water particles will move out of the cloth and into the air by diffusion. The warmth will make the molecules move around faster and the wind will blow them away.

Luigi uses a tumble drier to dry the cloths on cold, wet days.

A good drying day.

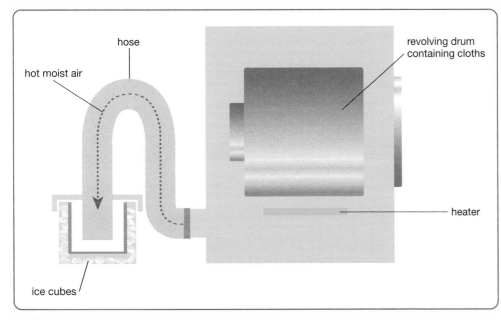

A tumble drier.

Tumble driers work by passing warm air through a revolving drum. The escaping warm, moist air causes dampness in the room so an air vent is often put through the wall. Sometimes this is not possible, so a container filled with ice cubes is used. The water can be emptied out of the container.

12 Explain why a cold wet day will be a poor day for drying tablecloths.

13 Explain why an increased temperature can increase the rate of diffusion.

14 Describe how a tumble drier makes the water in tablecloths evaporate.

15 How can a tumble drier cause dampness in a room? Include in your answer the words 'evaporates' and 'condenses'.

16 Describe the effect the ice cubes will have on the warm, moist air escaping from a tumble drier.

2.3 Osmosis

Alice preparing chips.

Alice the trainee chef

Alice goes on day release and works with Luigi at the café. She is training to be a chef. She has noticed that if she puts raw vegetables, such as potato chips, in strong salt water they go soft and floppy.

What happened to Alice's chips?

The chips go soft because more water is leaving them than is entering them. This is caused by a special type of diffusion called **osmosis**. If potato chips are put in pure water, the water enters all the cells by osmosis, making the chips hard and rigid. If the chips are put in salt water, water leaves the cells, making the potato chips soft and floppy.

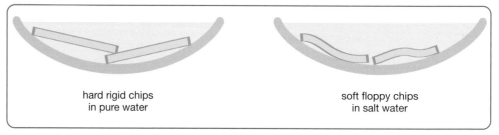

hard rigid chips in pure water

soft floppy chips in salt water

The effect of salt water on chips.

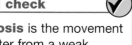
Word check

Osmosis is the movement of water from a weak solution to a stronger solution through a partially permeable membrane.

Membranes

There are several different types of membrane. The polythene covering that is used in packaging will not let anything through and is waterproof. Cellophane and **visking tubing** have microscopic holes and let only water through.

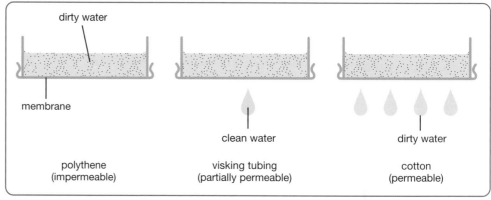

dirty water

membrane

clean water

dirty water

polythene (impermeable)

visking tubing (partially permeable)

cotton (permeable)

Different types of membranes.

The membranes that surround every living cell are **partially permeable**, like visking tubing. This means some things can get through easily, others have more difficulty and some can't get through at all. Water can get through easily.

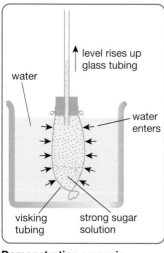

level rises up glass tubing

water

water enters

visking tubing

strong sugar solution

Demonstrating osmosis.

see Cells, page 26

Demonstrating osmosis

The picture shows a simple demonstration of osmosis. Strong sugar solution such as golden syrup or honey is put inside some visking tubing. Some of the surrounding water enters by osmosis. This increase in the volume of water causes the sugar solution level in the tube to rise. The stronger the sugar solution, the higher the level will rise in the glass tubing.

2.3 Osmosis

Experimenting with potato chips (ACTIVITY)

The firmness of vegetables, such as potatoes, is important to a chef and to their customers.

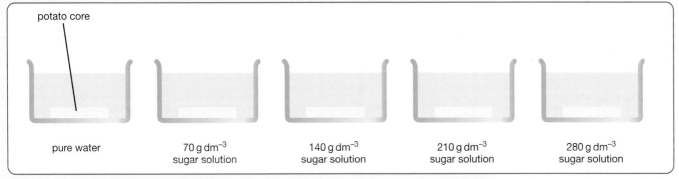

pure water   70 g dm⁻³ sugar solution   140 g dm⁻³ sugar solution   210 g dm⁻³ sugar solution   280 g dm⁻³ sugar solution

Potato cores in different sugar solutions.

Alice experimented with potato cores in different concentrations of sugar solution. A sugar solution has the same effect as a salt solution. She used a cork borer to get five cores from a large potato and cut them all to the same length (7.0 cm). She placed one core in each sugar concentration. After two hours, she measured them to see if they had increased or decreased in length.

Alice's results

Concentration/ g dm⁻³	Original length/cm	Final length/cm	Change in length/cm
0			
70			
140			
210			
280			

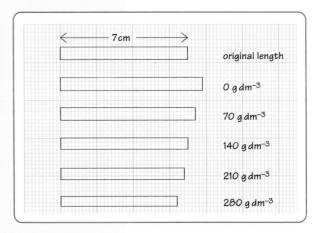

① Copy the table and fill in Alice's results.

② Draw a graph to show increase or decrease in length against sugar concentration.

③ Which core increased the most in length? What could have entered the core to make it longer?

④ Which core decreased the most in length? What could have left the core to make it shorter?

⑤ One core remained the same length. What does this tell you about the concentration of dissolved substances inside and outside the potato core?

2.3 Osmosis

Explaining osmosis

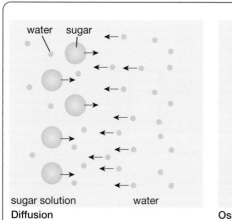

Movement of molecules.

Diffusion
Water and sugar molecules can diffuse.

partially permeable membrane

Osmosis
Only the small water molecules can diffuse because of the membrane.

Water enters or leaves living cells by osmosis. Water molecules move from where there are many of them to where there are fewer. Dilute solutions have more water molecules than concentrated ones. This means that in osmosis water passes through a partially permeable membrane from a dilute solution to a concentrated solution.

Without a partially permeable membrane, both sugar molecules and water molecules will diffuse. If a partially permeable membrane is put in the way, only small molecules, such as water (H_2O), will diffuse through it. Large molecules, such as sugar, ($C_{12}H_{22}O_{11}$), cannot get through the membrane because they are too big. Osmosis is sometimes called a 'frustrated diffusion'.

Osmosis is important for animals and plants

Animals living in fresh water have a problem if too much water gets into their bodies by osmosis. Fish have kidneys to control the water content. They remove excess water.

6 What do you think would happen to the cells of a fish if too much water got into them by osmosis?

Kidneys regulate our water content and filter our blood. When people have kidney problems, the process of **dialysis** can be used to filter their blood.

Osmosis also explains how water enters plant roots. With a lot of water outside the root cells and a partially permeable membrane lining every cell, water will enter by osmosis. Large molecules of starch and proteins will remain inside the root cells, so the plant does not lose its stored food.

Word check

Dialysis separates large molecules from water and small molecules, such as urea, by using a partially permeable membrane.

Key words

dialysis

osmosis

partially permeable

visking tubing

Key facts

Copy and complete the sentences by choosing the correct word from the key words list.

1 Water enters cells through the cell membrane by _____ when there is a more dilute solution outside the cell.

2 Membranes in living cells are _____ _____.

3 Artificial membranes, such as _____ _____, can be used to show osmosis.

4 Kidney machines use _____ to remove waste products, such as urea, from the blood.

2.3 Osmosis

Using osmosis

CASE STUDY

In science laboratories, we use 'reverse osmosis' to produce clean water.

The dirty water is put under pressure so the small water molecules are forced through a partially permeable membrane. The membrane is made from cellulose acetate. This process removes:

85% of salt;

95% of calcium carbonate;

95% of solid particles;

100% of bacteria.

This laboratory water purifier uses reverse osmosis to produce very pure water.

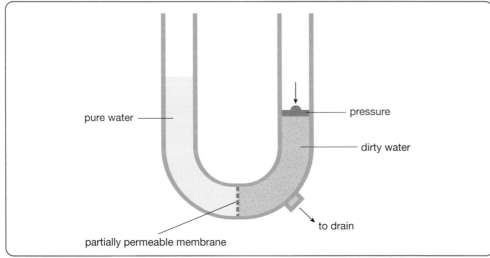

How a water purifier works.

The water is used in experiments as well as being safe to drink.

This process is similar to how your kidneys work. Blood entering the kidney is under pressure so unwanted substances are forced out of the blood and into kidney tubules. The waste urine collects in the bladder before the body gets rid of it.

7 Why can water purifiers be useful if water and sewage pipes are broken during an earthquake?

8 What do you think happens if the pressure produced by the pump is too high?

9 Many clothes use special fabrics to allow them to 'breathe' yet still remain waterproof. Look at labels of clothes such as Gore-Tex and Berghaus to find out how this works.

2.4 Characteristics

Mrs Bennett's new class

Amanda Bennett is a teacher. She teaches a new class every year. She makes drawings to help her recognise the students and to remember their names.

Every one of Mrs Bennett's students looks different.

Characteristics

Word check

A **characteristic** is any distinctive feature that helps to distinguish one organism from another.

She remembers Ben because he has red hair, freckles and blue eyes. These features are called **characteristics**. There is only one person like Ben in the whole world, even though there are about seven billion other people. Characteristics can often be grouped in pairs, for example, straight hair and curly hair.

❶ Apart from hair colour, how many other different pairs of characteristics are shown by Mrs Bennett's pupils?

❷ Who has (a) blond hair, blue eyes, no freckles and large ears?

(b) blond hair, green eyes, no freckles and small ears?

see Cells, page 26

Word check

The **nucleus** of a cell is the part that carries the code for inherited information.

What part do cells play?
All living things are made of cells.

The information about a person's inherited characteristics is carried in the **nucleus** of every one of their cells. The information about eye colour is carried in every nucleus, even in nose cells! However, this information is used only in eye cells; it is 'switched off' in other cells.

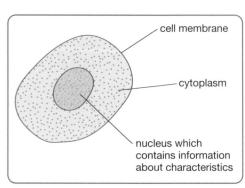

The nucleus of the cell carries the inherited information.

Discovering differences

ACTIVITY

Some of your characteristics are due to information in the nucleus of your cells. These are passed on from your parents; they are **inherited**.

Some other characteristics are caused by other things, such as your diet or exercise.

These characteristics are not inherited and are said to be caused by the **environment**.

❸ Look at another student in your class. Make a list of their characteristics that are inherited and a list of those which are not inherited.

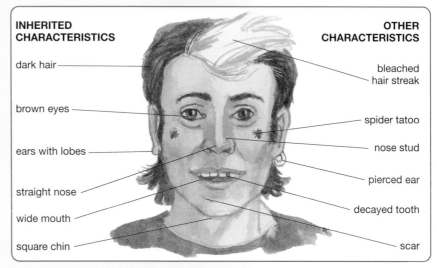

INHERITED CHARACTERISTICS

dark hair
brown eyes
ears with lobes
straight nose
wide mouth
square chin

OTHER CHARACTERISTICS

bleached hair streak
spider tatoo
nose stud
pierced ear
decayed tooth
scar

Do you know him?

We can see variation in characteristics of apples. Golden Delicious, Cox's Orange Pippin and Bramley cooking apples are different sizes, colours, smells and shapes even though they are all apples. They also taste completely different from each other. This gives us a choice of which to buy.

This sort of comparison is best shown in a table.

❹ Draw up a table to show as many differences as possible for these three types of apple.

You can find by eating them not only how they taste but also whether they are crisp or soft to bite, have thick or thin skins, or if they turn brown quickly.

All these differences are important. If organisms,such as apples, were all exactly alike, they would only grow in the same conditions and be vulnerable to the same pests and diseases. This is also true for other living things.

❺ Suggest why a supermarket sells many different types of apple. Visit your local supermarket and make a list of all the different types of apple and where they come from. (Remember to get permission from the supermarket.)

❻ Will a Golden Delicious apple taste the same if it is grown in France or in England? Give an explanation for your answer.

Apples come in many varieties.

2.4 Characteristics

Chromosomes

Great-grandmother, mother, grandmother and son.

There are four generations in this family. They all show many similar characteristics. The great-grandson has one important difference. He is a boy and information to make him a boy is carried in every cell of his body.

When a cell is specially treated, stained with a dye and examined under a microscope, you can see small thread-like **chromosomes** inside the nucleus. The chromosomes are arranged in pairs. In human male and female body cells, there are 46 chromosomes (23 pairs).

If the chromosomes in a dividing plant cell are stained, you can see them clearly with a light microscope.

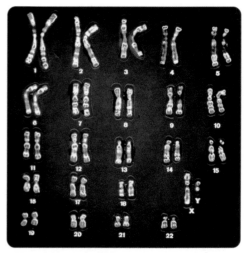

Human chromosomes.

One pair of chromosomes, the **sex chromosomes**, has a special function. In girls these sex chromosomes are exactly the same and are called **XX** chromosomes. In boys, the sex chromosomes are different sizes and are called **XY** chromosomes. The picture shows human chromosomes that have been photographed, then rearranged. In this way, a technician can check whether there are any problems.

7 Are these chromosomes from a man or a woman?

To check for cheating in the Olympic Games, the athletes are given a sex test by having the chromosomes from their cheek cells examined. A top male sprinter can still beat a top female sprinter because of his greater physical strength.

8 Look at your school Sports Day records and compare the times and distances for girls' and boys' events.

9 Use websites to compare male and female Olympic records for various events.

10 In which sports events do men and women compete together? Suggest why this is possible.

2.4 Characteristics

Identifying suspects using E-fit   CASE STUDY

Like Mrs Bennett, Bill Newstead needs to be able to identify faces. He is a Facial Identification Officer in the West Yorkshire police force. Bill's job is to interview witnesses of a crime. He has to get valuable information without leading or misleading the witnesses.

Bill works with the E-fit system. This creates images using the world's largest database of hair styles, facial features and accessories, such as hats and sunglasses. It can create about 32 million individual faces. If Bill wants information about a suspect's hair, he will ask about the colour, length, type, parting, style, tidiness and thickness, displaying each possible variation on a lap-top screen. The database has to be regularly updated to include the latest hairstyles worn by footballers and pop stars! Every step of the process of building up an image is recorded in case it is challenged in a court of law.

Bill Newstead using the E-fit system.

Bill plays a crucial role in helping to identify suspects and in ruling out innocent people.

11 Look at the E-fit image for about one minute. Cover it up and try to describe the person shown by listing their facial characteristics.

If you have managed ten you have done well, yet the E-fit system has thousands of characteristics in its database.

The West Yorkshire police have recently developed another system called VIPER (Video Identification Parade Electronic Recording). Police can take video footage of their suspect and then take a selection of 'look-alikes' from the thousands of images stored on the VIPER database. The selection is made into a video parade so witnesses don't have to attend a traditional identification parade.

An E-fit image.

Key facts

Copy and complete the sentences by choosing the correct word from the key words list.

1 We look different from each other because we have different _____.

2 Characteristics such as eye colour, which depend on information from our parents, are _____.

3 Other characteristics that are not inherited are caused by our _____.

4 Information about our characteristics is carried inside the _____ of every cell.

5 The nucleus contains thread-like structures called _____.

6 Special chromosomes called _____ _____ determine whether someone is male or female.

7 Males have _____ sex chromosomes and females have _____ sex chromosomes.

Key words

characteristics

chromosomes

environment

inherited

nucleus

sex chromosomes

XX

XY

2.5 Cells dividing

Luke at two weeks old.

Luke is born

When Luke was only a few minutes old, the nurses recorded his length and weight.

He started life as a microscopic fertilised egg and grew rapidly in his mother's womb for 40 weeks.

Luke will continue to grow until he is about 18 years old.

How will baby Luke grow?   **ACTIVITY**

All living things grow. Luke's height will be a result of **genes** inherited from his parents. It will also be affected by his diet and by chemical messengers called hormones in his body.

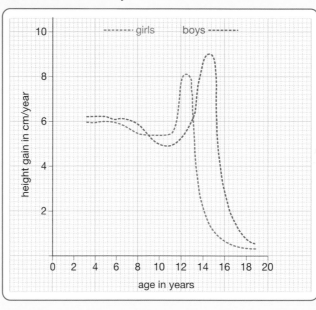

Girls and boys grow at different rates at different times.

As Luke grows up he will find that:

• in junior school, he is around the same height as most girls in his class;

• in year 7 in secondary school, he is smaller than most girls in his class;

• in year 11 in secondary school, he is taller than most girls in his class.

More accurate information is shown in the graph.

❶ What is the biggest height gain shown by (a) girls, (b) boys?

❷ When is the period of fastest growth in (a) girls, (b) boys?

You could carry out a survey on average student height in classes throughout your school.

Knights going into battle in medieval times wore protective armour. These suits of armour show that the knights were only about 168 cm (5 ft 6 in) tall. The average height of a modern soldier is about 183 cm (6 ft) tall.

❸ What could have caused this increase in average height?

❹ Suggest why height may not be the best way of measuring human growth.

2.5 Cells dividing

Growth and mitosis

Skin cells live for only a few days. They are continuously replaced as the outer cells are rubbed off. The skin is often damaged so new cells are needed for repair. We also need new skin cells as we grow.

Growth is an increase in size. For this we need an increase in the number of cells.

Cells make copies of themselves by dividing in two. This process of **cell division** is called **mitosis**. The new cells are **identical** to each other and to the original cell. This means that new skin cells will be exactly the same as the original skin cell.

Onion roots can be grown by placing an onion bulb in a vase, so only the bottom part of the bulb touches the water. In warm, dark conditions, roots form in about two weeks. You can use a marker pen to make marks at equal spacings on a root. The distances between the marks are measured every day to show where most growth takes place.

To find out what happens inside the cells as they divide, you will need to use a microscope to look at specially stained cells.

Mitosis happens in the following stages.

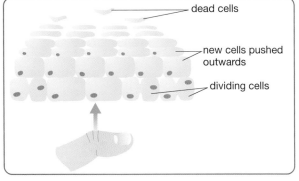

Skin cells are always being rubbed off and replaced.

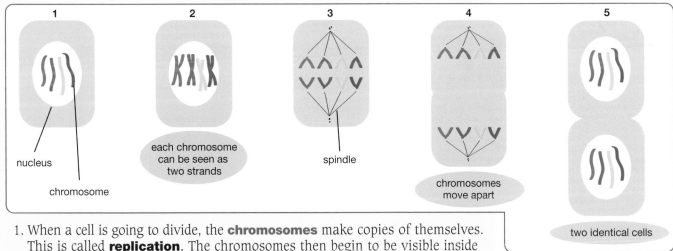

1. When a cell is going to divide, the **chromosomes** make copies of themselves. This is called **replication**. The chromosomes then begin to be visible inside the nucleus.

2. The chromosomes can be seen more clearly now. Each chromosome can be seen to be made up of two strands. The membrane around the nucleus disappears.

3. The chromosomes arrange themselves across the middle of the cell attached to the **spindle**.

4. The spindle contracts, pulling the chromosomes apart.

5. New membranes develop around each set of chromosomes, and in plant cells a new cell wall grows, forming two new daughter cells. These new cells are identical to the original cell and to each other. They have the same combination of genes in their chromosomes.

In mitosis, cells divide to make two identical cells.

Word check

Chromosomes are small thread-like structures in the nucleus of a cell. They carry coded genetic information.

see Cells, page 26

2.5 Cells dividing

Meiosis

Most plants and animals reproduce sexually. **Sexual reproduction** makes a new individual with a mixture of characteristics from its parents. With good luck you inherit good looks from one parent and intelligence from the other!

Sperm (or pollen in plants) and egg cells are produced by a type of cell division called **meiosis**.

see Characteristics, page 38

Most human cells have 23 pairs of chromosomes. There are 46 chromosomes altogether. This is called the diploid number of chromosomes.

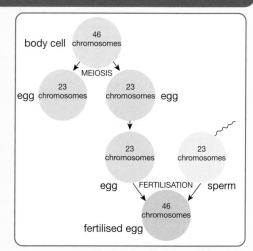

Meiosis produces gametes with only 23 chromosomes.

Eggs and sperm are different. They are the sex cells or **gametes**. They only get half shares, called the haploid number of chromosomes. They get only one chromosome from each pair. A human egg cell has only 23 single chromosomes. A sperm cell also has 23 single chromosomes. When the egg is fertilised by a sperm, the fertilised egg cell has 46 chromosomes (23 pairs).

If this halving of chromosomes did not happen before fertilisation, the fertilised egg would contain double the number of chromosomes of a normal body cell. After a few generations, all our cells would be full of chromosomes!

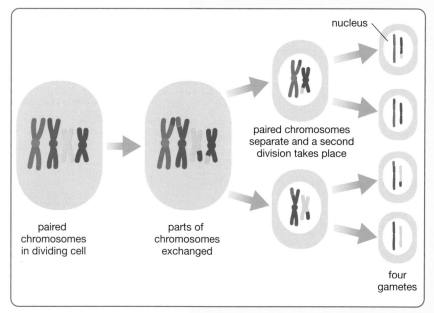

Meiosis.

Meiosis is different from mitosis in a number of ways.

1. Meiosis is involved in sexual reproduction, making gametes called eggs and sperm (or pollen).

2. In meiosis, the new cells have only half the number of chromosomes of the original cells. They have one set, not two.

3. In meiosis, the chromosomes twist, snap and rejoin. This means they now carry a different combination of genes, making each new individual unique.

4. In meiosis, four new cells are produced, not two.

5 Make a table to show the differences between mitosis and meiosis.

6 Make a large wall display of these processes using lengths of coloured string to represent chromosomes.

2.5 Cells dividing

Luke can be tested even before birth   CASE STUDY

Luke's mum and dad want to make sure that he is going to be born fit and healthy. One of the tests that can be performed on Luke is called an amniocentesis. It is performed about 16–20 weeks after a woman becomes pregnant.

The test sounds a good idea, but there is a problem. One in a hundred tests can result in the fetus being aborted (born before it is big enough to survive). It is a difficult decision for Luke's mum and dad to make. Do they risk the test to find out if Luke has a problem? Do they gamble and just hope that he will be born healthy?

The test involves inserting a needle into the mother's abdomen. The needle draws some of the amniotic fluid that surrounds the fetus up into a syringe. The fluid will contain some of the fetus' cells.

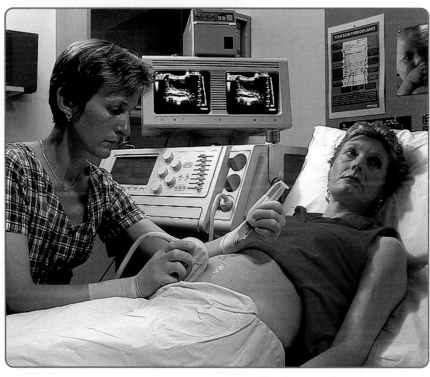

Checking the fetus.

The cells are then grown for several days. Highly magnified photographs of the cells are taken. The photographs are cut up and rearranged to produce a 'karyotype' of all the fetus' chromosomes.

see Characteristics, page 38

Key facts

Copy and complete the sentences by choosing the correct word from the key words list. Each word may be used more than once.

1 New cells are made by a process of _____ _____.

2 As cells divide, the behaviour of _____ is important since they carry _____.

3 Mitosis is involved in _____ and meiosis is involved in _____ _____.

4 In mitosis, the chromosomes make copies of themselves by _____. Cone-shaped _____ are formed. The new cell is identical to the original cell.

5 Eggs and sperm are called _____. They are produced by the cell division called _____, not by _____. They contain one set of _____. Normal body cells contain two sets of _____.

Key words

cell division

chromosomes

gamete

gene

growth

meiosis

mitosis

replication

sexual reproduction

spindle

2.6 Inheritance

A recipe for human beings

Winston King is a science teacher. He explains to his class that thousands of scientists across the world have been working out the sequence of genes in human cells, to crack our 'genetic code'.

Winston gives out lots of different cake recipes: chocolate, fruit cake, ginger. Each recipe is a unique set of instructions. He tells the students that, in the same way, each human has a unique set of instructions that is used to make that person.

The genetic code

The instructions to make a human being are carried by the chromosomes in every cell. The chromosomes are made of genes, which carry the coded instructions. These coded instructions form our **genetic code**.

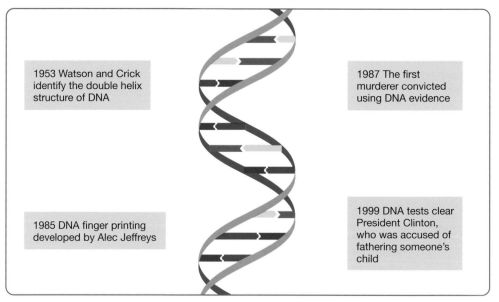

1953 Watson and Crick identify the double helix structure of DNA

1987 The first murderer convicted using DNA evidence

see Cells dividing, page 42

1985 DNA finger printing developed by Alec Jeffreys

1999 DNA tests clear President Clinton, who was accused of fathering someone's child

The double helix structure of DNA.

In 1944, Oswald Avery realised that the chemical called **deoxyribonucleic acid (DNA)** in our chromosomes carried this genetic code.

In 1953, James Watson and Francis Crick worked out the chemical structure of DNA. They discovered that DNA is made up of two parallel chains twisted to form a **double helix**. It looks like a twisted ladder with the rungs carrying the coded instructions. The story of this fascinating discovery is told in their book, *The double helix*.

You can find out about other important codes, such as the Morse Code and digital signals in photography and television.

2.6 Inheritance

Growing tomato seeds   ACTIVITY

The class have learned about different characteristics in plants and animals. They know that characteristics can often be grouped in pairs, for example, blue or brown eyes and dark or blond hair.

They decide to look at inheritance in plants. They grow some tomato seeds from a genetics kit.

The original parent plants were pure-breeding types. So the green-stemmed parent plants carried only genetic information for green stems. The purple-stemmed parent plants carried only genetic information for purple stems. After fertilisation had taken place between these parents, the seeds were collected. These seeds were in the kit. The students planted 100 of the seeds.

1 What conditions should they use for quick germination?

After ten days, the class looked at the results.

All the plants had green stems.

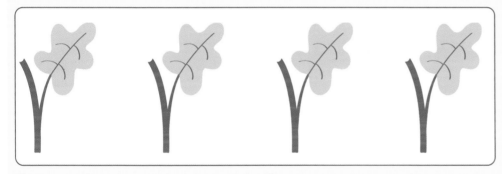

The tomato plants that grew from the parent seeds.

This showed that green stems are **dominant** over purple stems and purple stems are **recessive** to green stems.

The genetics kit also contained seeds collected when this first generation, called the F_1, had reproduced.

The students then germinated 100 of these tomato seeds. After another ten days they found that some tomato plants had green stems and some had purple stems. They counted them and found that this generation, the F_2, contained 74 green stems and 24 purple stems. Two seeds had not germinated.

Since there are about three times as many green stems as purple stems, this gives a ratio of three green to one purple. This ratio of 3:1 is called the **monohybrid ratio**.

The tomato plants that grew from the F_1 seeds.

2 Make a large wall poster of these results to show what happened in the experiment. If you do this investigation, you could use the school's digital camera to record your results.

2.6 Inheritance

Gregor Mendel

Winston King's class wanted to find an explanation for the results from growing tomato plants.

They found that Gregor Mendel carried out some research in 1860. He investigated the inheritance of different characteristics in garden peas and discovered the basic laws of inheritance.

Modern discoveries about chromosomes, genes and DNA are now used to explain his results.

The diagrams show how we can use symbols to explain the results of the tomato experiments. The letter G represents the **allele** (form of a gene) for green stems. It is a dominant allele.

The allele for purple stems is represented in the diagram by g and is recessive.

> ### Word check ✓
>
> **Alleles** are different versions of a gene. For each characteristic, you inherit one allele from each parent on a pair of chromosomes.

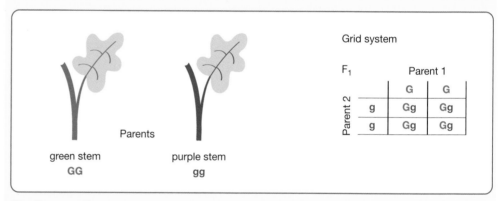

The F₁ generation.

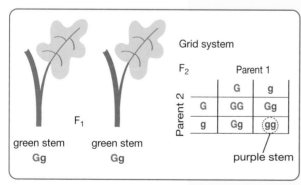

The F₂ generation.

When gametes (eggs and pollen) are made by the plant, these alleles are separated. During fertilisation they are combined at random.

You can use a grid to work out what happens.

The F_1 generation are all Gg and have green stems. These plants are called **heterozygous** because they contain two different alleles for stem colour.

❸ Why did all the F_1 plants have green stems?

The F_2 generation shows a ratio of three green to one purple stem. This 3:1 ratio is called the monohybrid ratio.

Some of these green-stemmed plants have only one sort of allele (GG). All the purple-stemmed plants also have only one sort of allele for stem colour (gg). They are both called **homozygous**.

2.6 Inheritance

The Human Genome Project   (CASE STUDY)

Since 1985, thousands of scientists around the world have been involved in the Human Genome Project.

Their aims are to:

• identify all the 30 000 human genes;

• find out the sequence of chemicals in human DNA, the human genetic code;

• make a computer database of all the information;

• consider the ethical, legal and social issues which would result from their research.

A first draft of their work was published in June 2000. The US President and the UK Prime Minister called it 'the most wondrous map ever produced'.

The position of disease-causing genes on particular chromosomes is now known.

In the future, this knowledge can be used to treat or prevent a wide variety of diseases. However, many people are worried that this knowledge could be misused. Others believe that open access to the information is necessary so a variety of people can use it.

If it is known that a person's genetic code contains some unwanted or harmful characteristics, they may be unable to get health insurance or a permanent job.

A human chromosome.

chromosome 7
Cystic fibrosis causes excess mucus production.

chromosome 4
Huntington's disease causes progressive nerve damage.

1   2   3   4   5

6   7   8   9   10   11   12

chromosome 11
Sickle cell anaemia causes abnormal haemoglobin.

13   14   15   16   17   18   19   20

21   22   XX

chromosome X
Haemophilia causes lack of blood clotting factor.

The genes that cause some inherited diseases can now be located on human chromosomes.

❹ Do you think all this information on genetic codes should be available to everyone?

Key facts

Copy and complete the sentences by choosing the correct word from the key words list.

1 Sections of chromosomes called _____ carry the genetic information inside the nucleus of every cell.

2 Coded instructions on chromosomes form our _____ _____.

3 Deoxyribonucleic acid, or _____, looks like a twisted ladder since it forms a _____ _____.

4 Genes for the same characteristic are called _____.

5 In humans, brown eyes are _____ over blue eyes, blue eyes are _____ to brown eyes.

6 When an organism has two identical alleles for a characteristic, it is said to be _____ for that characteristic. When the alleles are different, it is said to be _____.

7 The ratio of 3:1 is called the _____ _____.

Key words

allele

DNA

dominant

double helix

gene

genetic code

heterozygous

homozygous

monohybrid ratio

recessive

49

Review questions

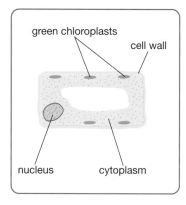

green chloroplasts

cell wall

nucleus

cytoplasm

1 Scientists discover a new plant. Using a microscope, they look at one of its cells (see diagram).

(a) Name TWO of its structures that are found only in plant cells and explain what they do. [5]

(b) Name TWO of its structures that are found in both plant and animal cells. [2]

2 The plant gives off a scent.

Explain how the scent reaches the scientists' noses. [3]

3 The scientists put some of the cells in various solutions.

What would you expect to happen to the plant cells in:

(a) water [2]

(b) strong salt solution? [2]

4 Using a microscope, the scientists study the membrane surrounding the cytoplasm.

(a) What name is given to this type of membrane? [1]

(b) Explain the function of this membrane. [2]

(c) Describe how you would prepare the cells to view with a microscope. [3]

5 The scientists decide to carry out breeding experiments on an animal.

Copy and complete the following sentences using some of these words:

chromosomes, cytoplasm, F$_1$, gametes, heterozygous, XX, XY.

The characteristics of this organism are carried on the _____ inside the nucleus.

The reproductive cells, called _____, contain only one set of chromosomes.

They think it is a female organism because its sex chromosomes are

_____. [4]

6 The scientists investigated the growth of a plant. Their results are shown in the table.

Time in weeks	Increase in length/cm at 10°C	Increase in length/cm at 20°C
1	0.5	0.7
2	0.6	0.8
3	0.5	1.0
4	0.5	1.0

(a) Which type of cell division is involved in growth? [1]

(b) How much did the plant grow in four weeks at 10°C? [1]

(c) Suggest why there is a difference between the growth rates at 10°C and 20°C. [2]

2 Living organisms

FOOD AND FARMING

Contents

Practical activities linked to this section:

Racing mustard and cress

Starch in leaves

Plants, animals and their environment

Use the following to check your progress.

Unit 1

You will:

- understand how to make a temporary stained slide and use a light microscope to examine it — see page 53

- analyse and interpret results — see pages 54, 57, 58, 63

- evaluate investigations. — see page 57

Unit 2

You will:

- understand how plants make their food by photosynthesis — see pages 53–59

- know that plants need minerals from the soil — see pages 60–63

- know why plants need nitrates and magnesium — see page 61

- know about organic farming and intensive farming — see pages 64–71

- know what is meant by biological control — see page 69

- understand and describe the process of selective breeding — see pages 72–75

- learn about genetic engineering. — see pages 76–79

Unit 3

You will:

- understand how to improve the yield of a plant — see pages 54–55, 60–63

- understand the link between the environment and the behaviour and growth of organisms. — see pages 52–71

2.7 Photosynthesis

The importance of being green

The garden centre.

David works in a garden centre. He understands how plants make their food. This makes plants different from animals. He has learnt during his studies that green plants carry out complex reactions to make their food. This process is called **photosynthesis**.

The process of photosynthesis

Only plants with special pigments can carry out photosynthesis. Inside green plant cells are **chloroplasts** which contain green **chlorophyll** pigments. Most leaf cells and some cells in the stem therefore look green. Other **pigments** such as carotene (orange) and phycoerythrin (red) are also found in plants.

Carbon dioxide and water are both needed for photosynthesis. Although only 0.04 per cent of the air is carbon dioxide, this is enough for photosynthesis. Carbon dioxide gets into plant leaves through tiny holes in the leaves called **stomata**. Water enters the root hairs on plant roots by osmosis and is carried up the stem in specialised **xylem** cells. The diagram shows the entry of these materials.

A number of reactions take place in the chloroplasts.

- Energy from sunlight is used to split water into hydrogen and oxygen atoms.

- The oxygen may be used in the plant for respiration, or released to be used for animal respiration.

- The hydrogen is combined with **carbon dioxide** using a number of **enzymes** to produce glucose.

- The glucose is either used by the plant to grow and repair itself or is stored as insoluble starch grains in the cells.

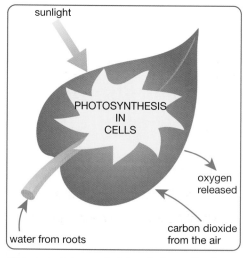

The materials needed for photosynthesis.

The overall equation for photosynthesis is

$$\text{carbon dioxide} + \text{water} \xrightarrow[\text{chlorophyll}]{\text{sunlight}} \text{glucose} + \text{oxygen}$$

$$6CO_2 + 6H_2O \longrightarrow C_6H_{12}O_6 + 6O_2$$

Word check

A **pigment** is a substance that gives colour to the cells of a plant.

 see Cells, page 26

 see Osmosis, page 34

Word check

Xylem are long, thin cells thickened with a chemical called lignin.

 see Exchange of gases, page 56

Word check

An **enzyme** is a biological catalyst that speeds up reactions in cells.

2.7 Photosynthesis

Looking inside potato cells ACTIVITY

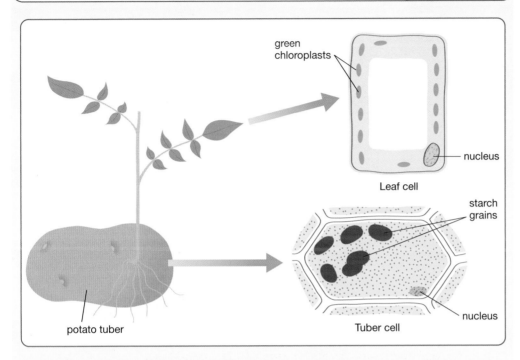

green chloroplasts

nucleus

Leaf cell

starch grains

nucleus

Tuber cell

potato tuber

Inside a potato plant.

The leaves of a potato plant photosynthesise in the summer, producing a lot of glucose. This changes into starch and is stored in the tuber to last through the winter.

Cells from a potato tuber are easily examined using a microscope. A core is taken from a tuber using a cork borer. Thin sections are cut and placed on a slide. When iodine solution is added, the starch turns black. The diagram above shows what the cells look like.

Cells from potato leaves are more difficult to get. By bending a leaf, then tearing the two halves apart, you can obtain a thin strip of cells. This thin strip of cells is placed on a slide with a drop of water. A coverslip placed over the top keeps everything in place. In some cells, it is difficult to see any detail. If you remove the coverslip and add iodine solution, any starch grains are stained black.

During winter, little photosynthesis is possible, so only the potato tuber survives. This is because:

• temperatures are too low for efficient enzyme action for photosynthesis;

• water is often frozen and therefore unavailable to the plant;

• daylight hours are few and light intensity is low, so sunlight is in short supply.

❶ Scientists are trying to develop plants with more chloroplasts in their cells. Explain how this would produce better plants.

❷ Potato plants are just one type of plant that stores food underground. Make a list of other plants that store food underground. Divide them into those we eat and those we do not. For example, we do not eat daffodil bulbs.

2.7 Photosynthesis

Selecting a plant for Mothers' Day.

Growing plants from seeds

David grows some plants from seed. He wants the plants he grows to be ready at the right time for special occasions, such as Mothers' Day. This takes a lot of knowledge and planning. If the plants flower too early, or flower too late, he will lose a lot of money. To do his job properly, David needs to understand the growth of seeds. This process is called germination.

Germination and growth

Seeds contain a large store of food and an embryo, which will grow into a new plant. David is doing some research into germination. He germinates maize seeds and grows them under different conditions.

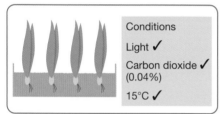

Conditions
Light ✓
Carbon dioxide ✓ (0.04%)
15°C ✓

A These maize plants grew looking very healthy and green in colour.

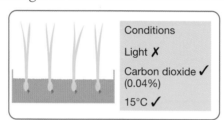

Conditions
Light ✗
Carbon dioxide ✓ (0.04%)
15°C ✓

B These plants grew taller but were pale yellow with thin stems.

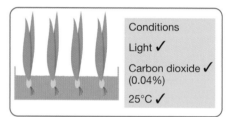

Conditions
Light ✓
Carbon dioxide ✓ (0.04%)
25°C ✓

C These plants grew tall, green and healthy very quickly.

The rate of photosynthesis can be increased by:

• increasing the level of carbon dioxide in the air;

• increasing the amount of light available;

see Exchange of gases, page 56

• increasing the temperature.

3 Why are the plants in batch B pale yellow?

4 What factor caused the plants in batch C to grow quickly?

5 David decides to grow some plants in a greenhouse with a paraffin heater. Give two reasons why these plants will grow tall and healthy very quickly.

Key words

carbon dioxide

chlorophyll

chloroplast

enzyme

photosynthesis

pigment

stoma (plural: stomata)

xylem

Key facts

Copy and complete the sentences by choosing the correct word from the key words list.

1 Plant cells make food by the process of _____.

2 Special green structures called _____ carry out this process. The green colour is caused by a _____ called _____.

3 Gases enter and leave a leaf through special openings called _____.

4 Water travels up the stem in specialised _____ cells.

5 In photosynthesis, the energy from sunlight is used to split water. Hydrogen from the water is combined with _____ _____ using many _____.

2.7 Photosynthesis

Growing healthy plants CASE STUDY

David enjoys looking after plants at the garden centre. With such a huge variety of plants to look after, he has to be familiar with the different growing conditions needed for a variety of plants. People buying plants know he is an expert and ask his advice.

Plant labels have a lot of useful information for the purchaser to make sure the plant has the best chance of growing well and looking good.

David advises people on different conditions plants need, but also suggests they look carefully at the advice on the labels.

David enjoys working in the garden centre.

Bunny ears cactus
Opuntia microdasys

Needs plenty of light.
Prefers warm conditions.
Too much watering will cause rotting.
Needs very little fertiliser.
Slow growing.
Spikes can damage skin so handle with care.

Cast iron plant
Aspidistra eliator

Prefers shady conditions.
Needs cool conditions to grow well.
Needs very little water.
Needs very little fertiliser.
Wash leaves frequently to remove dust.

Dumb cane
Diffenbachia amoena

Prefers some shade.
Needs warm conditions.
Grows quickly and needs a lot of fertiliser.
Water well.
Use gloves when handling this plant. If sap touches lips or tongue it will cause painful swellings.

6 Which plant should a customer buy for a sunny conservatory? Explain your choice.

7 Which plants would survive being neglected for a few weeks? Explain your choice.

8 A couple purchasing some plants have young children. Which plants should they not buy? Explain why.

9 Suggest why some plants need a lot of fertiliser.

10 Why will removing the dust from the leaves help the plants to photosynthesise?

2.8 Exchange of gases

Ali's fish tank

Tropical fish in a pet shop.

Ali keeps tropical fish. After a few months, some of the fish do not look very healthy. Ali goes to a pet shop for advice. Lindsay, the assistant, tells Ali that she should put some live plants in the fish tank instead of using plastic ones. The real plants will provide **oxygen** and use up the **carbon dioxide** produced by the fish.

Photosynthesis and respiration

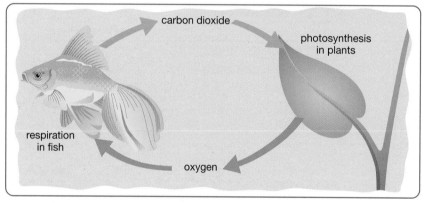

Fish need real plants in their tank to stay healthy.

Both **photosynthesis** and **respiration** are involved in keeping the environment in the tank healthy. Ali realises that the plants and fish are helping each other.

One of the fish's waste products is carbon dioxide. It is used by the plants and does not concentrate in the water. The plants make oxygen as the waste product of photosynthesis, so the fish will always have a good supply to breathe in.

The overall equations for respiration and photosynthesis are:

Respiration

$$\text{glucose} + \text{oxygen} \rightarrow \text{carbon dioxide} + \text{water} + \text{energy}$$

$$C_6H_{12}O_6 + 6O_2 \rightarrow 6CO_2 + 6H_2O + \text{energy}$$

Photosynthesis

$$\text{carbon dioxide} + \text{water} \xrightarrow[\text{chlorophyll}]{\text{light energy}} \text{glucose} + \text{oxygen}$$

$$6CO_2 + 6H_2O \longrightarrow C_6H_{12}O_6 + 6O_2$$

see Asthma, page 116

❶ Lindsay tells Ali to fit an air pump to the fish tank. Explain how this will help the fish.

❷ What do you notice about the equations for photosynthesis and respiration?

❸ In terms of energy, compare respiration and photosynthesis.

❹ Explain why respiration in plants results in carbon dioxide diffusing out of the leaves only when it is dark.

2.8 Exchange of gases

Ali does an experiment ACTIVITY

Ali decides to carry out some experiments in her science lessons on plants and animals.

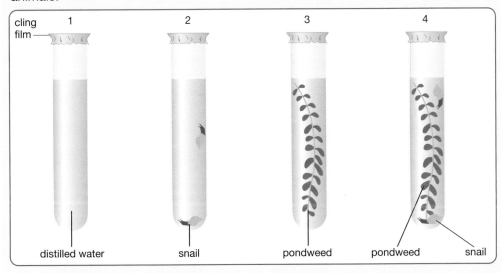

Experiment to show how plants and animals affect water pH.

She sets up four tubes containing:

1. only distilled water;

2. only water snails in distilled water;

3. only pondweed (*Elodea*) in distilled water;

4. both water snails and pondweed in distilled water.

She covers each tube with cling film and shines a light on all four tubes for a few hours.

She then uses a syringe to inject $2\,cm^3$ of bromothymol blue indicator into each tube. The indicator shows acid or alkaline conditions (pH) by changing colour. She notes the colours and pH of each tube and removes the pondweed and snails before they are affected by the indicator. Her teacher tells her she could have used an accurate pH probe to get better results.

If there is plenty of carbon dioxide, it will react with the water, producing an acid called carbonic acid. A pH of less than 7 shows an acid solution, a pH of more than 7 is alkaline, a pH of 7 is neutral.

Ali writes down her results.

Tube 1 pH 6.5   Tube 2 pH 6   Tube 3 pH 7   Tube 4 pH 6.5

5 Describe how Ali tried to make her experiment a fair test.

6 Why did Ali shine a light on the experiment?

7 Explain why the tubes were covered with cling film.

8 Explain why the water in tube 3 was the least acidic.

9 Explain why the water in tubes 1 and 4 had the same pH.

2.8 Exchange of gases

Limiting factors

If conditions such as light, heat and carbon dioxide are not correct, the rate of photosynthesis will be reduced or *limited*.

These conditions are therefore called **limiting factors**.

Scientists have carried out experiments to find out how fast photosynthesis can take place and what stops it from going faster.

They measured the rate of photosynthesis as the light intensity increased.

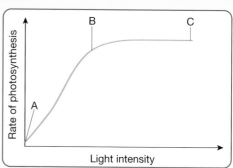

Between A and B, as the light intensity increased, so did the rate of photosynthesis.

Between B and C, although the light intensity increased, the rate of photosynthesis stayed the same.

Therefore, some other factor, such as temperature or the amount of carbon dioxide, was limiting photosynthesis.

The scientists then measured the rate of photosynthesis at different temperatures as the light intensity increased.

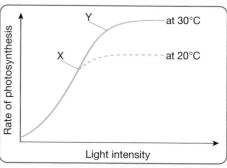

10 What is the limiting factor at X?

11 Suggest what could be the limiting factor at Y.

12 Ali keeps her fish tank in her bedroom. The water temperature is set at 25°C. She keeps plenty of plants in the fish tank. Suggest one factor which could be limiting the plants' growth.

Key words

carbon dioxide

limiting factors

oxygen

photosynthesis

respiration

Key facts

Copy and complete the sentences by choosing the correct word from the key words list.

1 During the day, green plants use up _____ _____ and produce _____. This process is called _____.

2 Green plants also carry out _____ to release energy from food.

3 Light, temperature and carbon dioxide can each be _____ _____ for photosynthesis.

2.8 Exchange of gases

Keeping tropical fish

The pet shop is so successful that Lindsay decides to set up another fish tank.

She has to think about a number of things.

Heating. To keep the tank at a reasonable temperature, a five watt heater is required for each four litres of water.

Number of fish. Each two centimetre length of fish require four litres of water to prevent overcrowding.

Lighting. The size of the bulb needed to provide a reasonable amount of light can be calculated:

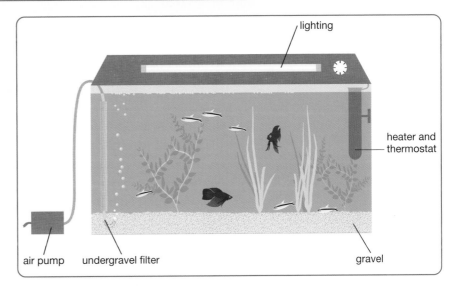

$$\frac{\text{length of fish tank in cm} \times 12}{\text{number of hours of lighting/day}} = \text{bulb size in watts}$$

pH. The water is best kept at about neutral, between 6.8 and 7.2.

Filtration. An undergravel filter system works by pulling dirty water through the gravel. Sediment in the gravel is broken down by bacteria. This prevents the build-up of organisms that cause disease.

Lindsay is interested in keeping these fish in her tank:

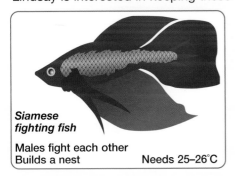

Siamese fighting fish

Males fight each other
Builds a nest   Needs 25–26°C

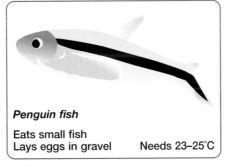

Penguin fish

Eats small fish
Lays eggs in gravel   Needs 23–25°C

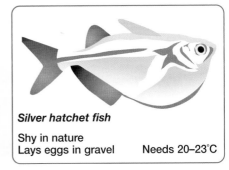

Silver hatchet fish

Shy in nature
Lays eggs in gravel   Needs 20–23°C

Lindsay's manager tells her this is not a good idea.

13 Suggest why Lindsay's manager thinks this.

For a project, you could find out a lot more detail about keeping and breeding tropical fish. The project could be based on:

• selecting a size of tank;

• working out how many and what type and size of fish to keep;

• working out the cost of setting up a fish tank;

• working out running costs (heating, lighting, feeding);

• developing a controlled breeding programme for one type of fish.

2.9 Minerals

How the Greeks thought plants grow

Long ago, Greeks and Romans believed that the growth of plants was due only to things in the soil.

In about 1600CE, Jan van Helmont set out to prove this wrong. He grew a small willow tree in a pot and watered it with rainwater for five years. The tree and soil were separated and weighed. The tree had gained 75 kg but the soil had lost only 0.0275 kg.

The gain in weight we now know was a result of the willow tree making its own food by photosynthesis.

The loss in weight from the soil was not caused by errors in weighing. The roots of the willow tree had taken up certain **minerals** from the soil. These minerals can be added to the soil as **fertilisers**.

 see Photosynthesis, page 52

 see Exchange of gases, page 56

Word check

A **fertiliser** is a substance that is added to soil to make plants grow better.

So the Greeks and Romans were partly right: plants do use something from the soil.

How modern scientists think plants grow

Plants remove small amounts of minerals from the soil. Farmers need to return these minerals to the soil. They can use natural fertilisers such as animal manure or manufactured fertilisers.

Animal waste products can be used as natural fertilisers.

Manufactured fertilisers contain compounds of nitrogen (N), phosphorus (P) and potassium (K).

Natural fertilisers. These come from dead plants and animals as well as animal wastes. Bacteria and fungi cause rotting, recycling the minerals.

Manufactured fertilisers. The first factory-made fertiliser was superphosphate, produced in 1842. It was made by adding sulphuric acid to bones. In 1919, after the First World War, many factories that used nitrates changed from making explosives to making fertilisers.

2.9 Minerals

Growing healthy tomatoes   ACTIVITY

Scientists have found that plants need some elements in large amounts (macronutrients) and some in small amounts (micronutrients).

Many elements are taken up by plant roots as compounds dissolved in water, for example, nitrogen as nitrates (NO_3) and phosphorus as phosphates (PO_4).

Plants also need carbon, oxygen and hydrogen. These come from carbon dioxide (CO_2) and oxygen (O_2) from the air and water (H_2O) from the soil.

The pictures show the results of an experiment with tomato plants. Some plants are missing some minerals.

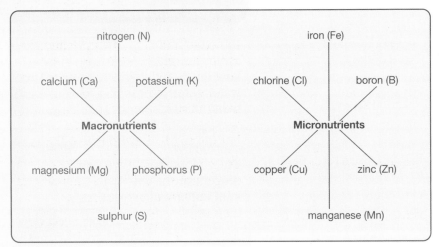

nitrogen (N)
calcium (Ca)   potassium (K)
Macronutrients
magnesium (Mg) | phosphorus (P)
sulphur (S)

iron (Fe)
chlorine (Cl)   boron (B)
Micronutrients
copper (Cu)   zinc (Zn)
manganese (Mn)

Minerals that plants need.

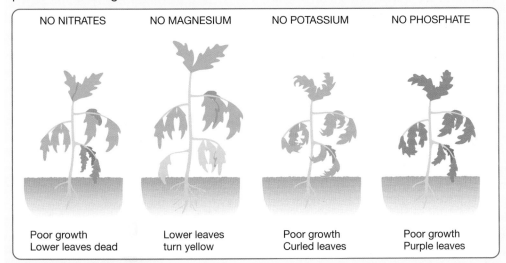

NO NITRATES	NO MAGNESIUM	NO POTASSIUM	NO PHOSPHATE
Poor growth Lower leaves dead	Lower leaves turn yellow	Poor growth Curled leaves	Poor growth Purple leaves

The effects of lack of minerals on plant growth.

Nitrates are used to make protein so a shortage will cause poor growth. **Potassium** and **phosphates** are also needed for healthy growth. **Magnesium** forms part of the chlorophyll molecule so a shortage will cause less chlorophyll to be made and the plant leaves will be yellow instead of green.

Farmers use a lot of fertiliser called NPK, named after the three elements it contains: nitrogen (N), phosphorus (P) and potassium (K).

Look at a label from a bottle of fertiliser for house plants and list the minerals it contains.

❶ Susie grows tomatoes. She finds she needs a high nitrogen fertiliser when her tomato plants are young. Suggest why.

❷ Susie's dad has been growing tomato plants in his greenhouse for many years. Each year his crop has been smaller. What advice should Susie give him so he can get a better tomato crop?

2.9 Minerals

Active transport

see Diffusion, page 30 and
Osmosis, page 34

Diffusion and osmosis explain how gases and water enter living things.

The bar chart shows how water plants concentrate minerals in their cells.

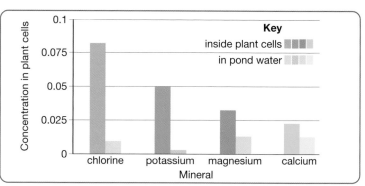

Plants select certain minerals.

Scientists were baffled as to how plants managed to take up various minerals. Then in 1938 they discovered that an increase in mineral uptake was matched by an increase in the rate of respiration. This meant that **energy** was being used to take up minerals.

They also found that plants could select certain minerals and take up different minerals in different amounts.

We now know that the uptake of minerals is carried out by a process called **active transport**.

see Cells, page 26

Carriers in the cell membrane move minerals into the cell, even though the concentration of minerals in the cell is higher than in the surroundings. This is why energy is needed.

How active transport works.

❸ Scientists have found that one mineral sometimes slows down the uptake of another mineral. Using information in the diagram, explain how this could happen.

Food in space

One of the problems of space travel is providing food for very long journeys lasting years. Scientists have tried growing small green plants called algae. Fertilisers are automatically supplied to the growing algae. After a few weeks' growth, the algae are harvested and eaten.

❹ Suggest where the fertilisers could come from.

❺ Suggest how, apart from food, these algae might be useful to astronauts. (Hint: exchange of gases in plants and animals.)

❻ Suggest why algae and not other plants, such as cabbage, are thought to be best for growing in space.

❼ Design equipment which could be used to grow and harvest algae in a spaceship.

2.9 Minerals

The Rothamsted experiment CASE STUDY

In 1843, after much argument about the use of fertilisers, a long-term experiment was set up on the Rothamsted Estate. Fertilisers containing nitrogen (N), phosphorus (P), and potassium (K) were used on wheat and potato crops in the same fields for about 160 years.

Results of the Rothamsted experiment.

Fertiliser added/kg ha^{-1}			Crop yield/tonne ha^{-1}	
N	P	K	Wheat	Potatoes
0	0	0	1.69	9.47
96	0	0	3.68	8.3
0	77	107	2.04	16.63
96	77	107	6.6	38.57

Nitrogen, phosphorus and potassium are all needed to produce a good crop of wheat.

The experiment showed that both wheat and potato crops needed fertilisers containing all three minerals to produce good crops. Nitrogen makes leaves grow well. Phosphorus is necessary for good root growth. Potassium is needed for overall growth, photosynthesis and disease resistance.

When too much fertiliser is used, some is washed out into rivers and lakes. This leads to rapid growth of green algae living there. When they die and rot, the oxygen in the water is used up so animals, such as fish, die. This process is called **eutrophication**.

see Intensive farming, page 64

8 Suggest why using a fertiliser containing only nitrogen produced a smaller crop of potatoes than using no fertiliser at all.

9 Explain why, in the Rothamsted experiment, one field had no fertiliser added.

10 Suggest other factors, apart from fertilisers, which might affect the potato and wheat crops.

11 Draw a time line of dates relating to fertilisers.

Key facts

Copy and complete the sentences by choosing the correct word from the key words list.

1 Although plants use photosynthesis to make food, they need _____ for healthy growth. They are supplied by _____.

2 Chlorophyll needs the mineral _____ and _____ are needed to make proteins.

3 Two other important minerals which are required for healthy growth are _____ and _____.

4 Minerals are taken up from soil water by _____ _____. This requires _____ which is released by respiration.

Key words

active transport

energy

fertiliser

magnesium

minerals

nitrate

phosphate

potassium

2.10 Intensive farming

Farming as it used to be.

How we used to grow food

Our ancestors used 'slash and burn' methods to grow crops. They cleared an area of forest by cutting down trees and burning them. Crops grew well in the soil, rich in minerals from the ash. After a few years, the crops were poor, so they moved on to another area and started again.

With small populations, this worked for hundreds of years.

In recent times, with rapidly increasing populations requiring food, most countries use **intensive farming** methods.

How we grow food now

Modern farming.

Intensive farming uses large amounts of:

see Minerals, page 60

- artificial fertilisers to get big yields of healthy crops;
- **herbicides** to kill unwanted plants;
- **pesticides** to kill unwanted animals such as insect pests;
- **fungicides** to kill fungi which cause plant diseases.

A modern farmer can use about 70 different manufactured substances on his farm.

1 If you lived very close to farmers' fields, what risks might you be exposed to?

In 1970, people in the UK spent 25 per cent of their income on food, yet today we spend only 10 per cent. Intensive farming, together with other improved farming techniques, has produced more food at a cheaper price.

see Types of microorganism, page 86

Since intensive farming uses large amounts of chemicals, pollution can be a problem. Keeping large numbers of animals, such as hens and pigs, in confined areas can easily spread disease. Creating large fields to use big mechanical harvesters has led to the removal of many hedgerows. This destroys important plant and animal communities. Many people have also blamed intensive farming methods for the spread of BSE in cows and the spread of foot and mouth disease in 2001.

2.10 Intensive farming

Energy levels in food production — ACTIVITY

Food production is about **energy transfer**.

In photosynthesis, plants use light energy to produce food. Plants are eaten by animals such as cows.

see Photosynthesis, page 52 →

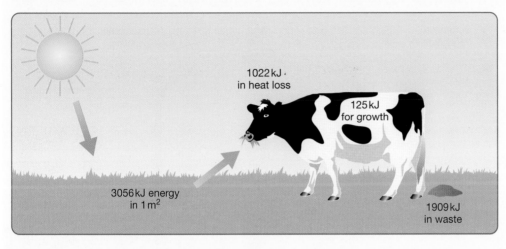

1022 kJ in heat loss

125 kJ for growth

3056 kJ energy in 1 m²

1909 kJ in waste

Energy transfer.

The diagram shows how of 3056 kilojoule (kJ) of energy in grass, only 125 kJ is used for a cow's growth.

It is a very inefficient way of transferring energy!

❷ Calculate this efficiency using the formula:

$$\text{efficiency} = \frac{\text{energy used for growth (output)}}{\text{energy supplied (input)}} \times 100\%$$

Intensive farming cuts down this energy loss by:

• stopping other animals eating the grass;

• keeping the animals close together in special sheds.

More energy will be saved by:

• using insecticides to prevent disease, and thus slower growth, in cows;

• using herbicides to stop weeds competing for minerals.

❸ Explain how keeping animals, such as cows, together in sheds saves energy.

❹ What problems could occur when cows are kept in sheds for long periods?

Small animals, such as hens, are suitable for intensive farming. Hens are kept in small cages called batteries. Their activity is limited so less energy is wasted in movement. Their diet is strictly controlled to get the maximum weight gain or high egg production.

Many people object to this 'battery farming' because they believe it is cruel. They prefer 'free range' hens. These hens have a more natural life. They are kept in fields and have the use of hen huts.

❺ Use the Internet to find more information about battery farming. Produce a leaflet showing arguments for and against this method of keeping hens.

2.10 Intensive farming

Greenhouses

see Movement under control, page 267

Large greenhouses are often used in intensive farming. They use automatic systems to get the best possible conditions for plant growth.

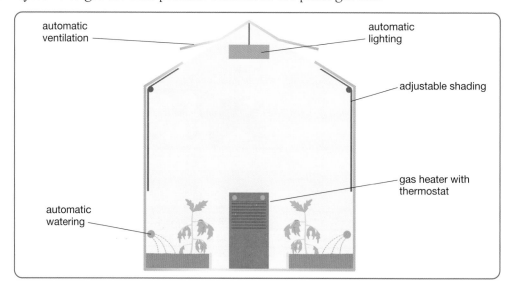

Automatic systems in a greenhouse.

6 Which conditions are being automatically controlled in this greenhouse?

To reduce costs, long polythene tunnels are often used instead of expensive glass greenhouses. Small tractors can be used inside to help in the cultivation and collection of the crop.

Green algae form a thick scum on a stagnant pond.

Farmers should not apply more than 210 kg of nitrogen fertiliser per hectare. When larger amounts are used, more is wasted by drainage. It drains away into ponds, rivers and lakes.

The fertiliser has the same effect in water as it has on land. It encourages plant growth. The microscopic green algae in the water grow and reproduce so quickly that the water looks like pea soup. When they die, the decay process uses up large amounts of oxygen from the water. This lack of oxygen kills most animal life, including fish. This is called eutrophication and is a major problem in many lakes throughout the world.

Using high levels of nitrate fertiliser has another bad effect. Some can end up in our drinking water. A European Union Directive suggests a maximum nitrate level of 25 mg per litre of water, as bacteria easily change nitrates to nitrites. Nitrites combine with haemoglobin in our red blood cells, preventing it from combining with oxygen. In babies, this can be fatal.

see Blood donor, page 112

see Chemical analysis, page 196

The mineral content of bottled water is shown on the labels. You could look at a variety of bottled waters and compare their mineral content, especially that of nitrates. You could also contact your local Water Authority to find out the amount of nitrates in your tap water.

2.10 Intensive farming

The miracle of fish in the desert   CASE STUDY

Fish are a valuable source of protein in our diet. Over-fishing and pollution have drastically reduced the fish stocks in the North Sea.

Fish farming, using salmon or cod, now takes place in a number of sea lochs and sheltered bays in the UK. The fishes' growth is carefully monitored and controlled. The fish are kept in large cages and feed on concentrated pellet food. Losses are kept low by preventing entry of predators and using drugs to control disease.

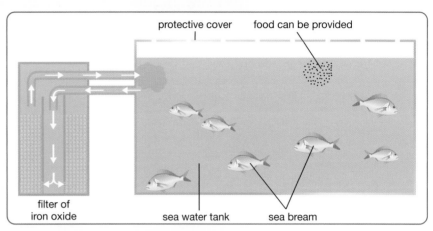

Removing poisonous waste from the tank at a fish farm.

The main problem of this type of intensive farming is the waste produced by the fish. Bacteria act on the waste, turning it into toxic hydrogen sulphide. If this is pumped back into the fish tanks, it will kill all the fish. Professor Mike Krom at Leeds University has developed an early warning system for this toxic chemical. His research was carried out on a fish farm in the middle of the Israeli desert.

The water is passed over tiny beads covered with orange iron oxide. This reacts with any toxic hydrogen sulphide, producing black iron oxide. A light-sensitive detector reacts to this change and stops the pump putting back the toxic waste. Clean water is pumped in to the tank instead.

In a pilot scheme, Professor Krom produced sea bream weighing about 0.5 kg each in one year in a small tank. Further trials in Israel and Greece have been set up, each holding 2400 fish.

7 Explain why fish farming could be so important to a mainly desert country such as Israel.

8 Describe the conditions which can be easily controlled in fish farming.

9 Explain why fish farming can be very productive.

10 Suggest how fish farming can be damaging to the environment.

Key facts

Copy and complete the sentences by choosing the correct word from the key words list.

1 Farmers try to produce more food using _____ _____ methods.

2 They use _____ to kill unwanted plants, _____ to kill unwanted pests and _____ to kill unwanted fungi.

3 _____ _____ takes place from plants to animals when they eat the plants.

4 Pollution by fertilisers can cause _____ in lakes. The oxygen in the water is used up, causing fish to die.

Key words

energy transfer

eutrophication

fungicides

herbicides

intensive farming

pesticides

2.11 Organic farming

Sam's allotment

Sam working on her allotment.

Sam has an allotment. She grows fruit and vegetables using organic farming methods. She wants to know exactly what is in her food.

Sam does not use manufactured chemicals such as pesticides, herbicides, fungicides or artificial fertilisers. She realises that her allotment will produce less because some crops will be eaten by pests such as slugs and aphids or killed by diseases such as club root in cabbages.

However, she will not need to buy any manufactured substances. She knows other ways of controlling the pests.

Controlling pests without using pesticides

Sam knows the dangers of using pesticides. They kill useful insects, such as ladybirds and bees, as well as harmful insects such as aphids.

 Explain how insects, such as bees, are useful.

② Name two other useful insects and two other harmful insects. Explain how they are useful or harmful to crops.

Sam knows that insecticides can be concentrated in **food chains**.

> ### Word check ✓
>
> A **food chain** shows how energy is transferred from plants to herbivores (plant eaters) and then to carnivores (animal eaters).

1 aphid receives 5 molecules of insecticide	A lacewing larva eats 100 aphids	A tit eats 10 lacewing larvae	A hawk eats 5 tits
5	500	5000	25000

Amount of insecticide in one organism

Insecticides build up as they move through a food chain.

Insecticides can build up to very high levels in predators such as hawks, affecting egg production or even causing their death.

Even though the insecticide called DDT was banned more than 20 years ago, long-living animals, such as polar bears and whales, have been found to contain very high levels of DDT.

2.11 Organic farming

Biological control

Aphids are a problem for many gardeners and farmers. They suck the sap from the stems of young plants, restricting and distorting their growth. Aphids grow rapidly, taking only seven days to become adult. Each adult aphid can produce four young aphids each day. After a week, these new aphids will also be reproducing.

Over 70 years ago, a Hampshire farmer discovered some black aphid larvae. He sent them to a horticultural research station. The scientists found that, instead of the larvae becoming aphids, a tiny wasp appeared. The wasp, called *Encarsia formosa*, had used the larvae to carry its eggs. When the eggs hatched out, the young stage of the wasp ate the aphid larva.

The wasp is a **predator** and the aphid larva is its **prey**. Scientists have used this discovery to develop a natural method of controlling pests. The recent interest in **organic farming** has meant that this **biological control** is now popular.

Aphids can give birth to four live young each day.

You can grow tomato plants in simple one metre square cages of curtain mesh, as shown in the diagram. Tomato plants are easily grown from seeds. Aphids for the experiment are easily found in gardens in spring and summer.

curtain mesh

tomato plant

tunnel opening

Using biological control to protect tomato plants.

After the tomato plants have been in the cage for one week, the aphids are introduced through the tunnel opening. Cards containing the young stages of the parasitic wasp (obtainable from most garden centres) are put into the cage.

After another week, you can remove a tomato leaf. Using a hand lens, you can count the number of black aphid larvae (affected by the wasp) and the number of pale larvae (unaffected by the wasp). This sampling is repeated over a number of weeks to find out how well this type of biological control works.

2.11 Organic farming

Large-scale production

Organic farming tries to create a humane and environmentally friendly system of producing food from plants and animals.

Although organic farming uses only 2.3 per cent of the total farmed area in the UK, it is rapidly increasing.

Supermarkets have reported that the market in organic produce increased by 55 per cent between 2000 and 2001. Surveys show that people in the UK believe that organic farming provides better tasting, healthier food, produced in an environmentally friendly way.

It is believed that organic farming will be more common than intensive farming by 2020.

see Minerals, page 60

To be an organic farmer, you must:

- recycle animal manure and crop waste to provide essential minerals for healthy plant growth;

- use crop rotation systems to avoid a build-up of disease in the soil;

- use plants such as clover to put nitrates back into the soil: special nodules on their roots can 'fix' nitrogen from the air into nitrogen-containing compounds in the plant;

- use natural methods such as introducing predators to control animal pests;

- use hand or mechanical weeding to control weeds;

- vary seed planting times to avoid times when plant pests are more numerous;

- avoid stress and cruelty to farm animals, conserve wildlife and natural habitat.

The nodules on clover roots 'fix' nitrogen in the air so the clover can use it to make proteins.

Visit your local supermarket and list the types of fruit and vegetable available. Compare prices of organic produce with those of the traditionally produced foods. If there is a difference in price, think why there is.

③ Draw up a table to compare the advantages and disadvantages of intensive farming and organic farming.

2.11 Organic farming

Composting waste

Every year, millions of tonnes of kitchen and garden waste go into our dustbins. They end up in landfill sites.

Many local authorities, such as Calderdale Council in West Yorkshire, actively encourage composting this material by providing compost bins at reduced prices. Calderdale Council has a full-time Compost Adviser.

Materials such as vegetable peelings, grass cuttings, leaves, shredded paper and even pet hair are ideal to compost. The rotting process is caused by aerobic **bacteria**, so **oxygen**, water and warmth are required. Many other small organisms, such as earthworms, also help to break down the material.

After a few months, the **compost** should be dark brown and crumbly without any unpleasant smell.

It will be rich in minerals. The compost can then be added to garden soil, creating a more productive and attractive garden. The problem of overflowing dustbins will also be solved. Sam has one of the compost bins on her allotment.

Find out if your local authority encourages composting. If it doesn't, write a letter pointing out the advantages. Design a leaflet, which could be circulated to households to encourage them to compost kitchen waste. Attach the leaflet to your letter.

Councils encourage people to compost their garden waste.

Word check

Bacteria (singular: bacterium) are single-celled microorganisms.

CALDERDALE COUNCIL

COMPOST ADVISER
Scale 4 £13,764 - £15,342
(Pay Award Pending)
Six Months Fixed Term Contract
Post No. EH1042

The Council's Home Composting initiative is a continuing success, helping to keep down the amount of Calderdale waste going to landfill. A Compost Adviser is to be appointed to encourage, support and further develop home composting in order to achieve further improvement in waste diversion.

The position will be initially for six months. The post may be extended for a further twelve months if funding is obtained.

The post holder will have a good understanding of composting and associated matters. He or she will have extensive direct contact with householders, and must possess excellent communication skills. You must be able to make clear progress reports to managers and have the ability to work unsupervised for significant periods. The post holder must be educated to at least GCSE standard and possess a clean current driving licence.

A career opportunity?

Key facts

Copy and complete the sentences by choosing the correct word from the key words list. Each word may be used more than once.

1 No artificial herbicides, pesticides, fungicides or fertilisers are used in
_____ _____.

2 Insecticides can accumulate in different animals in a _____ _____.

3 An example of _____ _____ is shown by the *Encarsia* wasp.

4 This wasp is a _____ on aphids. The aphids are its _____.

5 The rotting of kitchen and garden waste can be done in a _____ bin.

6 The rotting process is due to living organisms such as _____. They need _____ to carry out aerobic respiration.

Key words

bacterium (plural: bacteria)

biological control

compost

food chain

organic farming

oxygen

predator

prey

2.12 Selective breeding

Susie goes clubbing

It's the male peacocks who wear the beautiful feathers.

Susie goes out clubbing with her friends on Saturday night. It takes her ages to get dressed in her latest gear and put on her make-up, but she knows it's worth it to have a good time. Pity some of the boys don't make as much of an effort as she does to look good.

Unlike humans, the males of most wild animals are the ones who 'dress up'. The males develop special features and courtship displays to make sure their genes are passed on to the next generation. A male peacock displaying its colourful feathers is an impressive sight, especially to a peahen.

Variation

Charles Darwin, in his famous studies on evolution, recognised that animals are different from each other. All peacocks may look the same but there are differences in size, weight, calls and colour. This **variation** results in some male peacocks being more attractive to peahens than others. These peacocks attract more females and so produce more offspring, who will also show these characteristics. Over many generations, the tail feathers of male peacocks have become more and more impressive. The females have only a dull colour.

Our knowledge of genetics supports Darwin's theory of **natural selection**.

Sometimes conditions change and animals can no longer survive.

see Inheritance, page 46

Word check ✓

The theory of **natural selection** explains how organisms that are best suited to their environment will survive.

1 Can you name the animals in the picture, which are now extinct? Carry out some research to find out the names of other animals which have become extinct or are threatened with extinction.

These animals have all become extinct.

Humans keep many animals such as cats, dogs, sheep, goats, deer and cows. These **domesticated** animals have been used as food, for hunting, clothing and protection. Many thousands of years ago, farmers started to choose individual animals to keep. They ignored the smaller, weaker ones and chose animals with useful characteristics, such as fine hair in sheep, high milk production in cows and high egg production in hens. They used only these individual animals to breed. This was the start of **selective breeding**.

2.12 Selective breeding

Modern farming (ACTIVITY)

A modern farmer develops this technique of selective breeding.

The Jersey cow produces small amounts of very creamy milk.

The Friesian cow produces large amounts of milk, but it is not very creamy.

A Jersey cow produces small quantities of very creamy milk. A Friesian cow produces large quantities of slightly creamy milk.

Mr Entwhistle, a dairy farmer, plans his selective breeding programme using these two varieties of cow. He:

- chooses the Friesian cows that produce the most milk;
- chooses the Jersey cows that produce the creamiest milk;
- cross-breeds bulls with these selected cows;

see Characteristics, page 38

- selects from these cross breeds individual cows that produce a large amount of creamy milk.

2 Explain why Mr Entwhistle's programme will take a number of years.

Sometimes **cross-breeding** does not work well. Cross-breeding a male donkey with a female horse produces a mule. Mules are much stronger than either of their parents and are often used to carry heavy packs in difficult conditions. However, since the mule's chromosomes are unable to pair up in gamete production, mules are sterile and cannot breed.

see Cells dividing, page 42

3 Suggest which animals are the parents of the cross-breeds, zedonk and tiglon.

4 Design a poster to announce the discovery of a new cross breed. Draw your new animal and give it a name.

Selective breeding programmes can cause problems. Harmful **recessive** characteristics would rarely survive naturally. Animal breeders can deliberately choose to keep such characteristics as very long ears in rabbits or extremely short legs in dogs. Selective breeding can result in less variation, so varieties of plants and animals can easily become extinct.

see Inheritance, page 46

2.12 Selective breeding

Choice

Susie likes to grow tomatoes. She looks at tomato seed packets and finds there are many different types of tomato plant. The choice is very confusing.

She decides to ask all her friends which type they would like.

Copy down some of the information about these three different types. Then carry out a survey among your friends about their choice and a reason for their decision. Some may prefer a small, sweet variety; others may prefer a large, heavy-cropping variety.

With such a wide variety of different characteristics in plants, farmers have used selective breeding techniques. They have selected plants which:

- grow faster and mature early, for example, cereals;
- have a distinctive scent, taste or colour, for example, strawberries;
- grow bigger and stronger, for example, cabbage;
- are resistant to disease, for example, fungus-resistant wheat;
- freeze well, for example, Brussels sprouts;
- last a long time on shop shelves, for example, lettuce.

Key words

cross-breeding

domesticate

natural selection

recessive

selective breeding

variation

Key facts

Copy and complete the sentences by choosing the correct word from the key words list. Each word may be used more than once.

1 In his theory of _____ _____ Charles Darwin recognised that _____ was important.

2 Thousands of years ago, humans started to keep animals and _____ them.

3 By choosing desirable characteristics and breeding from them, farmers are using _____ _____ .

4 Breeding between different varieties is called _____ _____ .

5 Selective breeding can cause an accumulation of _____ characteristics and a reduction in _____ .

2.12 Selective breeding

How daffodils got to Britain　　CASE STUDY

Some of you will recognise the lines:

'When all at once I saw a crowd,

A host, of golden daffodils'

William Wordsworth 1770–1850

The original daffodil bulbs were introduced into Britain by the Romans and now there are about 200 different varieties. The daffodils seen by Wordsworth in the Lake District were probably a variety of *Narcissus*. They are small, growing to a height of about 15 cm. They have small delicate flowers. This variety still grows around Ullswater in the Lake District.

Narcissus pseudonarcissus.

THE TIMES TUESDAY MARCH 19 2000

Wordsworth daffodils threatened by invaders

By Russell Jenkins

THE host of golden daffodils fluttering and dancing in the Lake District breeze that so captivated William Wordsworth has an enemy at the gate.

The original bulbs, believed to have been introduced to Britain by the Romans, risk being contaminated, and perhaps overrun, by much bigger and voracious common varieties on sale in garden centres.

Daffodil experts have advised the National Trust to take urgent action to halt the kind of cross-pollination that would turn the famed hedgerows and byways from a poetic vision into a scene no more entrancing than a suburban garden.

The carpet of naturally occurring daffodils have drawn visitors ever since

Wordsworth and his sister Dorothy walked along the Ullswater valley 200 years ago and came across them near Glencoyne Bay. The sight prompted the poet to write *Daffodils*.

The covering of daffodils is much thinner now than in Wordsworth's day, and many visitors go to Dora's Field, in Rydal, for a more spectacular show. The threat by *Narcissus "Carlton"* to *Narcissus pseudonarcissus* could further damage its attraction.

The alarm was raised by Jan Dalton, president of the Daffodil Society, who spotted the advance of cultivated daffodils growing across the road from the wild species. He has urged the Trust to remove the introduced bulbs.

Local people are worried that many common varieties of daffodil, such as *Narcissus* 'Carlton', could compete with it and force it into extinction. There could also be cross-pollination between the two varieties, resulting in new varieties and even more competition.

The original daffodils that Wordsworth saw thrived because they were ideally suited to a cool, wet and windy climate. Some people say their survival is not important since they were foreign plants about 2000 years ago. Some scientists believe that these daffodils will not survive in the Lake District as the climate becomes warmer.

Narcissus 'Carlton'.

5 Do you think the original 'Wordsworth' daffodils should be protected? Explain your reasons.

6 Suggest how the daffodils could be protected if it was decided to do so.

7 Why do some people think that it is not worth protecting the daffodils?

2.13 Genetic engineering

Friend or foe?

Genetically modified (GM) food crops first went on sale in 1996 but the debate about the advantages and disadvantages of GM crops has continued to this day.

 see Selective breeding, page 72

Some people believe that this new technology is really just a type of selective breeding and is safe. They believe that the extra food produced could feed the world's population. New medical discoveries using GM organisms could also save thousands of lives.

Other people believe that GM crops could cause serious damage to the environment. They think that long-term risks are not fully understood. They also believe that medical advances will cause ethical problems. Who should or should not be treated using this new technology?

The increasing use of GM crops

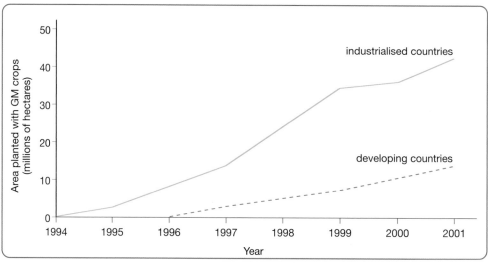

The area of land planted with GM crops has rapidly increased since 1994 as the graph shows. In 2001, GM crops covered nearly 55 million hectares of land worldwide.

The GM trial sites in the UK can be traced through various websites.

1 Suggest why the increase in area planted in industrialised countries slowed down in 1999.

2 Suggest why there is a difference in GM crop area between industrialised and developing countries.

2.13 Genetic engineering

Collecting evidence
ACTIVITY

Jake and Shareen read about genetic engineering. They start to collect newspaper cuttings about genetic engineering and display them on a notice board in the laboratory.

They divide them up into those that support using GM techniques and those that do not.

Using information in this topic, the Internet and your school library, add more information to support each side of the argument. Find out if there is a local GM trial site and ask for information. Ask your teacher to set up a debate to present your findings.

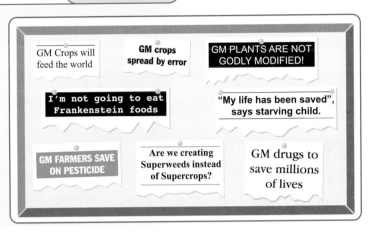

GM Crops will feed the world

GM crops spread by error

GM PLANTS ARE NOT GODLY MODIFIED!

I'm not going to eat Frankenstein foods

"My life has been saved", says starving child.

GM FARMERS SAVE ON PESTICIDE

Are we creating Superweeds instead of Supercrops?

GM drugs to save millions of lives

The science behind genetic engineering

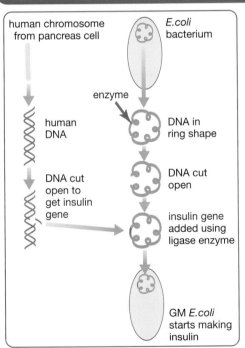

human chromosome from pancreas cell

E.coli bacterium

enzyme

human DNA

DNA in ring shape

DNA cut open to get insulin gene

DNA cut open

insulin gene added using ligase enzyme

GM E.coli starts making insulin

Chromosomes in the nuclei of cells contain DNA. This DNA carries the genetic code for living organisms.

see Inheritance, page 46

Scientists are now able to take a single gene from an organism's DNA and put it into the DNA of another organism while it is developing. This creates a **transgenic** organism that contains the new gene.

see Diabetes, page 132

Diabetics cannot produce enough insulin in their pancreas. A diabetic usually gets insulin by daily injections, so large quantities of insulin are required. Genetically engineered bacteria can now be used to make human insulin in large quantities. They reproduce very quickly, forming billions of new bacteria in a few hours.

The main stages in genetic engineering are:

- the **selection** of a certain characteristic from an organism;

- the removal or **isolation** of that gene from DNA. This is done using special enzymes. It must be done very precisely so that other genes are not moved as well;

- sometimes, the copying or **replication** of the gene;

- putting in or the **insertion** of the new gene into the DNA of another organism. The DNA is first opened up using special enzymes.

Some people believe this process could cause unknown effects, because it interferes with the DNA of the original organism. They think that new and dangerous organisms could be created.

2.13 Genetic engineering

The continuing debate

GM maize needs to be sprayed with herbicide less often than normal maize.

Most GM crops are designed in one of two ways.

- They can be **herbicide** tolerant. This means farmers can spray the fields to kill weeds without harming the crop.

- They can be modified to contain a bacterial toxin (Bt) gene. This gene is inserted from a bacterium. The GM crops can then produce the bacterial toxins, which act as a 'built-in' **insecticide** and prevent damage by insects. The expense and dangers of using manufactured insecticides are then avoided.

In September 2000, a health scare hit the headlines in the US. A corn (maize) variety had been genetically engineered to contain a Bt gene. When people realised that it could cause human allergies, it was approved only for animal feed. However, traces of this corn were found in taco shells, a popular American fast food. No allergic reactions in humans were reported but it was not clear how the GM corn had got into human food. This variety of corn is no longer on sale.

Bt cotton plants are popular in China, with 20 per cent of the total crop being genetically modified.

By using GM cotton, the application of toxic pesticides has been drastically cut by 80 per cent. This causes less environmental damage, as pesticides do not build up in food chains.

American scientists were excited when they genetically engineered a tomato plant that could grow in very salty water. This would allow tomatoes to be grown in new areas of the world. However, in 2002, British scientists discovered that some tomato plants were good at tolerating salt water and some were good at keeping it out. By cross-breeding, they produced a tomato plant that was just as good as the GM tomato. A 'hi-tech' solution was not necessary.

Other main uses of genetic engineering have been:

- to increase resistance in plants to disease or climate conditions;

- to modify microorganisms to produce large quantities of useful chemicals, such as insulin;

- to get fruits to ripen without going soft;

- to repair genetic defects;

- to modify pigs' hearts for transplant into humans without being rejected;

- to make organisms that can produce human growth hormones.

2.13 Genetic engineering

Paper from poplars | CASE STUDY

An international team of researchers at Dundee University has been busy. The team has produced the first paper made from genetically modified trees. The modified poplar trees were grown on a number of sites in Britain and France.

There are two main problems in papermaking. One is how to break down the chemical, lignin, which gives trees their hardness and strength. This requires strong alkalis. These can contaminate rivers and lakes and destroy living things if released into the environment.

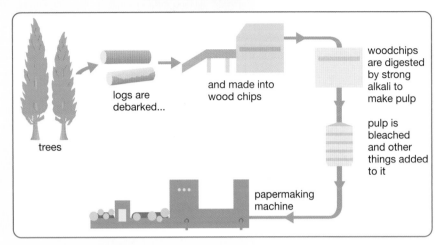

trees

logs are debarked...

and made into wood chips

woodchips are digested by strong alkali to make pulp

pulp is bleached and other things added to it

papermaking machine

The papermaking process.

Another problem is the bleaching of the wood fibres so the paper looks white. Chlorine is used to do this. Chlorine is a poisonous gas and easily reacts to make hydrochloric acid. This too can cause environmental problems.

The poplar trees were genetically modified so that the lignin was easy to break down. This meant using less alkali and chlorine as well as increasing the yield of paper.

No effects on wildlife living near these poplar trees were recorded. It seems a great success.

The making of paper is an interesting study. Find out how to make your own paper. Use the Internet to research the history of this use of plant material.

❸ The GM poplar trees have lignin which is easily broken down. Suggest how this could be a problem for the trees.

❹ Some scientists are concerned about possible effects on natural poplar trees growing nearby. Suggest why.

Key facts

Copy and complete the sentences by choosing the correct word from the key words list.

1 A GM crop is one that has been _____ _____.

2 The process of genetic engineering has these main stages:

(a) the _____ of a desired characteristic;

(b) the _____ of the actual gene;

(c) the production of more copies by _____;

(d) the placing of the new gene into the DNA by _____.

3 GM crops can be _____ tolerant so they are not damaged by herbicides, or made to produce _____ to prevent damage by insects.

4 A _____ organism has DNA that contains a gene from a different organism.

Key words

genetically modified

herbicide

insecticide

insertion

isolation

replication

selection

transgenic

Review questions

1 Neil grows tomato plants in a growbag.

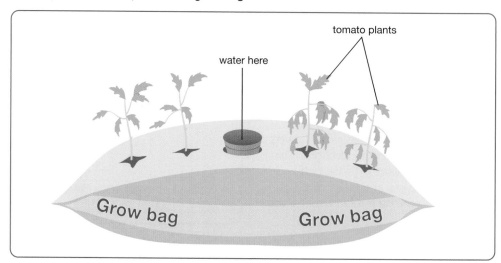

Copy and complete the following instructions. Use these words:

light   magnesium   minerals   phosphates   photosynthesis   temperature

- Make sure the soil does not dry out since plants need water for _____.

- You do not need to add extra fertiliser at first because the soil contains many _____.

- The chloroplasts in the plant cells will need plenty of _____.

- When tomato fruits develop, you should add a fertiliser containing _____ and _____.

- If you use this growbag in a greenhouse you can control conditions such as _____.   [6]

2 The instructions state that certain limiting factors may slow down the rate of photosynthesis.

  (a) Explain what is meant by the phrase 'limiting factors'.   [2]

  (b) Explain which limiting factors may be involved.   [2]

3 Neil wants to grow the tomatoes organically.

  (a) What is meant by 'organic farming'?   [2]

  (b) Why do many people believe that organic farming produces better food?   [1]

  (c) Suggest how:

       (i) weeds   (ii) animal pests   (iii) plant pests

       can be controlled by organic methods.   [3]

4 Genetic engineering is used to produce GM crops and for medical uses. George supports it, Neil does not. What arguments can Neil and George use to support their views?   [4]

2 Living organisms

MICROORGANISMS IN ACTION

Contents

Assignments and practical activities linked to this section:

Investigating microorganisms;

The production of yoghurt from milk.

Long live cabbage

Microorganisms, milk and yoghurt

Investigating the action of antibiotics

Use the following to check your progress.

Unit 1

You will:

- learn how yeast is used in brewing

see pages 82–85

- carry out simple calculations.

see pages 90, 95

Unit 2

You will:

- know how microorganisms can be used to make food and medicines

see pages 82–85

- know about different kinds of microorganisms such as bacteria, fungi and viruses

see pages 86–89

- know that microorganisms can cause disease and know some examples

see pages 90–93

- describe methods to prevent infection and contamination

see pages 94–97

- understand how immunisation can protect us and other animals from harmful microorganisms

see pages 98–101

- know that some bacteria, but not viruses, can be killed by antibiotics.

see pages 102–105

Unit 3

You will:

- understand that microorganisms need particular conditions to grow well.

see page 84

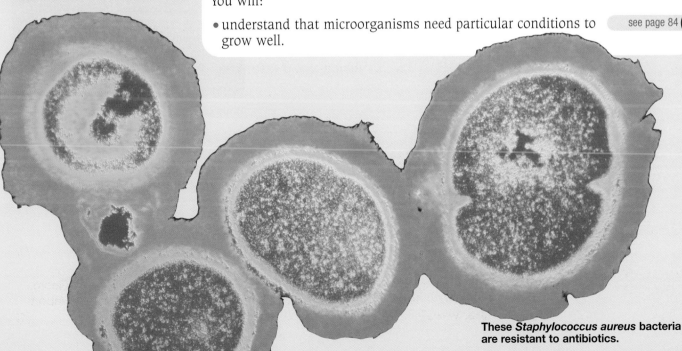

These *Staphylococcus aureus* bacteria are resistant to antibiotics.

2.14 Fermentation

Mansfield Brewery

Mansfield Brewery.

The Mansfield Brewing Company was started in 1855 by two farmers from Mansfield and a brewer from Sheffield. Although the original factory in Mansfield has closed down, the beer is still made at a new plant in Burton-on-Trent. The process of beer-making is possible because of a microorganism called yeast. **Yeast** is a single-celled fungus that lives by feeding on sugar. The yeast breaks down the sugar to **alcohol** and **carbon dioxide**. This process is called **fermentation**.

The brewing process

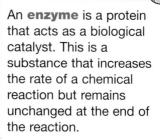

Malt

The sugar that is used by the yeast is called **maltose**. Maltose is produced when barley seeds are soaked in water and start to germinate. **Enzymes** in the malted barley seeds (malt) are activated and convert stored starch into maltose to provide energy for germination. Large brewers like Mansfield Brewery can produce batches of over 200 tonnes of malted barley at a time. The malted barley is ground to a coarse flour called grist which is then mixed with hot water. The liquid, or wort, is then extracted.

Hops give beer its bitter taste.

Hops

In order to give beer its special flavour, hops are added. The hop is a climbing plant that produces its seeds in a cone. These are collected and dried before they are added to the fermenting beer. They give the beer a bitter taste.

❶ Suggest why beer is sometimes called 'bitter'.

Brewing the beer

Hops are added to the wort and the mixture is boiled. The liquid is then removed and finally yeast is added. The mixture is left to ferment. Within a few days, the yeast has produced the alcoholic drink we call beer.

2.14 Fermentation

Designing a flow chart ACTIVITY

Scientists often use flow charts to simplify complicated procedures. Look at the case study on page 85, for Mansfield Brewery. You will see a flow chart. It explains the procedure for the complicated process of making beer.

Another process that uses yeast is bread-making. The pictures below show all the steps carried out when bread is made. However, they are not in the correct order. They have short labels and there are no arrows linking them together.

Imagine you are a master baker. You want to produce a flow chart to teach some trainee bakers how to bake bread. Use the pictures to produce a leaflet called 'How to make good bread'. Your leaflet should contain a flow chart with written explanations.

You may need to do some research into how bread is made.

water

dough

Flour

bag of flour

yeast

bread left to rise

loaf of bread

loaf tin

Stages in bread-making.

2.14 Fermentation

Getting the right conditions

It is important when making beer to get the conditions just right. Mansfield Brewery take great care to control factors, such as temperature, very carefully. The more care that is taken, the better the beer will be.

Temperature

Because yeast is a living organism, it prefers to live in an environment that is not too cold and not too hot. The **temperature** of the fermentation should be between 25°C and 55°C.

If the temperature is too high, enzymes in the yeast are denatured and will not work.

If the temperature is too low, the reactions occur very slowly.

❷ If you can, try making beer at three different temperatures, 15°C, 37°C and 65°C. Describe how quickly you think fermentation will happen at the three different temperatures.

Water

Water is needed for fermentation. This is because yeast is a living organism.

Absence of air

Yeast normally respires just like we do. It breaks down sugar in the presence of **oxygen**, to make carbon dioxide and water. This is not much use if we are trying to make beer. However, yeast can also respire without oxygen. This type of respiration is called anaerobic respiration.

 see Oxygen debt, page 124

$$\text{sugar (glucose)} \longrightarrow \text{ethanol (alcohol)} + \text{carbon dioxide}$$
$$C_6H_{12}O_6 \longrightarrow 2C_2H_5OH + 2CO_2$$

It is important to ensure that no oxygen gets into the fermentation vessel.

❸ Explain how an air lock prevents oxygen getting to the mixture.

Even when the beer has been made, it is important to keep oxygen away from it. If oxygen gets into the vessel, bacteria will respire by aerobic respiration and will turn the alcohol into vinegar.

 see Aerobics, page 120

Key words

alcohol

carbon dioxide

catalyst

enzyme

fermentation

maltose

oxygen

temperature

yeast

Key facts

Copy and complete the sentences by choosing the correct word from the key words list. Each word may be used more than once.

1 Brewers use _____ to convert starch in barley to maltose.

2 An enzyme is a biological _____.

3 During _____ yeast converts _____ into _____ _____ and _____.

4 _____ works best at a _____ between 25 and 55°C.

5 It is important that _____ is prevented from getting to the yeast, or the alcohol will turn into vinegar.

2.14 Fermentation

Mansfield Brewery   **CASE STUDY**

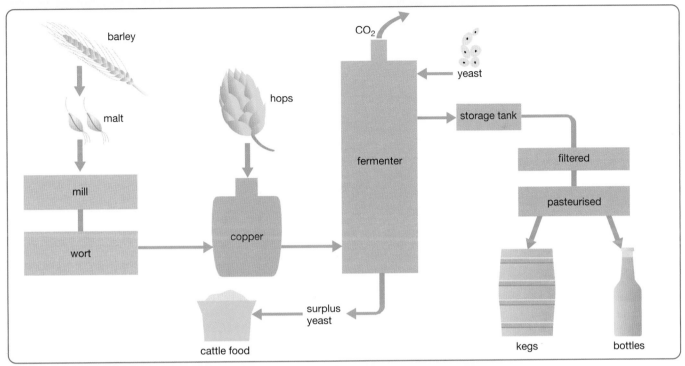

A flow chart of the brewing process.

Copy the flow chart that shows how the brewery makes the beer, or use the above copy and enlarge.

Add the following labels to your diagram.

Malted barley is added to the mill and ground into grist.	Hops are added to the wort.	The sweet wort is placed in the copper.
Yeast is added to the hops and wort liquid.	The beer is heated to kill any remaining microorganisms.	The beer is filtered to remove all the yeast.	The beer is put into kegs or bottles.

4 Describe at which points enzymes are used to make the beer.

5 Suggest why it would not be a good idea to have live yeast in the beer in the sealed keg.

6 Explain why the brewery never has to buy any fresh yeast.

7 Explain what the surplus yeast can be used for.

8 Make a list of as many Health and Safety issues as you can think of connected to the making of beer.

Fermentation is a process that has many other uses. For example, yoghurt, wine and antibiotics can all be made using similar methods. Fermentation by bacteria or fungi is also used to make proteins, such as enzymes, for industrial use.

2.15 Types of microorganism

Foot and mouth

Wendy and Gerry's bed and breakfast on the edge of the North Yorkshire Moors.

Wendy and Gerry were worried. It was early summer in 2001 and they owned a house on the edge of the North Yorkshire Moors where they ran a small business doing bed and breakfasts. In a normal year they would have lots of bookings as walkers and visitors to the moors came to stay with them. This was no normal year. A few weeks earlier, **foot and mouth** had broken out in the area. The whole village was sealed off and visitors were banned from entering the village. Wendy and Gerry knew that, without visitors, their bed and breakfast business would soon be in serious financial trouble. They knew that the disease attacked cattle and sheep and was caused by a microorganism called a **virus**.

What are microorganisms?

Microorganisms are very small living things. They are so small that they are invisible to the naked eye. They can only be seen with a powerful microscope.

see Antibiotics, page 102

Although they are very small, some microorganisms are very useful to us. They can be used for making proteins, bread, beer, wine and yoghurt. Some provide us with drugs, such as antibiotics. Other microorganisms can cause disease. They are responsible for much pain and suffering. **Athlete's foot** is another disease caused by a microorganism. However, this disease is caused not by a virus, but by another type of microorganism called a **fungus** (plural: **fungi**).

Microorganisms that live in or on other living things and cause harm are called **parasites**. Both the foot and mouth virus and the fungus that causes athlete's foot are parasites.

1 Suggest why it was a long time before people discovered the presence of microorganisms.

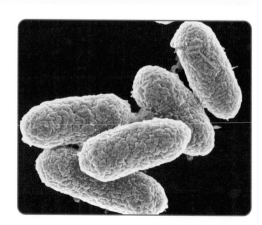

Salmonella bacteria, magnified multiplication × 109 000.

2.15 Types of microorganism

The foot and mouth slaughter | ACTIVITY

The UK is normally free from the disease of foot and mouth. When the 2001 outbreak occurred, it was decided that the best way to eliminate the disease was to slaughter all animals that had the disease. Even animals that did not have the disease were slaughtered if it were thought that they had come into contact with an infected animal.

The following table shows how many animals were slaughtered during the epidemic.

Foot and mouth – some interesting facts (from www.defra.gov.uk).

Type of animal	Animals on infected premises	Animals on neighbouring farms	Other dangerous contacts	Animals suspected of having the disease	Total animals slaughtered
Cattle	299 684	196 199	79 224	13 490	588 597
Sheep	977 511	992 192	1 372 790	108 499	3 450 992
Pigs	21 941	52 163	68 288	2498	144 890
Goats	791	713	670	293	2467
Deer	28	578	413	3	1022
Other	494	1848	6	3	2351
Total	**1 300 449**	**1 243 693**	**1 521 391**	**124 786**	**4 190 319**

Foot and mouth is not always a fatal disease in animals. Many of them recover with no long-term effects. It is also possible to vaccinate cattle against foot and mouth. European countries that do not have the disease will not import meat from those countries that have the disease.

see Immunisation, page 98

- If foot and mouth is not always fatal, suggest why the government went to so much trouble to get rid of it.

- State how many animals had been slaughtered by the end of the epidemic.

- Although deer are not normally kept on farms, Wendy and Gerry often see them close to their home. Suggest why 1022 of them were slaughtered.

- Suggest what is meant in the table in the column headed 'other dangerous contacts'.

2.15 Types of microorganism

Types of microorgansism

Bacteria

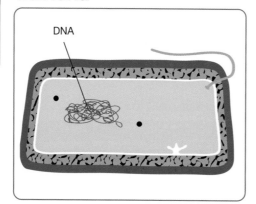

DNA

A bacterial cell.

A **bacterium** (plural: **bacteria**) consists of a single cell. Bacteria are much simpler than animals and plants. For example, they do not have a nucleus. Their **DNA** is found in the cytoplasm and is never contained inside a nucleus.

Bacteria can reproduce very quickly. Some can divide every 20 minutes. This means that, after a few hours, one bacterium can multiply to produce millions.

Fungi

see Fermentation, page 82

Unlike bacteria, a **fungus** (plural: **fungi**) can be made up of many cells. Unlike plants, fungi do not contain any chlorophyll. This means that they have to feed on other things as they cannot make their own food. Yeast is a single-celled fungus.

Athlete's foot is a disease caused by a fungus. The fungus grows on the soft damp tissue between people's toes. Most fungi feed on dead organisms but some, like athlete's foot, feed on the tissue of humans. The fungus secretes enzymes that digest the tissue of your skin and absorb it into the fungus.

6 Suggest why it is important that you wash your feet every day.

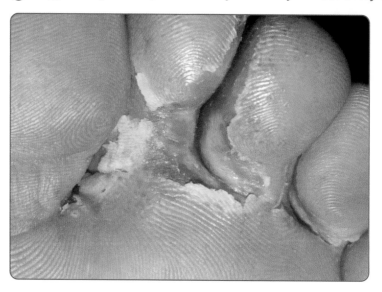

Athlete's foot.

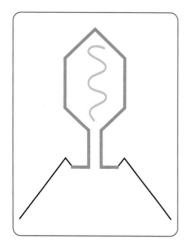

A virus – this particular type attacks bacteria rather than plants or animals.

Viruses

Viruses are much smaller than bacteria or fungi. They are so small that even with a light-microscope they are impossible to see. They live by invading other cells and getting the cells to make more copies of the virus. When the cells are full of viruses, they burst open and release the viruses to attack even more cells.

2.15 Types of microorganism

The foot and mouth outbreak of 2001 ⬤ CASE STUDY

Wendy and Gerry's bed and breakfast was next to a farm. They were very worried that the disease would reach the farm. They knew that foot and mouth was very infectious and was spread by animals and people carrying the virus from one farm to another. Once a farm was infected with the virus, all the animals on the farm, and on neighbouring farms, had to be killed. The bodies of the animals were then burnt in huge fires. In order to prevent the disease from spreading, the road leading to the village was closed off. Only people who lived in the village were allowed to use the road. Before they entered the village, they had to spray the wheels of their cars with disinfectant.

All the footpaths in the area were closed. Walkers and ramblers were prevented from walking across the moors. It was almost a year before Wendy and Gerry were able to open their home once more for bed and breakfasts.

7 Explain why the animals on neighbouring farms were slaughtered when an outbreak of foot and mouth occurred on a farm.

8 Explain why the bodies of the slaughtered animals were then burnt.

9 Explain why Wendy and Gerry had to spray the wheels of their car when they entered the village.

10 The virus was spread from one farm to another by cattle and vehicles. Suggest other ways in which the virus might be spread.

11 Explain why all the footpaths on the North Yorkshire Moors were closed to walkers.

Key facts

Copy and complete the sentences by choosing the correct word from the key words list.

1 Yeast is a type of _____ and is used in the brewing and baking industry.

2 _____ _____ _____ is a disease of animals caused by a _____.

3 _____ _____ is a human disease caused by a fungus.

4 Another type of microorganism is a _____.

5 _____ that causes harm is sometimes called a _____.

6 _____ is a chemical that contains the genetic code.

Key words

athlete's foot

bacterium (plural: bacteria)

DNA

foot and mouth

fungus

microorganism

parasite

virus

2.16 Microorganisms spreading

The 1918 influenza outbreak

During the final days of World War I, a new outbreak of flu spread across the world. **Epidemics** that spread across the world from one country to another are called pandemics.

Flu is a disease caused by a virus.

The flu virus mutates

Unfortunately for us, the flu virus is capable of evolving and changing the structure of its outer protein coat. These changes are called **mutations**. Each time this happens, the defence mechanisms in our body no longer work and we can catch the disease again. This is why, although we can become **immune** to diseases such as **polio**, we cannot become immune to diseases such as flu and the common cold.

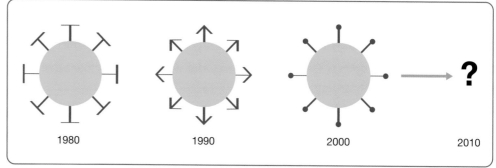

1980   1990   2000   2010

The flu virus mutates.

In some parts of the world, the death rate in 1918 was extremely high. In parts of Africa and India, the death rate rose to one person in twenty, while in some isolated parts of Australia, over half the population died.

Many more people died from the flu than were killed in the whole of World War I. Unusually, most of the people who died were in the younger age groups of 15–40 years old. Flu usually affects the very young and the very old.

❶ Find out the number of pupils at your school. Work out how many of them might have died from the flu if this were 1918.

❷ Suggest a possible reason why the very old were less affected by this outbreak of flu than younger people.

The outbreak of flu in 1918 was the worst ever recorded. In England, one person in every two hundred died of the disease.

❸ Explain why people who have flu jabs need a fresh flu jab each year.

Word check

An **epidemic** is an outbreak of a disease that affects a lot of people at the same time.

See Types of microorganism, page 86

Word check

Mutations occur when the coding of DNA changes.

Word check

Immune means being resistant to infection by a disease-causing microorganism.

2.16 Microorganisms spreading

Flu in Europe

ACTIVITY

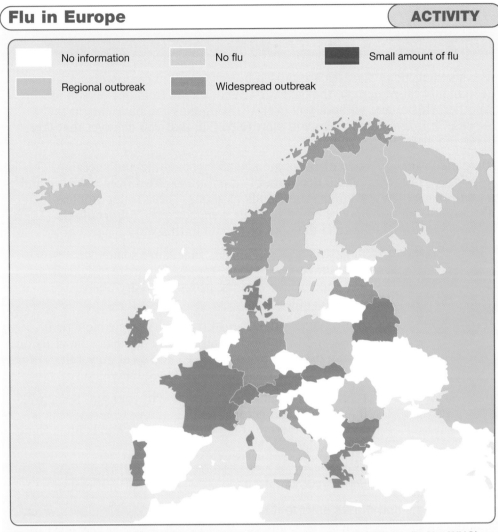

	No information		No flu		Small amount of flu
	Regional outbreak		Widespread outbreak		

The map shows the activity of the flu virus in Europe during April 2002 (from FluNet WHO).

4 Use an atlas of Europe to identify ten of the countries. Draw a bar chart to show the activity of the flu virus in the different countries.

5 The map seems to show that outbreaks of flu change between the borders of one country and another. Explain whether you think this is an accurate description of what happens with the flu virus.

6 The prevailing wind in Europe comes from the south west. Suggest one reason why countries such as Ireland and Portugal report only small amounts of flu.

7 Making a map like this requires accurate information. Suggest how a country such as the UK could collect information on the number of cases of flu occurring at any one time.

The map was produced by The World Health Organisation (WHO).

Use the Internet to find out more information about what this organisation does.

2.16 Microorganisms spreading

How diseases are spread

Because infectious diseases are caused by very small microorganisms (commonly called germs), they are very easily spread from one person to another. This occurs without you even realising that you have caught the disease. It is only later, when you start to feel ill, that you discover that you have the disease.

Droplets in the air. Many diseases are spread by coughing and sneezing. This is especially true of flu. Small **droplets** of water are expelled from the nose and mouth. Each droplet contains thousands of germs. These water droplets float through the air and may be breathed in by someone else. **Tuberculosis** (TB) is a disease caused by bacteria that can be spread in this way.

 see Antibiotics, page 102

Coughs and sneezes spread diseases.

Dust. The microorganisms that cause some diseases, such as anthrax, can produce spores. These are very resistant and can survive for long periods in a dry dusty environment.

Touch. Flu is often spread by touch. People blow their noses and then touch someone else and pass the virus on. Health experts advise that a good way of preventing flu outbreaks is to wash your hands regularly.

Faeces. Many microorganisms live in your gut. Some of these can be dangerous, such as the polio virus. This is why it is important that you wash your hands after going to the toilet.

Animals. Some animal diseases can be passed on to humans. There have even been cases where humans have caught diseases such as foot and mouth.

see Blood donor, page 112

Blood. Doctors and nurses have to take care by using disposable gloves when handling a bleeding patient. The National Blood Transfusion service takes particular care to ensure that all blood that is given to patients is free from infectious diseases. One of the most common causes of infection from blood is drug users sharing hypodermic needles. This has contributed to the rapid spread of diseases such as hepatitis and AIDS.

Key words

droplets

epidemics

immune

mutation

polio

tuberculosis

Key facts

Copy and complete the sentences by choosing the correct word from the key words list. Each word may be used more than once.

1 Microorganisms can be spread by _____ in the air, dust, touch, faeces, animals and blood.

2 _____ is an example of a disease that can be caught from faeces.

3 Large-scale outbreaks are called _____ and often happen because the microorganism undergoes a _____.

4 _____ is a disease of the lungs that is spread by bacteria in _____.

5 Being _____ to a disease-causing organism means you will not catch the disease.

2.16 Microorganisms spreading

The 1918 Project   CASE STUDY

Unravelling the mystery of the 20th century's greatest pandemic

In 1918, six miners who lived in the remote town of Longyearbyen in Norway died of the flu. Their bodies were buried in the Svalbard cemetery. The unusual thing about the graves is that the ground there is permanently frozen. This means that their bodies have been kept frozen for over 80 years.

Even though there were no medical records from the time, the bodies were found because of diaries kept by one of the mining company's engineers.

In 1997, Professor Kirsty Duncan headed a team of scientists who examined the frozen bodies, looking for the influenza virus that killed them. They wanted to isolate the virus so that they could study its DNA. This would give them important information about the virus so that the scientists could produce more effective treatment for the modern disease.

Svalbard cemetery.

see Inheritance, page 46

Professor Duncan said, 'We are grateful to the families of the young men and the people of Svalbard and Norway. I find this project extremely difficult. I believe that a person's final resting place is sacred and that a body should not be disturbed during its long rest. The only reason that I am able to continue the project is the strong conviction that something good can finally come from the 1918 tragedy. Perhaps we can at last learn the secrets of 1918 and use them to better international human health.'

8 Suggest why Professor Duncan found the experience extremely difficult.

9 Explain why the people who dug up the bodies had to wear biological safety suits.

10 Imagine you are one of the relatives of the dead men. Write a page for your diary explaining how you felt about having the bodies of your relatives dug up for scientific research. Try to include reasons for your happiness as well as your sadness.

11 Suggest why the flu virus could be preserved unchanged in the frozen ground of the cemetery.

2.17 Preserving food

Andy the butcher

Andy has a meat shop. He keeps it very clean. He knows that it is most important that he and his staff maintain very strict standards of hygiene.

Meat shops like Andy's have a particular problem in that they sell both fresh and cooked meat.

Keeping meat safe

Fresh meat

Fresh meat is meat that has not been cooked. Even if it has been handled very carefully, it is quite likely that it will be **contaminated** with a range of bacteria. As long as the meat is handled and cooked properly, these bacteria pose no danger to the people who eat it.

Word check

To **contaminate** means to make dirty or pollute.

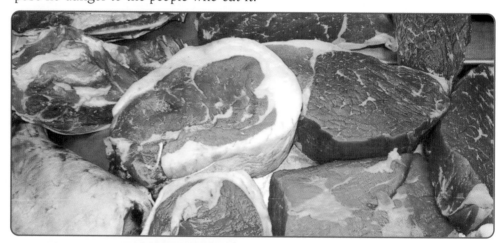

Fresh meat.

Cooked meats.

Cooked meats

Cooked meats are meats like ham. They have been cooked and prepared so that the customer can eat them straightaway. Because cooked meats will not be cooked again, it is most important that they do not become contaminated with the bacteria from fresh meat.

It is important that, each night when the shop has closed, Andy cleans down all the equipment and work surfaces.

see Types of microorganism, page 86

1 Explain why it is important that cooked meats, such as ham, do not become contaminated with harmful bacteria.

2 Why is it important that Andy cleans the work surfaces every night?

3 List as many ways as you can think of in which bacteria from fresh meat could contaminate the cooked meats in Andy's shop.

2.17 Preserving food

How to avoid food poisoning (ACTIVITY)

The following article is taken from a leaflet that explains the importance of **hygiene** for people working in places that sell food.

Food poisoning – how to avoid it

Food poisoning is caused when microorganisms grow on food that has been left in poor conditions. The microbes produce chemicals that make us feel ill and cause sickness and diarrhoea. Food poisoning is often a result of cross-contamination of food. Uncooked food like meat and chickens, when placed on work surfaces, may leave behind millions of bacteria. If other foods, such as cooked meats, are then placed on the work surface, they become contaminated with the bacteria. Bacteria grow and multiply in the warm conditions. This means that when the food is eaten, large numbers of food-poisoning bacteria are consumed. To prevent this from happening, cooked and uncooked food should always be prepared on different work surfaces. Shop assistants must always wash their hands after handling raw meat. Prepared food should always be stored in cold conditions, such as a fridge, to prevent the bacteria from multiplying. Any leftover food from meals should not be reheated as this encourages the bacteria to multiply. Food poisoning is preventable. By following simple and sensible precautions, we can ensure that food poisoning does not occur.

The leaflet is not very user friendly. Many shop assistants who received it would not bother to read it and would simply throw it away instead.

• Design a poster based on information contained in the leaflet, which could be placed in Andy's shop to remind him and his assistants how to handle food correctly. Keep your poster simple to get the message across. Use bright colours to make it more interesting.

• On a sheet of A4 paper, design a layout for a butcher's shop. Label each of the counters in the shop with the kinds of product that would be placed on them. Try to think of other facilities that would be needed in the shop and draw them on your plan.

4 In ideal conditions, bacteria can multiply on food very quickly. Imagine Andy left out some cooked ham overnight on a warm shop counter. Some bacteria can divide into two every 20 minutes. If one bacterium contaminated the ham, calculate how many bacteria could be on the ham the next morning, 12 hours later.

2.17 Preserving food

How Andy keeps his shop clean

There are various ways in which Andy ensures that the cooked meats do not become contaminated with bacteria from the fresh meats.

Using separate work surfaces

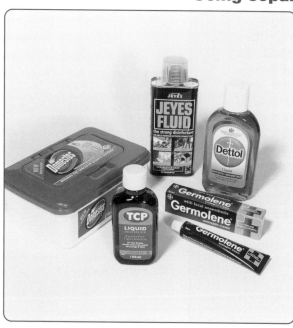

Disinfectants and antiseptics.

Cross-contamination can be avoided by making sure that the two types of meat never come into contact with each other. If you use separate work surfaces for fresh and cooked meats, any bacteria that are left on the work surface after the fresh meat has been prepared will not come into contact with the cooked meat.

Disinfectants

Disinfectants are chemicals that kill bacteria. They can be used on work surfaces and floors and ensure that any bacteria present are killed. They are usually used along with a cleanser for wiping down surfaces. They are not used, however, to clean hands, as they are quite harsh and may damage the skin.

Antiseptics are similar to disinfectants but may also be used in hand wash solutions. Many hand wash creams contain antiseptics. This ensures that hands do not just look clean, but also have fewer bacteria on them. This is very useful when handling food.

Sterilisation

We do not want knives and serving spoons to taste of disinfectants. These are usually cleaned by being washed in hot soapy water. However, it is possible to make them sterile by placing them in boiling water. Boiling water has a high temperature. It will kill bacteria within a few minutes. This process is called **sterilisation**.

Personal hygiene

Andy knows that it is important that his shop assistants wash their hands very well after visiting the toilet. This is good personal hygiene.

Key words

antiseptics

contaminated

disinfectants

hygiene

sterilisation

Key facts

Copy and complete the sentences by choosing the correct word from the key words list.

1 Personal _____ is very important to prevent food from becoming _____ with microorganisms.

2 _____ and _____ are chemicals that kill microorganisms.

3 _____ is the killing of all microorganisms using a high temperature.

2.17 Preserving food

Andy gets a certificate

Andy in his shop.

Andy has a visit from the public health inspector. It is the job of the inspector to ensure that all the food that is sold in Andy's shop is safe to eat.

The inspector checks that the shop is kept clean and tidy. This is particularly important in a shop like Andy's. Any bits of meat that are left lying around can act as breeding grounds for bacteria. These bacteria could then infect the clean food that is on sale to the public. This could lead to a serious case of food poisoning.

The inspector also checks that the toilet facilities for staff are suitable and that washing facilities are available for Andy's staff. It is most important that staff wash their hands before handling food for the customers. The inspector checks that work surfaces and equipment used for handling raw meat do not come into contact with cooked meats.

The inspector is very pleased with Andy's shop. Andy receives a certificate to say that his shop has been inspected and is fit for use.

5 Explain why Andy has two shop assistants, one who handles only raw meat and one who handles only cooked meats.

6 Explain why all food shops must have good toilet and washing facilities for their staff.

7 Carry out some research to find out more about the role of Public Health Inspectors and what they do when they visit food shops and restaurants.

8 Suggest why Andy and his staff wear hats while working in the shop.

9 Describe the differences between antiseptics and disinfectants. Explain which Andy would use in different situations.

2.18 Immunisation

Word check

A **vaccine** protects you from catching a disease.

Elliot gets the jab

Elliot's mum and dad are concerned that it is time that he should be immunised against the diseases measles, mumps and rubella. This means injecting him with the **MMR vaccine**. The process is called **vaccination** or **immunisation**.

Should Elliot be vaccinated?

His mum and dad know that some people think that the vaccine may have serious side effects such as autism. Some children who develop autism become very withdrawn and have difficulty communicating with other people. Elliot's mum and dad do not want him to become autistic.

Rubella is sometimes called 'German Measles'. It is usually a very mild disease and the symptoms are soon gone. However, if a woman catches rubella in the early months of pregnancy, the disease can cause serious damage to the unborn baby. For this reason it is especially important that girls are vaccinated against rubella.

Elliot's mum and dad decide to find out all about the vaccine.

They know that diseases like measles and mumps can be very serious and can cause permanent damage. Measles can sometimes cause permanent hearing damage. Mumps can be very painful and sometimes causes males to become sterile and not be able to have children.

They also know that, even though some people suspect that the vaccine may cause autism, large-scale studies have found no evidence that this is the case.

Although it is a hard decision to make, they decide to go ahead and have Elliot vaccinated with the MMR vaccine.

❶ If the 'R' in MMR stands for rubella, what do the two letter 'M's stand for?

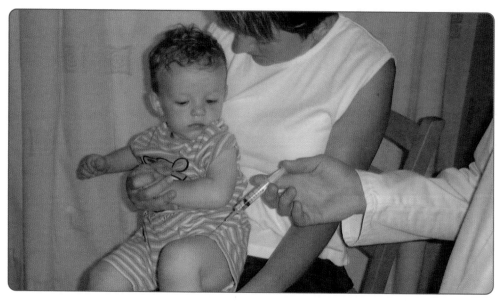

Elliot is vaccinated.

Although Elliot did not enjoy the needle being stuck into his thigh, it is soon forgotten and Elliot is back to his cheerful self.

2.18 Immunisation

The pros and cons ACTIVITY

When Elliot's mum and dad made their decision about whether to have Elliot vaccinated, they made a list of all the reasons to have, or not have, the vaccination.

- The injection might hurt Elliot.

- It has been a long time since the last epidemic of these diseases in the UK and resistance in the population will be low.

- If lots of children like Elliot are vaccinated, there is less chance of an epidemic starting.

- We have read claims in some newspapers that children might develop autism after the injection.

- Measles can result in a child being made permanently deaf.

- If a woman catches rubella in the early months of pregnancy, the baby may be born deaf and blind. So a rubella outbreak could affect our next child.

- The vaccine may not work and Elliot could get the diseases anyway.

- Statistics show that it is much safer to have the injection than to risk catching the diseases.

- These diseases are usually not serious and just a minor inconvenience.

- Mumps can make men sterile.

- There is no hard evidence that the vaccine causes autism.

Draw a table with two columns, headed PROS and CONS.

Copy down the above points from the list and write them in the correct column in your table.

Making a leaflet
Use the points to design a leaflet that could be given to parents who are trying to decide whether to have their child vaccinated with the MMR vaccine.

To make your leaflet, use a piece of A4 paper that has been folded in three.

Use colour to provide interest. Try to keep the message simple.

Making a leaflet.

2.18 Immunisation

What happens to Elliot when he is immunised?

Vaccines usually contain a harmless form of the disease. Sometimes this may be a weakened or dead form of the bacterium or virus. Sometimes it may be just a small piece of the microorganism. This process is sometimes called immunisation and we become **immunised**, or immune to the disease. This means that, even if we come into contact with the microorganism, we will not develop the disease.

When the vaccine is injected into Elliot's body, his body does not know that the microorganisms are harmless. It reacts as if he had just been infected with a live and dangerous microorganism. White bloods cells in Elliot's body start to attack the invaders. Some white blood cells attack the invading microorganisms and engulf them, rather like some computer games.

Other white blood cells attack the microorganisms by producing a chemical called an **antibody**. Antibodies are very specific. Each one is designed to attack one kind of microorganism and no others. Some antibodies cause the microorganisms to clump together so that they can be more easily attacked by the white blood cells.

see Blood donor, page 112

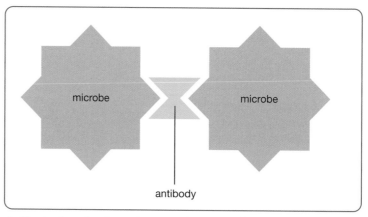

Antibody clumping two microorganisms together.

2 Suggest why we are not usually vaccinated with the live microorganism.

3 Copy the picture and add more antibodies to show how they could cause even more microorganisms to clump together.

It will take Elliot several days to start producing antibodies against the three microorganisms that cause measles, mumps and rubella. This means that his immunity to the diseases will not develop until some time after the vaccination. Vaccination does not give instant protection against the diseases.

When children catch the real diseases, they become ill. The body is in a race to produce antibodies to destroy the microorganisms, before they multiply and cause damage to the body. It is much better for Elliot to be vaccinated and have the antibodies ready in his bloodstream. They kill the microorganisms as soon as they enter his body, before the symptoms of the disease even appear.

2.18 Immunisation

Nurse in a family practice

Joy is a nurse who works in a family practice for a GP. She knows the importance of ensuring that young children are vaccinated against MMR. So many parents are concerned about MMR that she is getting more people than ever asking for her advice. She knows that parents find it difficult to make up their mind about whether to have their children vaccinated. Some parents decide to have the three vaccinations on separate occasions. Joy knows, however, that there is no hard evidence to say that this is a safer option. She feels that the MMR vaccine is still the safest policy.

4 Explain why a vaccination does not give instant immunity to a disease and why full immunity will take some time to develop.

5 Decide whether you would have your own child vaccinated with the MMR vaccine. Study the hazards of the diseases and the vaccine. Explain with reasons how you made your decision.

6 The graph shows the number of cases of measles in the UK. In which year do you think children in the UK were first immunised against measles? Explain your reasons.

7 Suggest why it may not a good idea for the body to have too many vaccinations at the same time.

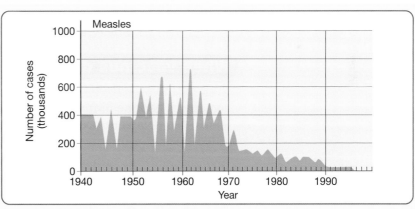

Cases of measles in the UK from 1940 to the 1990s.

Key facts

Copy and complete the sentences by choosing the correct word from the key words list. Each word may be used more than once.

1 When a person gets a disease, they produce _____ which attack the _____ that cause the disease.

2 _____ or _____ may use a _____ made from dead microorganisms which is injected into your body and causes it to make antibodies.

3 When you make antibodies, you are _____ against the microorganisms.

4 Most babies in the UK are vaccinated or _____ against _____.

Key words

antibodies

immunisation

immunised

microorganisms

MMR

vaccination

vaccine

2.19 Antibiotics

The miracle drugs

Most of us alive today are very lucky that we suffer from very few infectious diseases. This was not always true. Many years ago, people lived much shorter lives and many died from serious illnesses. One of the main reasons for this is that we have received vaccinations to protect us from most of the harmful diseases. We usually get these vaccinations when we are young children.

Measles, mumps and rubella

Most parents in the UK decide to protect their children from these three diseases by having them vaccinated in their early years. Each injection contains a vaccine that will protect the child from all three illnesses. The vaccination is sometimes called a triple vaccine, or MMR for short.

see Immunisation, page 98

TB (tuberculosis)

Most children are vaccinated against tuberculosis while they are at secondary school, usually in Year 9. In some parts of the UK, it is babies who are vaccinated. **Tuberculosis** is a very serious lung disease that can lead to complications and death. It is hard to treat and some new forms of the disease are very difficult to cure.

see Microorganisms spreading, page 90

Polio

Most children are vaccinated against this disease before starting school. The vaccine is not injected but swallowed on a lump of sugar. The vaccine protects against **polio**, which is a disease that can damage nerves and lead to permanent paralysis of parts of the body.

When vaccines don't work

Even when you have been vaccinated against many diseases, you still sometimes become ill from an infection. When this happens, you can sometimes help your body to fight the disease by taking drugs prescribed for you by your doctor.

see Types of microorganism, page 86

One type of drug that we often take when we are ill is called an **antibiotic**. Antibiotics are drugs that are obtained from **microorganisms**. The first antibiotic was made from a fungus. It is called penicillin. It was discovered by a scientist called Alexander Fleming in the year 1928.

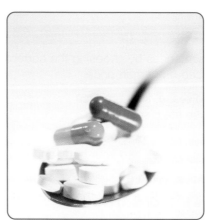

Antibiotic tablets and capsules.

2.19 Antibiotics

How antibiotics work   ACTIVITY

An experiment was carried out to find out how quickly antibiotics work.

Some **bacteria** were grown in a container. After ten hours, some penicillin was added.

The graph shows the number of bacteria over a period of time.

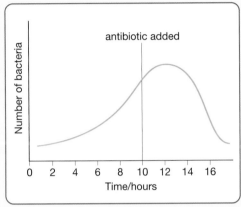

Graph of bacterial growth.

1 Copy the graph and draw an extra line to show what it would look like if the antibiotic had not been added.

2 Suggest why the number of bacteria did not fall straightaway.

One month later, the scientist was about to dispose of the container. To his surprise he noticed that bacteria were once again growing in the container. He suspected that the bacteria had become resistant to the penicillin: they had changed so that they were no longer harmed by the penicillin.

The picture shows the number of normal and resistant bacteria at the beginning of the experiment.

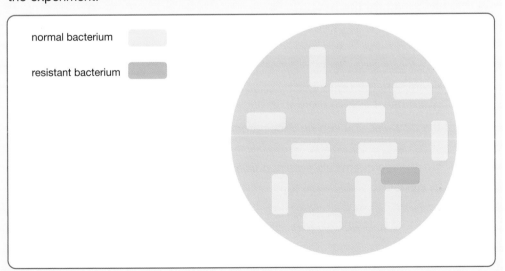

Draw the picture again, but this time show the number of normal and resistant bacteria at the *end* of the experiment.

2.19 Antibiotics

see Types of microorganism,
page 86

When antibiotics don't work

Although antibiotics have been called miracle drugs, they do not work on every kind of disease. They are very effective in killing bacteria but have no effect whatsoever against diseases caused by **viruses**. The table shows some common diseases and what type of microorganism causes them.

Bacteria	Viruses
pneumonia	cold sores
salmonella food poisoning	influenza
skin infections due to *Staphylococcus aureus*	polio
tuberculosis	mumps
whooping cough	measles
tonsillitis	rubella

Causes of disease.

3 Which diseases would a doctor use antibiotics to treat?

This is why, when you go to your doctor with a cold, they will not prescribe antibiotics but instead will tell you to go home, keep warm and drink plenty of fluids. Antibiotics will be of no use in treating a disease such as a cold, which is caused by a virus.

Sometimes, however, when you have a cold, bacteria take advantage of your weakened state and also infect your lungs and chest. When this happens, the doctor will prescribe antibiotics because they will help to kill the bacteria that are causing the secondary infection. *Staphylococcus aureus* is a bacterium that can cause secondary infections.

Key words

antibiotics

bacterium (plural: bacteria)

microorganisms

polio

tuberculosis

viruses

Key facts

Copy and complete the sentences by choosing the correct word from the key words list. Each word may be used more than once.

1 Two of the diseases you can be vaccinated against are _____ and _____.

2 _____ are chemicals obtained from some _____.

3 They can kill _____ but not _____.

4 This means that a doctor will only prescribe _____ for diseases caused by bacteria and not _____.

Sir Alexander Fleming

CASE STUDY

Sir Alexander Fleming was born in 1881. He trained as a doctor at St Mary's Hospital in London. One day, he was growing some bacteria on a Petri dish when he noticed that the dish had become contaminated with a mould (fungus) called *Penicillium*.

Most people would have thrown the dish away and started again, but Fleming noticed that an area around the mould was free from any bacteria. He realised that something was being produced by the mould and spreading out into the agar, killing the bacteria. It was this discovery that led to the production of the first antibiotic, called penicillin.

Penicillin was called a miracle drug as it saved the lives of thousands of soldiers who were injured during World War II. The soldiers would certainly have died without penicillin.

In recent years, however, the story has not been so happy. As a result of the overuse of penicillin and other antibiotics, bacteria have developed resistance to the drugs. There are now some bacteria that are completely resistant to all known antibiotics. This makes it very difficult for doctors to treat patients who are infected with these resistant bacteria.

Sir Alexander Fleming.

4 Imagine you are Sir Alexander Fleming. Write an account in your diary to explain what you saw and how you felt on the day of your great discovery.

5 Explain why your doctor should not give you an antibiotic to treat a cold.

6 Animals other than humans suffer from infections by viruses and bacteria. Foot and mouth is an infection found in cattle. It is caused by a virus. Do you think farmers should treat the disease by using antibiotics?

7 Some antibiotics have been used to make farm animals grow more quickly. Explain whether you think this is a good use of antibiotics.

Review questions

1 Sally makes beer as part of an experiment. She uses a microorganism called yeast. Name three other substances that she uses to make beer. [3]

2 Mansfield Brewery brews beer. It is a complicated process. Draw a flow chart to show the procedures that Mansfield Brewery use in the beer making process. [6]

3 Foot and mouth is a disease caused by a virus. Name two different kinds of microorganism and the diseases that they cause. [4]

4 Look at the pictures. What type of microorganism does each represent? [3]

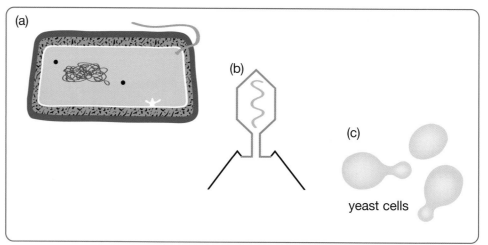

5 John gets the flu. He tries to find out more about it. He does not know what the following words mean. Explain the meaning of the following words for John.

(a) parasite

(b) epidemic

(c) pandemic

(d) mutation [4]

6 Flu can be spread by droplet infection when someone sneezes. Describe the ways in which other diseases can be spread. [3]

7 Andy is a butcher. Explain why he keeps cooked meats separate from raw fresh meats in his shop. [2]

8 Mary cooks a chicken. Describe how she should prepare and cook the chicken to avoid getting food poisoning when she eats it. [3]

9 Chemicals can be used to kill microorganisms. Make a list of the different kinds of chemical used to do this and explain how they would be used. [3]

10 Bob has antiseptics and antibiotics in his medicine cabinet. Explain the difference between an antibiotic and an antiseptic and say when each should be used. [2]

11 Elliot is vaccinated against measles, mumps and rubella. Explain how the vaccination prevents him from catching the diseases. [3]

2 Living organisms

HOW YOUR BODY WORKS

Contents

Practical activities linked to this section:

Plants, animals and their environment

Exercise and recovery rates

Use the following to check your progress.

Unit 1

You will:

- present data in graphs see page 129

- analyse and interpret results, and carry out simple calculations. see pages 121–123, 125, 126–127

Unit 2

You will:

- know the structure of the human heart and circulatory system see pages 108–111

- know how the heart and blood circulatory system work see pages 108–111

- know what blood is made of and what it does see pages 112–115

- know how humans breathe see pages 116–119

- know how aerobic respiration provides us with energy see pages 120–123

- describe how anaerobic respiration works without oxygen see pages 124–127

- describe how humans maintain a constant body temperature see pages 128–131

- know how glucose levels in the blood are kept constant. see pages 132–135

Unit 3

You will:

- understand the effect on the body of some physical activities see pages 120–127

- understand how receptors in the body respond to a stimulus see pages 136–137

- describe how neurones transmit information see page 138

- describe how effectors bring about a response to a stimulus see page 139

- understand penicillin and aspirin are used as medicines see page 140

- understand how antibiotic resistance develops in bacteria see page 140

- understand the use of social drugs, such as tobacco and alcohol see pages 142–143

- understand the medical implications of both illegal and social drug abuse see page 141

- understand how new drugs are tested. see page 144

2.20 Heart attack

George's heart attack

George is not well. He is in intensive care in hospital. Not many hours ago, George was feeling fit and healthy. Then he noticed that he was short of breath and had a pain in his chest, neck and arms. George was having a heart attack.

The doctors tell George that this time he is lucky. However, to reduce the risk of further attacks, he has to change his lifestyle: stop smoking, eat less fat and take more exercise.

George agrees and decides to find out more about what went wrong with his heart.

The blood system

George is surprised to discover that the blood in his body flows inside tubes called blood vessels. Some of these are so small that he would need a microscope to see them. These are called **capillaries** and take blood to all the cells of his body. It is the job of his heart to pump the blood through the **arteries** to the capillaries. The capillaries are linked back to the heart by **veins**.

see Blood donor, page 112

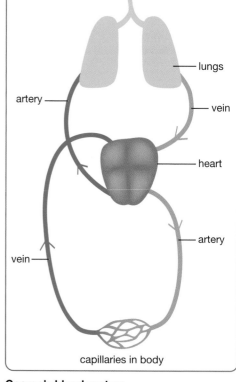

George's blood system.

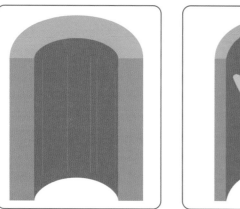

Section through an artery.

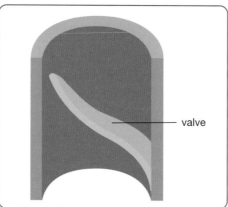

Section through a vein.

Arteries carry blood away from the heart.

They have thick, muscular, elastic walls to withstand the high blood pressure.

Capillaries are very narrow thin-walled blood vessels. The thin walls allow oxygen and glucose to pass out of the blood to the cells of the body. Carbon dioxide passes from the body cells into the blood.

Veins return the blood to the heart.

Because the blood pressure is now very low, the veins have thin walls and **valves** to prevent the blood from flowing backwards.

2.20 Heart attack

Georges's M. O. T.   **ACTIVITY**

George having his blood pressure taken.

The nurse takes George's blood pressure. She tells George that his blood pressure is '150 over 95'. The figure of '150' tells the nurse what the pressure is in George's blood when the heart muscle is contracting.

1 Suggest what the figure of '95' means.

Your teacher may have a piece of electronic equipment with which you can test your blood pressure. Try taking your blood pressure before and after exercise. Make a note of any differences that you find.

Ask if you can take the blood pressure of some of your teachers.

What differences do you see between their blood pressure and that of younger people?

George is then attached to a machine that produces an electrocardiogram (ECG). This is a picture which shows how the electrical impulse that causes George's heart to beat spreads through his heart.

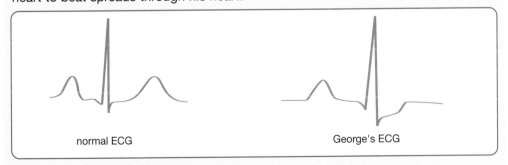

normal ECG

George's ECG

George's ECG.

2 Look at George's ECG. Describe any differences that you can see between it and a normal one.

3 Do you think George's heartbeat is normal?

The doctor tells George that there is some damage to his heart muscle but, with care, he should recover and be able to lead a normal life.

2.20 Heart attack

What happened to George's heart?

George wants to know exactly what happened to his heart.

George's heart

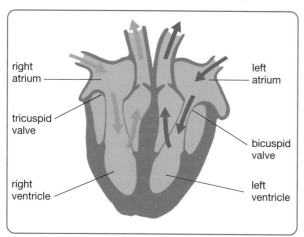

right atrium
tricuspid valve
right ventricle
left atrium
bicuspid valve
left ventricle

A section through a human heart.

George's heart is really two pumps, joined and lying side by side. One side of his heart pumps blood to his lungs to pick up oxygen and get rid of carbon dioxide, and then back again. The other side of his heart pumps blood all round the body. This double circulation means that higher pressure can be maintained in the blood vessels, which increases the rate of flow of blood to the tissues.

The blood enters the heart through the **atria** (singular: **atrium**). Then it is pumped into the **ventricles**, before it leaves the heart again. Valves stop the blood from flowing in the wrong direction.

George discovers that even though his heart is full of blood, it has a small blood vessel carrying blood to the heart muscle. This supplies the heart muscle with oxygen and glucose. The doctor tells him that one of the branches of this blood vessel became blocked. This prevented part of his heart muscle getting any blood, so that part of the muscle died.

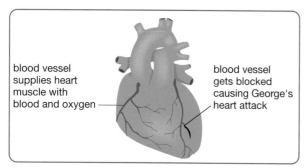

blood vessel supplies heart muscle with blood and oxygen
blood vessel gets blocked causing George's heart attack

Blood vessels supplying the heart muscle.

❹ The severity of the heart attack depends upon where the artery gets blocked. Suggest what you think would have happened if the artery had been blocked higher up, before it divided.

George is soon released from hospital. He decides to give up smoking and take up more exercise. Even George's dog benefits from the extra walks he is getting.

Key words	Key facts
artery atrium (plural: atria) capillaries circulatory system valves vein ventricle	Copy and complete the sentences by choosing the correct word from the key words list. Each word may be used more than once. 1 Blood is carried away from the heart through _____. 2 It is then carried to the body cells through very small vessels called _____ before being returned to the heart through _____. 3 The heart and the blood vessels make up the _____ _____. 4 Veins have _____ to stop blood flowing the wrong way. 5 Blood from the body and the lungs flows into the _____ of the heart and is pumped into the _____.

2.20 Heart attack

William Harvey

William Harvey was the first scientist to suggest that the human body had a **circulatory system**. He lived from 1578 to 1657. He noticed that blood travelled through blood vessels called arteries and veins.

Microscopes had not been invented at that time, but he correctly guessed that the arteries and veins must be linked together by even smaller blood vessels.

It may seem common sense to us now, but before Harvey, people believed the work of Galen who lived over 1000 years before Harvey was born. Galen thought that blood just went from one side of the heart to the other, without going though all the thousands of tiny blood vessels inside the organs of the body. He did not realise that the blood was responsible for transporting materials around the body.

Harvey correctly predicted the existence of capillaries. He also demonstrated that veins had valves to prevent the back flow of blood. He placed a tourniquet round the arm of one of his patients and could see the valves standing out as the tourniquet tried to push the blood backwards.

William Harvey.

Word check

The heart and the blood vessels make up the **circulatory system**.

5 Suggest why Galen did not realise that tiny blood vessels carry the blood in the organs of the body.

6 Suggest why veins have valves but arteries do not.

7 Suggest why George's doctor wants him to eat less fat and take more exercise.

8 Smoking makes the blood more sticky and likely to clot. Suggest why smokers are much more likely to have a heart attack.

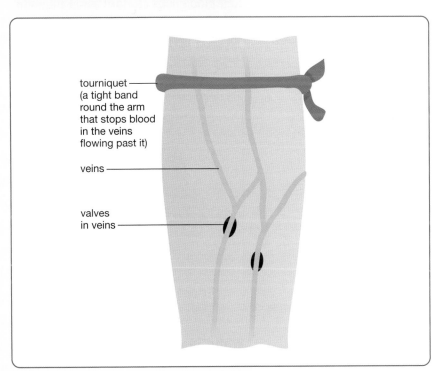

tourniquet (a tight band round the arm that stops blood in the veins flowing past it)

veins

valves in veins

Veins in the arm.

2.21 Blood donor

Giving blood

Chris and Beccy want to give blood. They have thought about being blood donors for some time, but have never got round to it. They contact the National Blood Service and find that there is a session at their village hall in two weeks time. The National Blood Service sends them some information about blood and how they use it.

What does blood do?

Blood is a **fluid** that **transports** (carries) substances such as oxygen, carbon dioxide, food and hormones around the body.

Blood also provides a defence against invading microorganisms.

Blood can clot and seal wounds in the body to prevent further loss of blood.

The components of blood

The liquid part of blood is a fluid called **plasma**. It is pale yellow and composed mainly of water. Dissolved in it are substances such as food, carbon dioxide, hormones and urea (a waste substance produced by the body).

Red blood cells carry oxygen around the body. They take it from the lungs and carry it to all the cells of the body.

Red blood cells contain a red pigment called **haemoglobin**. Haemoglobin combines with oxygen in the lungs to form **oxyhaemoglobin**. When it gets to cells that need oxygen, it releases the oxygen and turns back into haemoglobin.

$$haemoglobin + oxygen \rightleftharpoons oxyhaemoglobin$$

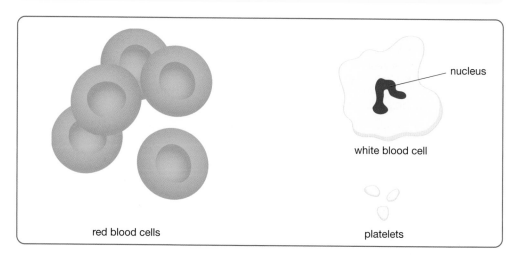

nucleus

white blood cell

red blood cells

platelets

Blood contains red cells, white cells and platelets.

White blood cells protect your body from infection. They can destroy bacteria that invade your body. Some do this by making antibodies. Others remove dead tissue and microorganisms.

Platelets are small pieces of cells. They contain chemicals that cause the blood to clot when the skin is damaged and you start to bleed. The clot prevents further blood loss and also stops bacteria getting in.

see Immunisation, page 98

2.21 Blood donor

"Do something amazing today – give blood" (ACTIVITY)

Did you know that only 6 per cent of people who could give blood actually do so?

The National Blood Service needs more people to give blood – just like Beccy and Chris.

Most people just never get around to giving any. They think they have not got the time, or that it might hurt.

Imagine you work for the National Blood Service. You need to get more people to donate some of their blood.

The leaflet shown is a page from a National Blood Service brochure to encourage people to give blood.

What's so *amazing* about giving blood?

When you give blood, you'll be doing one of the most amazing things anybody could dream of – saving a life.

You can enable someone to receive a desperately needed transfusion. Some operations, for instance, require literally pints and pints of blood. Or just as importantly, components extracted from blood, such as plasma, can play a key role in a range of procedures such as treating burns or preventing infection.

Diane Crawford has had Sickle Cell disease all of her life. She gave birth to a daughter, Chi, after receiving 19 units of blood during her pregnancy.

"Blood donors gave me the chance to have a family," says Diane. "Now I want to play my part in encouraging more people from African and Caribbean communities to help others like me by giving blood."

Use the following facts, and any others that you can research, to design your own leaflet to encourage people to give blood. The following website may help you: www.blood.co.uk.

Here are some facts to help you.

- Only 6 per cent of people who can give blood in the UK, do give blood.
- Giving blood saves lives.
- 10 000 units of blood are needed every day.
- Hospitals need 15 per cent more blood than they did five years ago.
- Some people who think they can't donate, in fact can.
- Giving blood makes you feel good about yourself.

2.21 Blood donor

The bag of blood's journey

Once the blood has been collected, it is bar-coded with its own unique number. This means that Chris and Beccy's blood can always be traced back to them. The bag of blood is then taken to one of the National Blood Service Centres.

One of the things that happens to the blood is that most of the white cells are removed. They are filtered out of the blood using a special filter. This makes the blood safer for those people who are going to receive it.

The blood is placed in a centrifuge. A centrifuge is a machine that spins at high speed. It separates heavier things from lighter things. This forces the blood to separate out into three different layers – red cells, platelets and plasma.

Finally, the blood, still in its original plastic pack, is placed in a machine that squeezes the bag and forces out the red cells, leaving behind the platelets. Platelets from four or five donors may need to be pooled to give one adult dose. The blood components are now ready to be used.

1 Suggest why concentrated red blood cells are given after an accident, rather than whole blood.

Key words

anaemic

fluid

haemoglobin

oxyhaemoglobin

plasma

platelets

red blood cells

transports

white blood cells

Key facts

Copy and complete the sentences by choosing the correct word from the key words list. Each word may be used more than once.

1 Blood is a _____ that _____ food, oxygen, carbon dioxide, hormones and urea around the body.

2 The liquid part of blood is called _____.

3 Blood contains _____ _____ _____ to carry oxygen, _____ _____ _____ to protect us from bacteria and _____ to clot the blood.

4 Red blood cells contain _____ that combines with oxygen to form _____.

5 If you are _____, there is not enough _____ in your red blood cells.

2.21 Blood donor

Chris and Beccy get the red card   CASE STUDY

Chris and Beccy decide to go along to donate some of their blood.

When they enter the village hall, they have to wait in turn to be seen. Soon their turn comes and they are asked a series of questions about what diseases they have had in the past, if they are taking any medication and personal questions about their lifestyle. It is most important that the donor is healthy so that the patients who receive the blood are not harmed in any way.

Finally, after all the questions are answered, they each have a simple blood test. The skin is punctured to release a small drop of blood. This small drop is tested to see if either of them is anaemic.

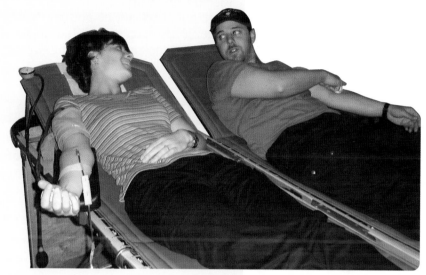

Beccy and Chris donate blood.

Anaemic means there is not enough haemoglobin in the red blood cells.

The test shows that they are OK to give blood and they go into another room. The room is full of trolley-beds. They lie on the beds and a nurse asks them if this is their first time. They are pleased to find how helpful she is. The nurse explains the procedure and places an inflatable cuff on their upper arm. The site of the vein is thoroughly cleaned before the needle is inserted into a vein and the blood flows into a bag. Both Beccy and Chris are surprised by just how easy and painless it is.

The nurse watches the weight of the bag so she knows when she has collected enough blood. The needle is removed. Once the donor's clotting system has done its work and a small clot has formed to stop further bleeding, a small plaster is placed over the site.

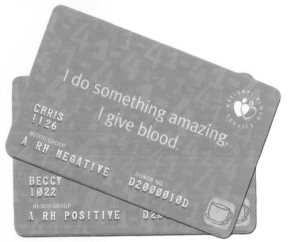

Beccy and Chris' donor cards.

Beccy and Chris stay on the beds for a short while, to check there are no problems.

A few weeks later their red cards arrive. These tell them their blood groups.

2 Suggest why Beccy should not give blood if she has recently had her ears pierced.

3 State what the word 'anaemic' means.

4 Suggest why Chris should not give blood if he is anaemic.

5 Suggest why people must not give blood if they have just had hepatitis.

6 Suggest why the nurse weighs the bag of blood as she is collecting it.

7 Suggest why three small samples of blood are also taken.

2.22 Asthma

Richard has asthma

Richard first learned of his asthma when he had difficulty breathing. When he exercised at school, he noticed that he soon became out of breath and started to wheeze. His parents took him to see the doctor. His doctor explained that the tubes that took air to his lungs sometimes got narrower. This made it much more difficult for him to breathe air in.

How Richard breathes

Word check

An **alveolus** (plural: alveoli) is a thin-walled air sac in the lung.

The doctor showed Richard a diagram of his lungs. She pointed to the **bronchi** (singular: **bronchus**) and **bronchioles** on the diagram and explained that these were the tubes that got narrower during an asthma attack. She told Richard that when he breathed in, air was taken into his lungs and oxygen diffused through the wall of his air sacs (**alveoli**) and into his blood.

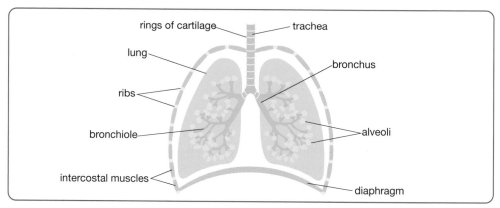

rings of cartilage — trachea
lung
ribs
bronchus
bronchiole
alveoli
intercostal muscles
diaphragm

Your lungs are contained in your **thorax** (chest).

 see Diffusion, page 30

In return, carbon dioxide diffuses from the blood into his lungs. So when Richard breathes out, he gets rid of the waste carbon dioxide. This is called **gaseous exchange**.

In order to be able to do all this, the alveoli in his lungs must:

• be thin – to allow oxygen to pass through;

• be moist – oxygen passes through more quickly in solution;

• have a large surface area – more surface for oxygen to diffuse through into the blood;

• have a good blood supply – to carry away the oxygen to all parts of the body, so that more can diffuse through.

Richard realises that the air that he breathes out must be different from the air that he breathes in. He can feel that it is warmer and has more moisture in it. The table shows some other differences.

	Nitrogen	Oxygen	Carbon dioxide
Air breathed in	79%	20%	0.04%
Air breathed out	79%	16%	4%

1 What percentage of the oxygen in the air does Richard's lungs absorb?

2.22 Asthma

How Richard breathes   ACTIVITY

Richard wants to know how air gets in and out of his lungs. This is called **ventilation**.

He decides to make a model of his lungs and chest. The diagram shows how he makes it.

Make a copy of Richard's model using the same equipment that Richard used. Your teacher will have prepared some of the equipment for you.

2 Which part of the model represents Richard's:

   (a) chest   (b) lungs
   (c) trachea (d) diaphragm?

Gently push the rubber sheet upwards to increase the air pressure in the jar.

3 What happens to the volume of the air in the glass jar when you push the sheet upwards?

4 What do you notice happens to the balloons?

5 Explain why you think this happens.

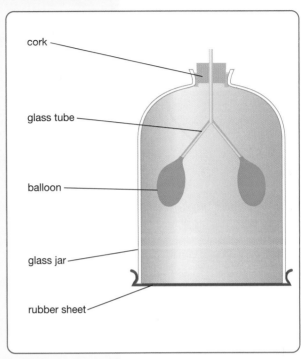

cork
glass tube
balloon
glass jar
rubber sheet

Model lungs.

Pinch the rubber sheet between your thumb and forefinger. Gently pull the rubber sheet downwards to decrease the air pressure in the jar.

6 What happens to the volume of the air in the glass jar when you pull the sheet downwards?

7 What do you notice happens to the balloons?

8 Explain why you think this happens.

Models do not always tell the full story.

When Richard really breathes in and out, it is not just his **diaphragm** that moves up and down. His **ribs** also move. When he breathes in (inhales), his ribs are pulled upwards and outwards by his intercostal muscles (**rib muscles**). This also increases the **volume** of his lungs and lowers the pressure, causing air to enter. When Richard breathes out (exhales), his diaphragm rises and his ribs fall.

When the volume of the lungs increases, the air **pressure** inside them decreases. The air pressure outside Richard's body is greater than it is inside his lungs, so air rushes in to the lungs.

The rings of **cartilage** in the walls of the bronchioles and bronchi stop them collapsing when the air pressure inside them drops.

2.22 Asthma

Controlling Richard's asthma

Most medical experts encourage asthmatics to take responsibility for their own condition. People with asthma are taught how to use the drugs as and when they need them.

Richard using his Ventolin.

This is Richard's diary.

Today is sports day at my school. I was very wheezy this morning and had difficulty in breathing in. I now use two different drugs to control my asthma. One of them is called Becotide and I take this every day, in the morning and before I go to bed. The other drug is called Ventolin and I take this drug whenever I feel short of breath. Each drug is in its own inhaler. The inhaler delivers a 'puff' of medicine which I breathe into my lungs. This makes sure that the drug is delivered exactly where it is needed. I take the Becotide to stop any asthma attacks occurring. It makes my lungs less sensitive to things that might irritate them and start off an attack. This is why I have to take it all the time. Sometimes, though, even this will not prevent an attack and then I take the Ventolin to open up my airways so I can breathe easily again.

I felt much better after I had used my inhaler. It means I should be OK for my school sports day this afternoon.

Key words

alveolus
(plural: alveoli)

bronchioles

bronchus (plural: bronchi)

cartilage

diaphragm

gaseous exchange

pressure

rib muscles

ribs

thorax

trachea

ventilation

volume

Key facts

Copy and complete the sentences by choosing the correct word from the key words list. Each word may be used more than once.

1 The chest or _____ contains the lungs.

2 Getting air into and out of the lungs is called _____.

3 Air enters the lungs by passing down the _____, _____ and _____.

4 The bronchioles divide and end in small air sacs called _____.

5 The lungs allow _____ _____ to take place.

6 Air is drawn into the lungs when the _____ lowers and the _____ _____ pull the _____ upwards.

7 This increases the air _____ in the lungs and reduces the _____ so air is drawn in.

8 Rings of _____ keep the bronchi open when the internal pressure drops.

2.22 Asthma

Dr Davies – a family GP   CASE STUDY

Dr Davies is a family doctor. Many of his patients suffer from asthma. He knows the importance of regularly monitoring these patients. One of the ways he does this is to use a peak flow meter. His patients take a deep breath and blow as hard as they can into the meter.

A peak flow meter.

The reading on the meter shows how much air his patients can blow out from their lungs in one second. The higher the reading is, the healthier the lungs are. Dr Davies checks the reading against a chart of the patient's age and height. This shows whether the lungs are being affected by the asthma and whether the medication is working properly.

Dr Davies thinks that patients should be encouraged to take responsibility for their own condition. Asthma is a life-threatening disease. However, he knows that most patients who successfully use their medication can lead normal healthy lives and take part in a wide range of physical activities.

Some patients are worried when they are prescribed Becotide. They know that it is a steroid. Steroids are powerful drugs. However, Dr Davies tells them not to worry. Because Becotide goes straight to the lungs, the dose needed is very small and safe.

9 Why does Dr Davies use a 'peak flow meter'?

10 Explain why Dr Davies encourages his patients to take responsibility for their own condition.

11 Suggest why asthma can be a life-threatening disease.

12 Why does Richard take Becotide twice a day, but Ventolin only when he feels he needs it?

13 Suggest why the air that Richard breathes out is warmer and contains more moisture than the air that he breathes in.

14 Explain why Richard finds it difficult to breathe when he has an asthma attack.

15 Why does Dr Davies tell his patients that it is very safe to take a steroid like Becotide?

2.23 Aerobics

David gets fit

David does not get enough exercise.

David is unfit. His job involves sitting at a desk for most of the day.

He knows that, for his age, he is slightly overweight because he does not always eat the right kind of food.

David knows that this kind of lifestyle can lead to ill health. He realises that he needs to devise a fitness plan.

He decides to visit an aerobics class to find out what it is all about.

Aerobic respiration

The aerobics instructor tells David that the carbohydrates in his food are broken down by digestion into a type of sugar. This sugar, called **glucose**, provides him with all his energy. The energy is released from the glucose by a process called **aerobic respiration**. This occurs inside all David's cells, including the cells of his muscles. Respiration involves 'burning' the glucose with **oxygen** that you breathe in. This releases the energy that your body needs. It also produces **carbon dioxide**.

see Fermentation, page 82

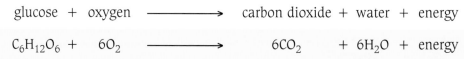

glucose + oxygen $\longrightarrow$ carbon dioxide + water + energy

$$C_6H_{12}O_6 + 6O_2 \longrightarrow 6CO_2 + 6H_2O + \text{energy}$$

The instructor tells David that an aerobics class will make him fitter in many ways.

- His lung area will increase so that he can absorb oxygen from the air more quickly.

- His heart will get larger and stronger so it can pump blood containing oxygen and glucose around his body more quickly.

- His muscles will increase in size and have a better blood supply. This will make them more efficient. It will enable them to get more glucose and oxygen and release the energy more quickly.

David realises that the fitter he gets, the more efficient his body will become. This will help with everyday activities. It will also enable him to exercise harder and for longer periods of time before he becomes exhausted.

David decides to give aerobics a try.

2.23 Aerobics

How much energy is in food?   ACTIVITY

David knows that the energy in food is measured in **kilojoules**. The problem is, he has no idea what a kilojoule is or just how much energy it represents. He decides to do an experiment to find out.

The aerobics instructor has told David that respiration is like burning. When you eat carbohydrates, your body 'burns' them to release energy.

David decides to burn some food that contains carbohydrate and use the heat given off to heat up some water. He thinks that this will show him just how much energy the food contains.

The diagram shows how David carried out his experiment.

He:

- placed 20 cm³ of water in a test tube;

- measured the temperature of the water;

- held a potato crisp between some tweezers and carefully set fire to it;

- held the burning crisp under the test tube until the crisp burnt out;

- measured the temperature of the water again. It had increased by 25°C.

1 The amount of heat energy needed to raise the temperature of 1cm³ of water by 1°C is 4.2 joules. How many joules do you think the potato crisp contained?

David thought that the experiment might not be as accurate as it could be. How could you make David's experiment more accurate?

Your body temperature is normally 37°C. This is nearly always much warmer than your surroundings. Where do you think the extra heat energy comes from to keep you at this temperature?

State the differences and similarities between respiration and burning.

Word check ✓

A joule (J) is a measure of energy in the international system of units (SI).
1000 joules (J)
       = 1 **kilojoule** (kJ)
Some people still use the old units called calories.

see Lighting power, page 244

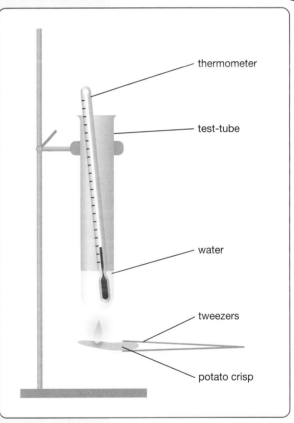

Measuring the energy in a potato crisp.

2.23 Aerobics

David does aerobics

David getting fit.

David turns up for his first aerobics class.

He decides to take his pulse before he starts and finds that his heart is beating at 78 beats per minute. He starts to follow the instructor and does the dance exercises set to the music. It is not long before he is feeling short of breath. His breathing rate has increased and he is also breathing more deeply. David decides to take a short break. When he takes his pulse again, his heartbeat has sped up to 121 beats per minute.

While he is resting, David looks at a wall poster. It shows the differences between the air we breathe in and the air we breathe out.

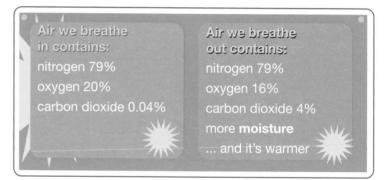

Air we breathe in contains:

nitrogen 79%

oxygen 20%

carbon dioxide 0.04%

Air we breathe out contains:

nitrogen 79%

oxygen 16%

carbon dioxide 4%

more **moisture**

... and it's warmer

5 State two reasons why David's heartbeat has sped up during the exercise.

6 Suggest why the air you breathe out contains more carbon dioxide and less oxygen than the air you breathe in.

7 Calculate the percentage of oxygen in the air that is absorbed by the body.

8 Suggest why you breathe out exactly the same amount of nitrogen as you breathe in.

Key words

aerobic respiration

carbon dioxide

glucose

kilojoules

moisture

oxygen

Key facts

Copy and complete the sentences by choosing the correct word from the key words list. Each word may be used more than once.

1 Energy in food is measured in _____.

2 _____ reacts with _____ to release energy.

3 This is called _____.

4 The gas _____ _____ is produced during respiration.

5 The air we breathe out contains more _____ _____ and less _____ than the air we breathe in.

6 It is also warmer than the air we breathe in and contains more _____.

2.23 Aerobics

Measuring David's fitness

Using a spirometer.

Breathing can be measured using a machine called a spirometer. The picture shows David breathing as he pedals an exercise machine. The air that he breathes out is collected in a bag. It is then analysed to see what it contains.

The computer also calculates how much air is being breathed in and out.

The data collected can be shown as a print out.

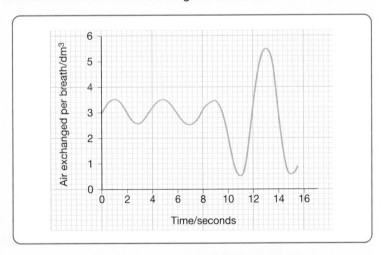

Spirometer print out.

Breathing rate is the number of breaths per minute. **Tidal volume** is the amount of air that is breathed in and out with each breath. **Vital capacity** is the *maximum* volume of air that can be breathed in and out with each breath. **Residual volume** is the small amount of air left in the lungs when you have breathed out as far as possible.

9 Determine David's tidal volume.

10 Determine David's vital capacity.

11 Determine David's breathing rate in breaths per minute.

12 Suggest how the graph will change when David has been going to his aerobics class for several weeks.

2.24 Oxygen debt

Wendy runs a marathon

Wendy trains to run a marthon.

Wendy wants to run a marathon to raise money for charity. She knows that running a marathon requires special training and she will have to get very fit.

Wendy has heard that marathon runners eat lots of carbohydrate ('carbohydrate loading') before a race. She does not understand why.

She decides to find out as much about marathon running as she can.

Anaerobic respiration

She wonders why, when she runs her first 100 metres, she is breathing hard when she stops running. It seems perfectly reasonable to be breathing hard when she is running, but she cannot understand why she is still breathing deeply for some minutes later. She asks her fitness trainer.

 see Aerobics, page 120

The trainer tells her that when she runs, she burns glucose with **oxygen** to release energy. She uses this energy to run. Unfortunately, the human body is not designed well enough to supply all the oxygen that Wendy needs. Even though her breathing rate speeds up and her heart beats more quickly, the muscles in her legs still cannot get enough oxygen to meet their needs. This means that the body will soon run out of energy and stop.

Wendy is puzzled because she knows that people who run marathons do not stop. They can carry on for mile after mile.

The trainer tells her that it is possible to break down glucose to release energy without using oxygen. This process is called **anaerobic respiration**.

Wendy is even more puzzled. She wonders why people bother to breathe at all if glucose can be broken down without oxygen.

Her trainer tells her that we can only do this for short periods of time. The problem is that far less energy is released from the glucose (the process is not very efficient) and a waste product called **lactic acid** is produced in our muscles.

$$\text{glucose} \longrightarrow \text{lactic acid} + \text{energy}$$

Lactic acid makes your muscles ache, which can be very painful.

When you stop running, you have to carry on breathing deeply to absorb sufficient oxygen to break down the lactic acid. In effect, you are paying back the oxygen. This is called the '**oxygen debt**'.

2.24 Oxygen debt

Measuring fitness
ACTIVITY

The Harvard step test

The Harvard fitness test can be used to work out how fit you are. It works by timing your pulse rate after doing some exercise. The exercise involves stepping up and down on a bench for 300 seconds.

Next, rest for one minute, then take your pulse count for 30 seconds.

Wait for 30 seconds, then take your pulse count for a further 30 seconds.

Wait another 30 seconds, then take your pulse count for another 30 seconds.

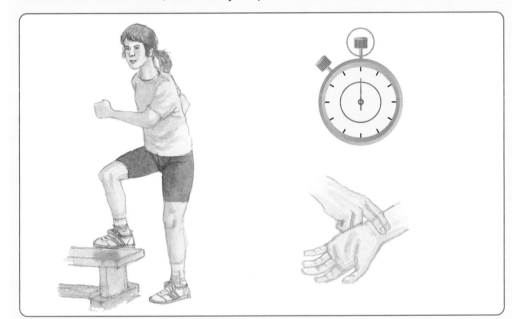

Doing the Harvard fitness test.

Wendy decided to find out how fit she is.

She did the test, then used the following formula to calculate her fitness:

$$\frac{\text{time spent on exercise} \times 100}{2 \times (\text{1st + 2nd + 3rd pulse counts})}$$

When Wendy first took the test, she could only do it for 200 seconds. Her pulse rates were 65, 60 and 55.

Her fitness is $\dfrac{200 \times 100}{2 \times (65 + 60 + 55)} = \dfrac{20\,000}{360} = 56$

1 How fit is Wendy?

After completing her training, she could complete the 300 seconds and had pulse rates of 60, 55 and 50.

2 Calculate her new fitness. How fit is Wendy now?

The reason you breathe faster during exercise is that the brain monitors the **carbon dioxide** level of the blood. The higher the level of carbon dioxide, the faster you breathe.

Fitness scale

90+ super fit

80+ very fit

70+ fit

60+ fair

less than 60 unfit

2.24 Oxygen debt

Wendy gets ready for the race

Wendy starts her training by running short distances. Each day she tries to run a little further, until she is able to run for several miles without stopping.

She notices that as she gets fitter, she is able to run further. She also notices that the time it takes her to pay back her oxygen debt gets shorter. She knows that this is because her heart and lungs are getting larger and more efficient. They are providing her muscles with oxygen and glucose more quickly.

She wants to know the most efficient speed she should run at in order to complete her marathon in the best possible time.

Her trainer tells her that if she tries to run too quickly, she will produce too much lactic acid and stop because of muscle fatigue. She must find the best speed to run at without her lactic acid level rising too high.

Wendy runs her race. The graph shows the level of lactic acid in her blood.

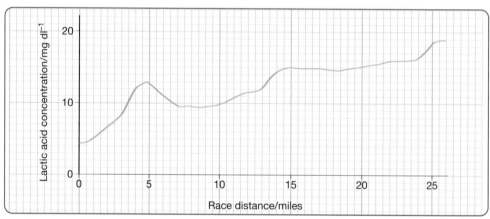

Wendy's lactic acid levels.

❸ Suggest what Wendy did at a distance of five miles into her race.

❹ Suggest what Wendy did just before the end of her race.

Key words

anaerobic respiration

carbon dioxide

lactic acid

oxygen

oxygen debt

Key facts

Copy and complete the sentences by choosing the correct word from the key words list. Each word may be used more than once.

1 During hard exercise, muscles break down glucose without _____.

2 This is called _____ _____.

3 Anaerobic respiration produces _____ _____ which can cause muscle fatigue.

4 Eventually, the lactic acid must be broken down with _____.

5 Paying back this oxygen is called the _____ _____.

6 Carbon dioxide levels in the blood are monitored by the brain. As the levels of _____ _____ rise, so does the breathing rate.

2.24 Oxygen debt

Is Wendy overweight? **CASE STUDY**

Before Wendy started training, she thought she was a little overweight. When someone is very overweight they are called obese. This happens when the body stores excess fat. It can be very unhealthy.

Half a kilogram of extra body fat represents about 14 700 kilojoules of energy.

To find out if a person is overweight, doctors use tables that compare weight with height. The problem is that some people are heavier than others but have less fat. This could happen to Wendy. As she trains, she will use up her fat, but make more muscle. Because muscle is heavier than fat, she could get fitter and still put on weight.

A better method of measuring obesity is the **B**ody **M**ass **I**ndex (BMI). It can be calculated as follows.

$$BMI = \frac{weight\ (in\ kg)}{height\ (in\ metres)\ squared}$$

For example, Wendy is 1.70 metres tall and weighs 73 kg.

Her BMI is $\dfrac{73}{1.70 \times 1.70} = 25.3$

Body type	BMI
underweight	< 18.5
normal	18.5–24.9
overweight	25.0–29.9
obese	> 29.9

see Heart attack, page 108

5 Is Wendy her correct weight?

6 Fat contains 39 kJ per gram. How many kilojoules would you need to burn to lose 6 kg in mass? (6 kg = 6000 g)

2.25 Keeping warm

Paul goes on his Duke of Edinburgh's Award Scheme

Paul and his friends set off on their long walk.

Paul goes on an outward-bound course as part of the Duke of Edinburgh's Award Scheme. In order to get his Gold Medal, he has to undertake a fifty-mile walk through rough country. He knows that in bad weather he is in danger of suffering from hypothermia. He wants to find out more about hypothermia in preparation for his walk.

Word check

Homeostasis is the name given to any process that keeps body temperature, or levels of substances in the blood, constant.

 see Diabetes, page 132

Hypothermia – the facts

Paul's normal body **temperature** is 37°C. This is usually much warmer than his surroundings (the temperature of a comfortable room is about 20°C). He is therefore in danger of cooling down. In order to keep his body temperature at 37°C, he constantly releases heat energy into his body from the process of **respiration**. There is a careful balance between the heat energy released by respiration and how quickly his body is losing the heat energy to the environment.

Maintaining a constant body temperature of 37°C is an example of **homeostasis**.

If Paul's body loses heat energy too quickly, his core body temperature will drop and he will suffer from hypothermia. This can happen when you find yourself in very cold or very wet conditions and are unable to get warm. Hypothermia can be very dangerous. People who have hypothermia feel cold and tired. They may fall asleep, fail to wake up and die.

Paul realises that he will have to take precautions on his walk to prevent hypothermia from happening to him. He knows that if he gets wet, he is much more likely to suffer from hypothermia.

1 Suggest which kind of weather conditions would be most dangerous for Paul.

2 Suggest what equipment Paul should take with him to avoid hypothermia.

3 Suggest why it would be a good idea for Paul to get a weather report before he leaves.

2.25 Keeping warm

Measuring hypothermia

ACTIVITY

Body temperature

You normally take your body temperature by using a clinical thermometer. It can be placed in the armpit or under the tongue.

Another way is to place a temperature-sensitive strip on your forehead. The colour that it turns will tell you your temperature.

If you took your temperature with a clinical thermometer and a temperature-sensitive strip, they might not give you the same result.

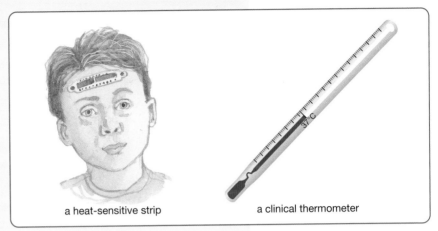

a heat-sensitive strip

a clinical thermometer

A clinical thermometer or a heat-sensitive strip can be used to measure body temperature.

4 Suggest why the two temperatures may be different.

Hypothermia experiment

Paul wanted to know how likely he was to get hypothermia if he got soaking wet. He decided to do an experiment using a model.

He filled two soft drinks bottles with warm water. A thermometer was placed in each bottle. The bottles were wrapped in cotton wool. Paul soaked the cotton wool round one bottle with water and left the other bottle dry. He measured the temperature of each bottle every minute.

These are Paul's results:

Time/minutes	Temperature/°C	
	Dry bottle	Wet bottle
0	65	65
1	63	61
2	61	58
3	59	55
4	57	52
5	56	49
6	55	47

wet

dry

Experiment to show what happens to your temperature when you get wet.

Draw a single graph showing both sets of results.

5 State which bottle cooled the fastest.

6 Explain what might happen to Paul if he gets soaking wet on his long walk.

129

2.25 Keeping warm

Controlling body temperature

Paul has two problems. If he gets cold and wet, his body may lose heat too quickly and he will suffer from hypothermia. However, if it is a hot day and he walks too fast, he may not be able to lose the heat quickly enough and his body will overheat. He could end up with heat stroke.

Shivering. When Paul gets too cold, he will start to shiver. This will cause the muscles in his body to respire more quickly (burn more fuel) and so produce more heat. This will help to keep him warm.

Sweating occurs when Paul is in danger of overheating. It causes the surface of his skin to become wet. As the sweat **evaporates**, it removes heat from his skin. This is why you feel cold if you have been sweating and then sit around after exercising, even on a warm day. In other words, sweating transfers heat from your body to the environment.

Normally you do not walk about shivering or sweating, even though the temperature around you is constantly changing. You manage to make small changes to how quickly you are losing heat by **vasoconstriction** and **vasodilation**.

If the air temperature around you increases, the diameter of the small blood vessels in the skin increases (vasodilation). This allows more blood to flow near the surface of the skin. If you have pale skin, it turns pinker in colour. The body loses more heat from the warm skin. You cool down.

If the air temperature around you falls, the small blood vessels in your skin get narrower (vasoconstriction). Less blood flows near the surface of the skin. Pale skin turns whiter in colour. Less heat is lost from the cold skin.

The thermoregulatory centre in your brain **monitors** the temperature of your blood all the time. If the temperature is too high or too low, the brain sends messages to start these temperature control mechanisms.

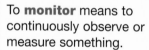

Word check

To **monitor** means to continuously observe or measure something.

Key words

evaporates

homeostasis

monitors

respiration

shivering

sweating

temperature

vasodilation

vasoconstriction

Key facts

Copy and complete the sentences by choosing the correct word from the key words list. Each word may be used more than once.

1 The normal _____ of the human body is 37°C.

2 Heat released from _____ is used to maintain body temperature.

3 _____ releases more heat, as the muscles respire more.

4 _____ cools the body as the liquid _____ and removes heat from the surface of the skin.

5 _____ and _____ alter the flow of blood to the surface of the skin by changing the diameter of blood vessels, and thus control heat loss.

6 Sweating and shivering are controlled by the brain, which _____ the _____ of the blood.

7 Keeping your body temperature constant is an example of _____.

2.25 Keeping warm

The Patterdale Mountain Rescue Team — CASE STUDY

Dave is a member of the Patterdale Mountain Rescue Team. The team consists of volunteers who are called into action when an emergency happens on the hills. Dave and his team never quite know what to expect. Sometimes it is someone who has gone missing. Sometimes it is someone who has had an accident and been injured.

Dave in action.

Dave knows that the hills can be a dangerous place. He also knows how important it is for people who walk in the hills to use the proper equipment. A sensible precaution is to always get a weather report. Make sure that someone has a copy of your route and expected time of arrival.

People who do not take the proper precautions cause many of the accidents that Dave is called out to. Speed is very important in an emergency. Dave and his team practise regularly to ensure that they can provide the best care as quickly as possible.

7 Suggest how Dave and his team could be contacted in an emergency.

8 Explain whether you think people who behave irresponsibly on the hills should have to pay for calling out the Mountain Rescue Service.

9 Make a list of the equipment that Paul should put in his rucksack before starting his expedition.

Diabetes

Geoff and diabetes

Geoff with his doctor in the surgery.

Geoff was not feeling well. For some time he had been feeling tired and lacking energy. He also felt thirsty and was going to the toilet more often than usual. Sensibly, he decided to go to see his doctor.

His doctor told him that he thought he had **diabetes**. However, before he could be sure, he needed to do some tests. Geoff had heard of diabetes, but did not know what it was. His doctor told him that 1.4 million people in the UK have diabetes and this total is expected to double by 2010. The doctor then explained diabetes to him.

Controlling blood sugar

When you eat food, some of it is broken down in your gut into a sugar called **glucose**. The glucose enters your blood. The body would like to receive glucose in a slow steady supply. But it does not work like this.

We tend to eat quite a lot of food during a meal and then wait several hours before we eat any more. So glucose tends to enter the blood in large amounts after a meal. This is difficult for the body to manage.

In order to work properly, the body needs to have a constant level of glucose. If the level in your blood rises too much or falls too much, you can go into a coma. It can even lead to death.

When glucose enters the blood after a meal, the spare glucose is stored in the liver as a substance called **glycogen**. This ensures that the glucose in the blood does not rise to dangerous levels. Between meals, when the level of glucose in the blood is falling, glycogen in the liver is turned back into glucose. It enters the blood again. This makes sure that the glucose level does not fall back too far between meals.

The body normally controls the level of glucose in the blood by using a **hormone** called **insulin**. The insulin is produced in a gland called the **pancreas**. This hormone lowers the level of glucose in the blood in several different ways.

As with the levels of oxygen, carbon dioxide and temperature, it is important to keep a constant level of glucose. This balancing act is called homeostasis.

The best way to think of homeostasis is to imagine a car travelling at 30mph. To speed it up you need an accelerator and to slow it down you need a brake.

Insulin is the brake that keeps the glucose levels in the blood down.

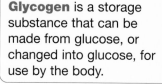

Word check

Glycogen is a storage substance that can be made from glucose, or changed into glucose, for use by the body.

Word check

A **hormone** is a chemical messenger that travels to different parts of the body in the blood.

2.26 Diabetes

Testing Geoff ACTIVITY

The doctor explained that if Geoff had diabetes, his urine would contain glucose.

1 Why do you think that Geoff's urine would contain glucose if he had diabetes?

The doctor tested Geoff's urine with a clinistix. This is a plastic stick with a piece of paper on the end that changes colour when placed in urine. The colour tells you how much glucose is in the urine.

2 Look at the picture of the clinistix and the chart. Do you think Geoff has too much glucose in his urine?

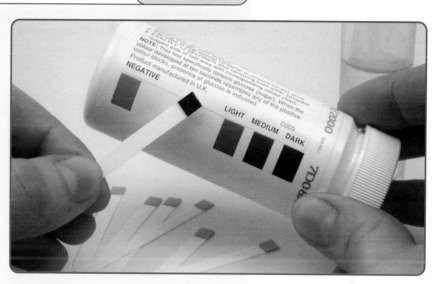

Clinistix and colour chart.

The doctor decided that he needed to do further tests, just to be sure. He took a sample of Geoff's blood and tested it on a small machine. The machine gives a read-out of how much glucose is in the blood.

The normal reading for blood glucose level is between 4 and 7 mmol l⁻¹. Geoff has a reading well above 7.

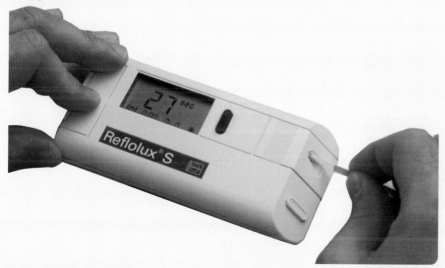

Geoff's blood testing machine.

3 An untreated **diabetic** has values greater than 7 mmol l⁻¹. Do you still think that Geoff has diabetes?

4 Find out about the types of tablets diabetics can take and how they work.

5 There are different types of diabetes. Find out what you can about Type 1 and Type 2 diabetes.

You can find out more about diabetes in leaflets at a doctor's surgery, or on the Internet at www.diabetes.org.uk.

2.26 Diabetes

Controlling Geoff's diabetes

Geoff wants to know how it is going to affect him. The doctor tells him that there are three main ways to treat the disease.

Diet

Because the glucose level in the blood rises after eating a meal, and falls between meals, the doctor tells Geoff to eat smaller meals, but more often. Snacking will drip-feed glucose into his blood all the time. This is better than eating one or two large meals. It means that Geoff will have to plan his meal and snack times, and must not forget to take a meal. He will also have to check the glucose level in his blood regularly to ensure that the glucose level is not too high and not too low.

Tablets

Geoff's pancreas is not making enough insulin. Geoff thinks that he could take insulin tablets. Insulin is a protein.

6 Why is it not possible to take in insulin by swallowing tablets?
(Hint: Think about what happens to the proteins we take in with our food.)

There are tablets that can be taken to make the pancreas work better or to encourage the body to take more sugar out of the blood.

Injecting insulin

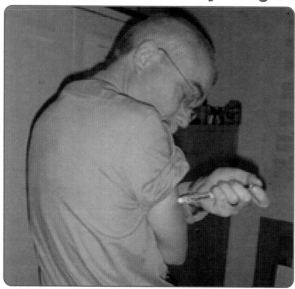

Because Geoff's pancreas is not making enough insulin, he may have to inject himself with insulin every day.

7 Geoff is told that taking regular exercise may help his glucose levels. Why is this?

Life is going to be different for Geoff from now on.

8 State where the glucose in the blood comes from.

9 Explain why Geoff cannot control the level of glucose in his blood without medical help.

10 Apart from glucose, state two other things that the body has to keep at a constant level.

11 Explain how diabetics can control the level of glucose in their blood.

Geoff injecting himself with insulin.

The future

Geoff's doctor tells him that things are looking brighter in the future. New research into stem cells may mean that his pancreas can be repaired and will start to make insulin again.

Stem cells are cells that can turn into any other kind of cell. In the future, it might be possible to inject them into Geoff's pancreas and turn them into insulin-making cells.

2.26 Diabetes

Rebecca the optician

Rebecca is an optician. Most people think that an optician just tests eyes to see if a patient needs a pair of glasses. In fact, the job of an optician is much more than this. One of the things that Rebecca looks for when testing someone's eyes is to see if there is any evidence of diabetes. She looks very carefully at the back of the eye to examine the state of the blood vessels.

The back of the eye is called the retina. It is supplied with blood through lots of tiny blood vessels. When someone is suffering from diabetes, the blood vessels get leaky and patches of blood can be seen at the back of the eye. When Rebecca sees this, she completes a special form called a 'referral form' and instructs the patient to go and see their doctor. The doctor will then perform tests to see if the patient really is a diabetic.

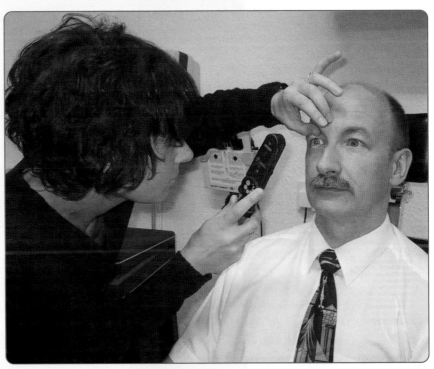

Rebecca looks for signs of diabetes when testing eyes.

Opticians like Rebecca are responsible for finding many cases of diabetes when the patient is completely unaware that anything is wrong. The sooner that diabetes is discovered, the better it can be treated.

12 Suggest why diabetics must have regular tests of eyes and feet every year.

13 Explain how Rebecca knows that one of her patients has diabetes and why she fills in a referral form.

Key facts

Copy and complete the sentences by choosing the correct word from the key words list. Each word may be used more than once.

1 The level of _____ in the blood must be kept constant.

2 _____ is a _____ produced by the _____.

3 A person with _____ does not produce enough insulin.

4 Insulin can be injected into the blood of a _____.

5 The dose of _____ will depend upon diet and exercise of the diabetic.

6 Keeping the correct levels of substances in the blood is a process called _____.

7 Excess glucose in the blood is changed into _____ which is stored in the liver.

Key words

diabetes

diabetic

glucose

glycogen

homeostasis

hormone

insulin

pancreas

2.27 Cells and communication

Living is dangerous

We can only survive if we get information about what is going on around us.

The sense of smell.

Just imagine trying to cross a busy road if you were deaf, blind and could not feel anything. It would be a very dangerous thing to do. We can only survive because our brain receives information from our five different senses. These senses are sight, hearing, smell, taste and touch. These five senses are responsible for keeping us fully informed about what is happening in the world around us. It is only when we lose one of our senses that we realise how vulnerable we are.

Sense receptors

Our sense organs, the ears, the eyes, the tongue, the nose and the skin, contain receptor cells that monitor changes in the environment around us. When something in the environment changes, the receptor cells send the information to the brain to be processed. This is why we immediately notice a new smell or a sound that may alert us to important things like food or danger.

1 Which of the five senses do you think is most important? Explain your answer.

2 If you could choose to have a sixth sense, what would it be?

2.27 Cells and communication

Nerve cells are sensitive

ACTIVITY

Our senses are so good at sending information to the brain that the brain cannot cope with all of the data that it receives. It ignores most of it and just concentrates on what is important. Think about the chair you are sitting on. Suddenly, you can feel it underneath your body. Now think about the shoes on your feet and you can feel them touching your toes. Although receptor cells are sending this information to the brain all of the time, our brain mostly ignores it because it is not important. It concentrates on the really important things like the data coming from your eyes whilst you are reading this book.

Just how sensitive are our nerves?

For this activity, you need to work with a partner.

Take a pair of compass dividers and open the points so that they are five millimetres apart.

Ask your partner to look away and gently place either one, or both, of the points onto the skin on the back of your partner's hand. Ask them to tell you whether they feel one or two points touching their skin.

How many points? One or two?

To make sure that they are not guessing, repeat the process, sometimes touching them with one point and sometimes with two. You will find that they can only feel one point, even when you touch them with two.

Gradually open the dividers until your partner can always feel both of the points.

Measure the gap between the points and record it in a copy of the following table. Repeat the procedure for other areas of the body.

Position of skin	Distance between points (mm)
back of hand	
fingertip	
forearm	
upper arm	
back of neck	

Plot your results as a bar chart.

❸ Which area of skin is most sensitive? Suggest why.

We can only feel two points if the dividers are stimulating two different receptors.

❹ In which part of the body are the skin receptors closest together?

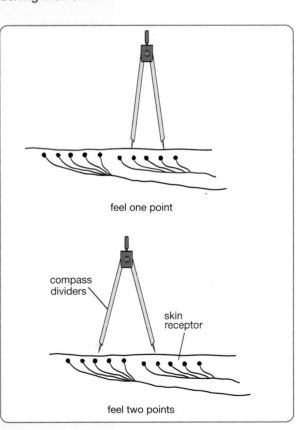

feel one point

compass dividers

skin receptor

feel two points

2.27 Cells and communication

How our senses work

Neurones

Neurones are nerve cells. They are the longest cells in our body. Some of them can be over a metre in length. Their job is to carry information from the receptors to our brain where the data can be processed. They then carry instructions from the brain to the effectors, or muscles of our body, to make them contract.

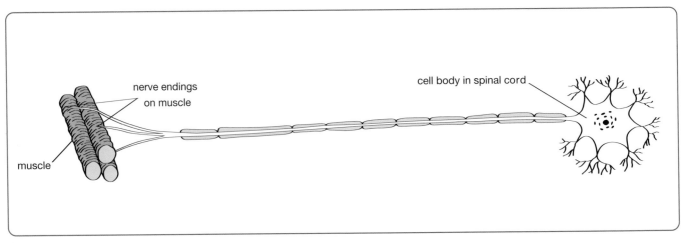

A neurone.

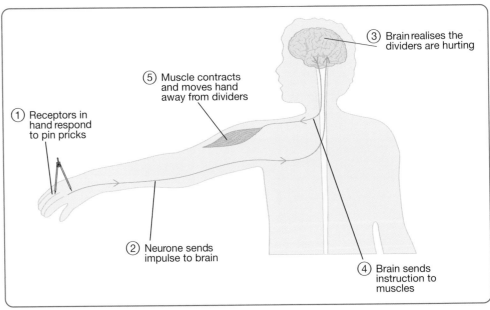

Neural pathway.

⑤ Suggest why nerve cells are so long.

⑥ You can test how fast your neurones work by doing a reaction time test. Type 'reaction time test' into a search engine to find a test. What was your reaction time and how does it compare with the rest of the class?

2.27 Cells and communication

Working with neurones CASE STUDY

Some nurses work in the neurology department of a hospital. They test patients with carpal tunnel syndrome. Carpal tunnel syndrome is when the nerves that pass through the wrist get compressed. It causes pain, numbness and tingling in the hand.

A simple test that can help diagnose carpal tunnel syndrome is the Phalen's test. The patient flexes their wrist at a sharp angle for one minute. Those with carpal tunnel syndrome will experience numbness and tingling.

Treatment

In the early stages, patients can wear a wrist support to restrict movement of the wrist.

Some patients can be treated with ultrasound to reduce inflammation and pain.

In severe cases, surgery can be used to relieve the pressure on the nerves as they pass through the wrist.

Phalen's test for carpal tunnel syndrome.

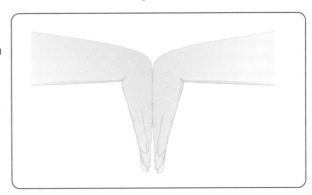

7 What is carpal tunnel syndrome?

8 Explain how it can be diagnosed.

9 Explain how it can be treated.

Key facts

Copy and complete the sentences by choosing the correct word from the key words list. Each word may be used more than once, or not at all.

1 _____ in the sense organs detect changes in the environment.

2 Information is sent along a _____ to the brain.

3 The brain sends instructions to an _____.

Key words

effector

nerves

neurones

receptors

2.28 Drugs and the body

What are drugs?

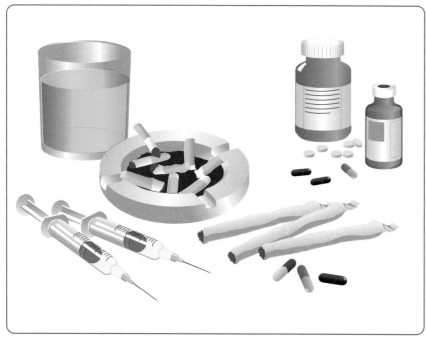

Drugs come in a wide range of sizes and colours.

Drugs are any chemicals that change the way in which the body works. They are found in food (for example, caffeine), may be prescribed by our doctor (for example, antibiotics) and can be used on social occasions (for example, alcohol and tobacco). They can also be abused, for example, cocaine and heroin.

Types of drugs

Different drugs have different effects on the body. Sometimes drugs can be useful. They can reduce pain and inflammation and kill bacteria that invade our body. Other drugs may be abused. They make us feel good for a short while but can seriously damage our health and even kill us. Many of these drugs are also addictive so that we need to continue taking even more larger doses.

Type of drug	Example of name of drug
anti-inflammatory	aspirin
painkiller	paracetamol
antibiotic	penicillin
anti-depressant	Valium
recreational	nicotine
	tobacco
	barbiturates
	heroin
	cocaine
	alcohol

Examples of different drugs.

Testing new drugs

New medical drugs have to be tested before they can be used on patients. First they have to go through a series of clinical trials to judge their effectiveness and safety. Sometimes the drug may be tested on animals. At other times human volunteers are used. If the drug passes these trials, it then has to be given a license by an organisation called NICE. Only then can the drug be prescribed by doctors.

❶ Explain the difference between medical and recreational drugs.

❷ Explain what happens to new drugs before they can be prescribed by doctors.

2.28 Drugs and the body

Who takes drugs?

Most people know that taking cannabis is illegal. Cannabis is a drug that is usually taken by smoking it. Even cigarette smoking is a form of drug-taking. The addictive drug in cigarettes is nicotine. However, cigarettes also contain many other harmful chemicals. Some countries have now banned smoking in public places so that non-smokers do not have to breathe in the harmful chemicals. This is called passive smoking.

The table shows the percentage of people in each age group who smoke.

Smoking cannabis is illegal.

Percentage of smokers															
	1974	1978	1982	1986	1990	1992	1994	1996	1998	2000	2001	2002	2003	2004	2005
All men aged 16 and over	51	45	38	35	31	29	28	29	30	29	28	27	28	27	27
All women aged 16 and over	41	37	33	31	29	28	26	28	26	25	26	25	24	25	24
Total for different ages															
16–19	40	34	30	30	30	27	27	29	31	29	28	25	26	25	25
20–24	48	44	40	39	38	38	39	39	40	35	37	38	36	36	35
25–34	51	45	38	36	35	34	32	36	35	35	34	34	34	34	33
35–49	52	45	39	36	34	31	30	30	31	29	29	28	30	29	28
50–59	51	45	41	35	29	29	27	27	28	27	26	26	25	25	25
60 and over	34	30	27	25	21	20	17	18	16	16	17	15	15	15	14
All men and women aged 16 and over	45	40	35	33	30	28	27	28	28	27	27	26	26	26	25

3 Describe the trend in the number of men and women aged 16 and over who smoke cigarettes.

4 Which group smokes the greatest number of cigarettes, men or women?

5 Draw a bar chart to show the percentage number of men and women who have smoked between the years 1974 and 2005.

6 Suggest why a lower percentage of people smoked cigarettes in 2005 than in 1974.

7 Do you think that smoking in public places is acceptable?

2.28 Drugs and the body

The effects of smoking and drinking on the body

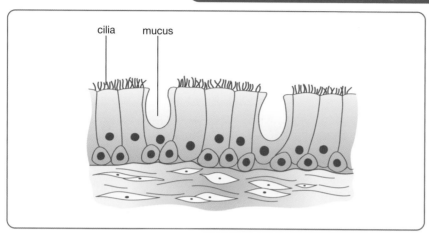

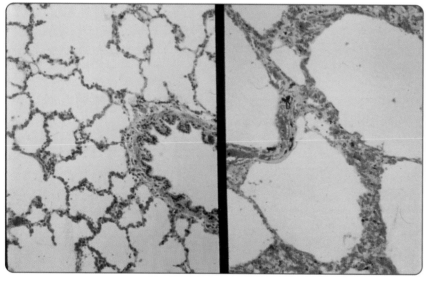

The lung on the left is healthy. The lung on the right has emphysema.

2 units   1 unit

Men should not drink more than this each day.

Smoking

Bronchitis

The cells of our trachea and bronchi are lined with mucus cells. The cells produce sticky mucus that traps dust and microorganisms. The mucus is then wafted up to the mouth by small hairs called cilia. Smoking paralyses these small hairs so that the mucus builds up in the lungs. This causes the smoker's cough and leads to bronchitis.

Emphysema

Over a period of time, the build-up of mucus causes infections. The infections and chemicals present in the cigarette smoke cause the walls of the air sacs in the lungs to break down. This causes permanent damage to the lung tissue and makes breathing very difficult. This is called emphysema.

Lung cancer

Cigarette smoke contains chemicals that cause lung cancer. The greater the number of cigarettes smoked, the greater the risk of getting lung cancer. About 90 per cent of people who die from lung cancer are smokers.

Drinking

Alcohol is a powerful drug. It affects nerve function in the brain, reduces our inhibitions and slows down our reaction time. This is why it is illegal to drink and drive. Alcohol is broken down by the liver. If too much alcohol is consumed, the liver becomes damaged and death can result. This is called cirrhosis of the liver.

Scientists think that a safe level of alcohol consumption for men is 21 units per week and 14 units for women.

2.28 Drugs and the body

Testing new drugs CASE STUDY

Russell is a computer programmer. He writes software for computers. New drugs are tested before use by using double blind trials.

A computer programme divides the patients into two groups: those who will receive the drug and those who will receive a placebo. A placebo is just a sugar tablet that is made to look exactly like the drug tablet. None of the patients will know whether they are taking the new drug or the placebo. Even the doctor who is giving out the drugs does not know which of his patients is getting the drug or the placebo. This is why it is called a double blind trial. Only the computer programme knows which patients are taking the drug. After a period of time, the patients are asked to judge the effectiveness of the tablets and describe any side effects. Their replies are analysed by the computer. If all the patients taking the real drug show improvement but those taking the placebo do not, then the new drug is proved to be effective and may be licensed for general use.

8 Suggest why the doctor does not know whether they are giving the drug or the placebo to their patients.

9 Explain why the drug trial is called a double blind trial.

10 Suggest why it is important that drugs are tested before they can be prescribed by doctors.

Key facts

Copy and complete the sentences by choosing the correct word from the key words list. Each word may be used more than once, or not at all.

1 Two legal recreational drugs are _____ and _____.

2 _____ is an anti-inflammatory drug.

3 Bacterial infections can be treated with _____.

4 Two illegal recreational drugs are _____ and _____.

5 _____ are given to people who are depressed.

Key words

alcohol

amphetamines

antibiotic

anti-depressants

anti-inflammatory

aspirin

barbiturates

cocaine

heroin

nicotine

paracetamol

penicillin

Review questions

1 Describe and explain what each of the following does:

   (a) artery   (b) vein   (c) capillary.   *[3]*

2 George has his blood pressure taken. It is 150 over 95. Explain what these two figures mean.   *[2]*

3 George has a heart attack. Look at the picture of his heart.

   (a) With reference to the picture, explain what happened when he had his heart attack.   *[3]*

   (b) Explain what George could do to help to prevent another attack.   *[3]*

4 Beccy and Chris donate some blood. It contains the following things:

   (a) red blood cells   (b) white blood cells   (c) platelets   (d) plasma

   Describe what job each of these does.   *[4]*

5 Richard has asthma. Look at the diagram and explain what happens when he has an asthma attack.

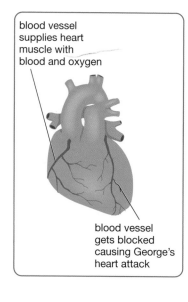

blood vessel supplies heart muscle with blood and oxygen

blood vessel gets blocked causing George's heart attack

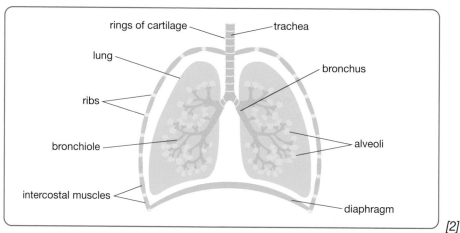

rings of cartilage — trachea

lung

bronchus

ribs

bronchiole

alveoli

intercostal muscles

diaphragm

    [2]

6 Wendy runs a marathon. Explain how she breaks down glucose to get the energy that she needs.   *[2]*

7 Paul goes on his Duke of Edinburgh's expedition. Explain how Paul's body will try to prevent his body temperature from dropping when he gets cold and wet.   *[3]*

8 Geoff has diabetes. He does not produce any of the hormone called insulin.

   (a) Explain what the word diabetes means.

   (b) Why does Geoff inject himself with insulin every day?

   (c) Give another example of homeostasis.   *[3]*

9 A pint of beer is two units of alcohol. A small glass of wine is one unit of alcohol. In order to avoid liver damage, men should not drink more than 21 units of alcohol per week. Dave drinks five pints on Friday, eight pints on Saturday and has four glasses of wine on Sunday.

   (a) How many units of alcohol has Dave drunk?   *[1]*

   (b) Is Dave exceeding his safe limit of alcohol consumption?   *[1]*

3 Useful chemicals

CHEMICALS FROM THE EARTH

Assignments and practical activities linked to this section:

The extraction of copper from an ore.

Elements, compounds and mixtures

Making saline solutions

Use the following to check your progress.

Unit 1

You will:

- learn about separating processes such as evaporation.

see pages 156–159

Unit 2

You will:

- know that gold and sulphur are mined and their uses

see pages 146–149

- know that gold is a metal and sulphur is a non-metal

see pages 146–149

- know that limestone and marble are mined and their uses

see pages 150–155

- know the composition of some building materials and how they are manufactured

see pages 152–153

- know the difference between an element, a compound and a mixture

see pages 150–155

- be able to work out the names of elements in a compound from its formula

see page 154

- know that salt must be separated out of rock salt and how this is done

see pages 156–159

- be able to explain what an ore is

see pages 160–163

- know how metals can be made from their oxides

see pages 160–163

- be able to describe what happens in a blast furnace.

see pages 160–163

Unit 3

You will:

- be able to write equations for the reactions in a blast furnace

see pages 160–161

- understand the industrial importance of the reaction of carbon with metal oxides.

see page 162

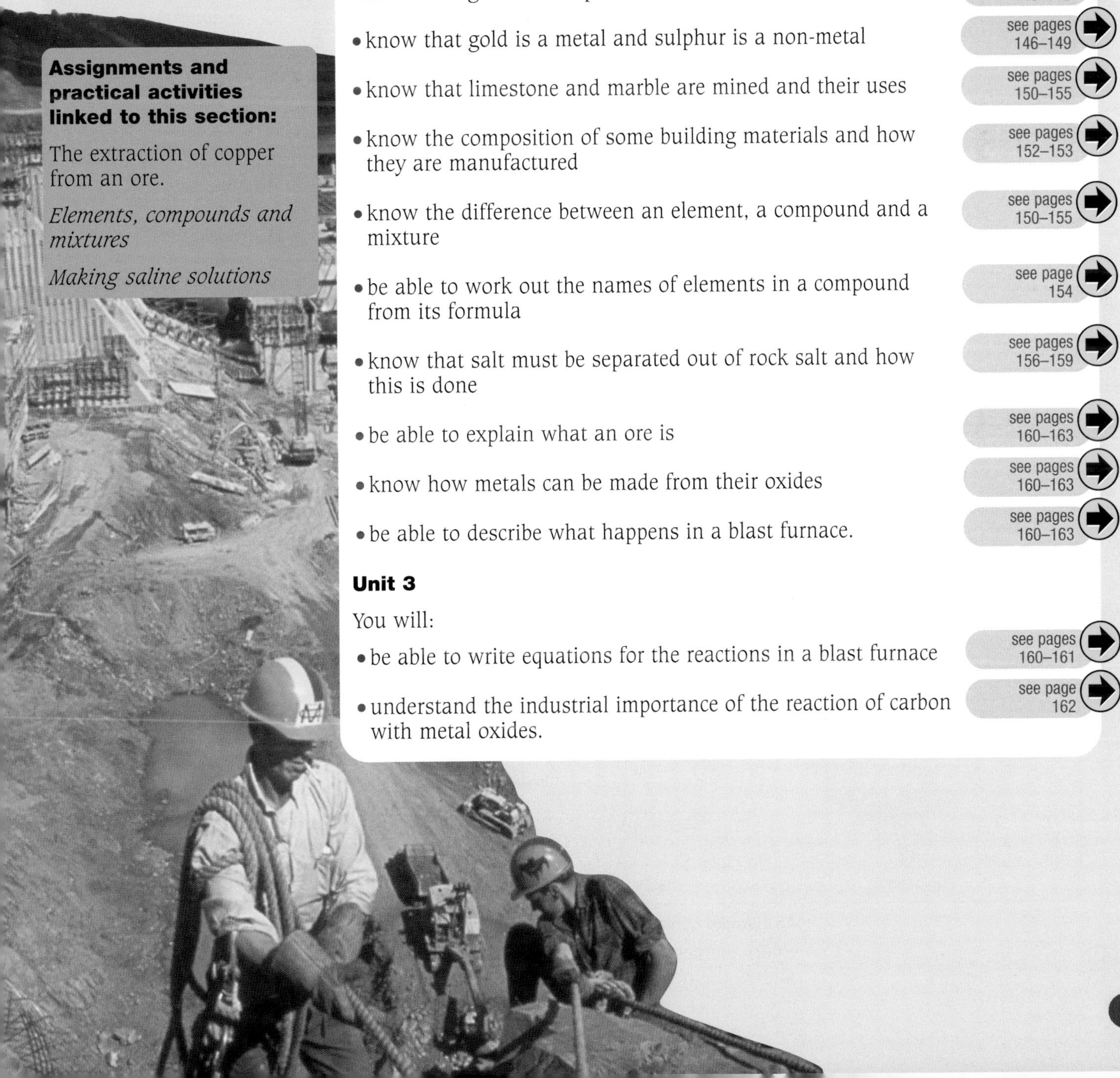

3.1 Elements from the Earth

Rubber and riches

The quality of gold must be tested before it is sold.

Volcanoes bring sulphur to the surface from deep in the Earth.

Sulphur and **gold** are both **elements** that are found in their natural state in the Earth. In some countries, people collect lumps of fresh sulphur from volcanoes. Most sulphur is mined from older deposits underground. Sulphur is used for making sulphuric acid (needed to make paints and detergents like shower gel). Older car tyres also contain sulphur.

There is hardly any gold left on the surface of the Earth. Modern gold mines are very deep. Gold has many uses besides making jewellery – did you know that the electrical contacts in car air bags are made from gold?

Elements

Gold and sulphur are both found in the ground as elements.

Elements are made of atoms. Every element has its own symbol. The symbol for gold is Au; the symbol for sulphur is S.

Word check

An **element** contains only one type of atom and cannot be split up into anything simpler.

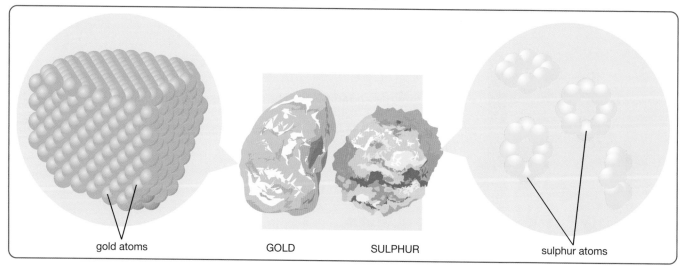

gold atoms   GOLD   SULPHUR   sulphur atoms

An element contains all the same type of atoms.

see Appendix 1, page 313

Every element we know about is listed in the Periodic Table. The Periodic Table shows the name and the symbol for every element.

3.1 Elements from the Earth

Mining and using gold and sulphur   ACTIVITY

1 Gold is mined by digging it out of deep mines. Underground sulphur deposits can be brought up by melting the sulphur using superheated water (at 170°C) and piping it to the surface.

(a) What does this information tell you about the melting point of sulphur?

(b) Why can't gold be mined like this?

2 The trade price for buying gold is about £10 per gram. The cost of sulphur is about £90 per tonne (1 kg = 1000 g and 1 tonne = 1 000 000 g).

(a) Work out the cost of 1 kg of gold and 1 kg of sulphur (1 kg of gold is about the same size as a bar of chocolate).

(b) Make a list of reasons why you think the costs of sulphur and gold are so different.

3 This table shows some information about the history of gold.

1350 BCE	Tutankhamen's coffin is solid gold and weighs about 1100 kg.
1927	Gold was shown to ease arthritis.
1947	The first transistor was made using gold for making connections.
1969	The astronauts on the Apollo 11 moon landing used helmets fitted with gold-plated sun visors to protect their eyes from the glare of the sun.
1987	Air bags for cars were given gold contacts to make them more reliable.

Make a collage of pictures from magazines or print outs from websites to show the uses of gold. Write captions to explain why gold is so well suited to each use.

4 Sulphur burns in oxygen to make sulphur dioxide. Sulphur dioxide is a toxic gas. It is used to bleach white paper and to kill bacteria in food. Foods labelled with 'E220' contain tiny amounts of sulphur dioxide.

(a) Look at some food labels. Which foods contain 'E220'?

(b) Why do you think numbers are used instead of names on food labels?

5 Archaeologists often dig up very old metal objects from the ground. Egyptian golden bowls may be 5000 years old, but still look shiny and new. Iron tools rust away completely in only a few years. How does this help us to understand why gold occurs in the Earth as an element, but iron does not?

3.1 Elements from the Earth

Metals and non-metals

Gold is a **metal** and sulphur is a **non-metal**.

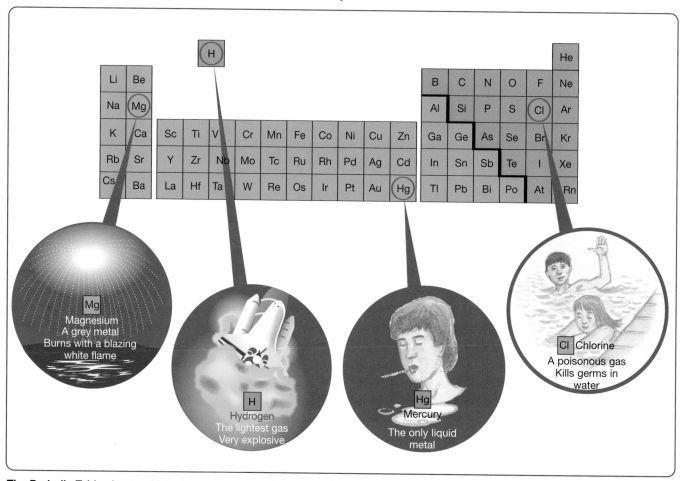

The Periodic Table shows which elements are metals and which are non-metals.

Metals are usually hard and shiny solids. (Mercury is the only metal that is liquid at room temperature.) All metals conduct electricity. At room temperature, a **non-metal** may be a solid (like sulphur), a liquid (bromine) or a gas (oxygen).

FACT CARD: HYDROGEN	
Name:	Hydrogen
Symbol:	H
Metal or non-metal:	Non-metal
Appearance:	Colourless gas
Uses:	Making ammonia and margarine. As a fuel
Other information:	Explosive when mixed with oxygen

Work in groups to carry out a data search on the 20 elements listed on page 314. Each group should cover about three metals and three non-metals.

- Make a 'fact card' about each element to summarise your findings. On the left is an example of a fact card for hydrogen.

- Work in a group to discuss the similarities you can find between all the metals. How are metals different from non-metals?

- Choose another element. Try to predict some information about it based on your findings so far. Then check to see if you are right.

3.1 Elements from the Earth

Working in a jeweller's shop — CASE STUDY

Ann works in a jeweller's shop. 'My job is to help people choose jewellery.'

If people are buying gold jewellery, they often need advice about what the hallmarks mean. Gold jewellery does not contain pure gold – the gold is made into an alloy by mixing it with other metals. Pure gold would be too dense and soft to make jewellery.

Jewellers may talk about gold purity using the words '9 carat' or '18 carat'. Nowadays gold has a stamp or hallmark with a number to show how pure the gold is.

Ann works in a jeweller's shop.

This table shows how much gold, copper and silver are found in gold with different 'carat' values.

Carat	Gold %	Copper %	Silver %
22	92	5	3
18	75	12.5	12.5
14	58	21	21
9	38	31	31

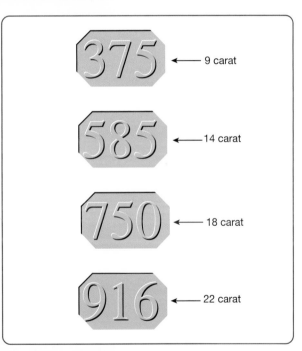

The hallmark shows how pure gold is.

6 Draw a graph with 'Carats' along the bottom and '%' up the side. Draw a separate line for each metal, to show the percentage of each metal in different gold alloys.

7 Predict the percentage of gold in 24 carat gold.

8 Which gold alloy will be the cheapest to buy? Look in a catalogue to check the prices of gold jewellery to see if you are right.

Key facts

Copy and complete the sentences by choosing the correct word from the key words list.

1 An _____ contains only one type of atom.

2 A shiny element that conducts electricity is a _____.

3 A _____ element may be a solid, liquid or gas at room temperature.

4 _____ and _____ are useful elements found in the ground.

Key words

element

gold

metal

non-metal

sulphur

3.2 Compounds from the Earth

Roads and houses

Joe is a builder. He works on buildings around Derby. He works to work every day on the Derby ring road. Joe's van travels over miles of limestone on the way to work. Crushed limestone is used as 'aggregate' underneath the tarmac on many roads.

Limestone 'aggregate' is used under roads.

Looking at limestone products

Limestone and marble are both rocks that are quarried from the Earth. Marble is similar to limestone, but is shinier and harder. It is used to make building blocks for buildings, gravestones and statues. Limestone can be used as blocks, or crushed to make fine powders or 'aggregates' (lumps). It is also used to make other products, such as **cement**.

neutralising acidic soil

making glass

making iron and steel for machinery

small lumps of limestone as road aggregate

powdered limestone in road marking paint

making cement, mortar and concrete

limestone blocks as building stones

This diagram shows how limestone is used around Joe's building site.

❶ Write down some uses of cut or crushed limestone.

❷ Do a 'window survey'. Write down the uses of limestone that you can see from your classroom window.

3.2 Compounds from the Earth

Should we build a new limestone quarry? (ACTIVITY)

In the UK, limestone is quarried in huge open quarries. Before a new quarry is opened, everyone has the chance to put forward their views. Here is a summary of the views of two people who have 'for' and 'against' views about a new quarry.

Liz Starks, Quarry spokesperson

- The limestone is needed for industry and the building trade.
- The quarry will provide money and jobs locally.
- Our company can limit problems by:
  - building banks and planting trees around the quarry;
  - spraying lorries to keep dust down;
  - not quarrying at night;
  - to build a fishing lake and golf course on the land when quarrying is finished.

Norman James, Local resident

- The quarry would ruin a hill that has been beautiful for millions of years.
- What about local wildlife? The birds are lovely up there.
- I don't want lorries, noise and dust upsetting everyone for years.
- Once the quarry is here it will attract other industry – we don't want our village to be spoiled by a cement works.

Choose to be either 'Liz, Quarry spokesperson' or 'Norman, Local resident'.

Liz: Produce an information leaflet with pictures and explanations. Your leaflet will be posted to all the local residents to persuade them that the quarry is needed.

Norman: Prepare information to take to a meeting with the quarry spokesperson. What photos might help? Produce a leaflet with pictures to put across your views.

3.2 Compounds from the Earth

Building materials from limestone

Limestone is used as a raw material for making other building materials. It is used to make **cement** which is then mixed with sand to make **mortar**, or sand and gravel to make **concrete**.

Cement

... is made by heating in a kiln...

- **powdered limestone**
- and **clay**.

Mortar

... is made by mixing together...

- **cement**
- **sand**
- and **water**.

Mortar is used to hold bricks together.

Concrete

... is made by mixing together...

- **cement**
- **sand**
- **crushed rock** (or **gravel**)
- and **water**.

Concrete is much harder than mortar – it can be used for construction.

Building sites usually buy large amounts of cement, sand and gravel from building merchants. Joe mixes mortar as he needs it on the site. He sometimes mixes small amounts of concrete. He buys larger amounts of concrete 'ready mixed'.

3 Look at the difference between mortar and cement. List reasons why mortar is the easiest to use for laying bricks and why concrete is more hardwearing.

4 (a) Find out where mortar and cement have been used around the school buildings. Find out how old the buildings are. What do the two materials feel like? How do mortar and cement change over time?

(b) Older brick buildings need 'repointing'. Find out what this means. Why do you think it is necessary?

3.2 Compounds from the Earth

Making glass   ACTIVITY

Limestone is also used as a raw material in making glass. The chemical structure of glass is the same as sand – glass is really just sand that has been melted and made into a flat sheet. Glass is not made from just sand, because the melting point of sand is 1610°C. It would take far too much energy and be far too difficult and costly to make glass at this temperature. Other ingredients are added to lower the melting point of sand so the process can be run at a lower temperature.

Raw materials used to make glass	
Raw purpose material	
Sand	Melts to form glass.
Sodium carbonate	Lowers the melting point of sand.
Limestone	Makes the glass more water resistant.
Recycled glass	Saves energy and saves raw materials.

Special types of glass		
Type of glass	**Properties**	**Uses**
Toughened glass	Does not break easily. No sharp edges when broken.	Glass doors, car windscreens.
Heatproof glass	Does not crack or melt at high temperatures.	Glass cooking pots, oven doors and cooker tops.
Self-cleaning glass	Has a catalyst coating that breaks down dirt.	Windows of very large buildings.
Low energy-emitting glass	Lets less heat through than normal gas.	Household double glazing.

The glass-making process

The raw materials are heated until they melt, mixed together and then poured onto hot molten tin. The molten glass spreads out to form a big sheet on the tin. When the glass cools, it goes solid and can be cut into smaller sheets.

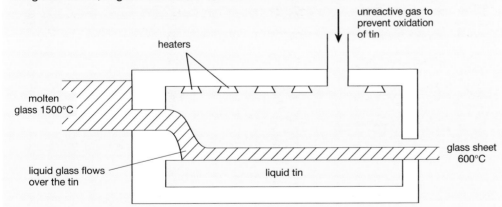

heaters

unreactive gas to prevent oxidation of tin

molten glass 1500°C

liquid glass flows over the tin

liquid tin

glass sheet 600°C

Glass is an important construction material.

Making glass sheets.

5 Why does industry prefer to run processes at the lowest possible temperature?

6 Look at the diagram of the glass-making process. Estimate the melting point of tin. Explain your reasoning.

7 (a) The furnace is filled with an unreactive gas. What would happen to the tin if oxygen was let in?

   (b) Which gas from the air could be used to fill the furnace?

8 Take some digital photographs of some different uses of glass at home or school. Which type of glass is used in each place?

3.2 Compounds from the Earth

Getting the formula

Remember that an element contains all the same type of atoms. Limestone and marble are mainly **calcium carbonate**. Calcium carbonate contains different types of atoms. It is a **compound**.

The **formula** (plural: **formulae**) for calcium carbonate is $CaCO_3$.

This is how we work out what that means:

$$Ca = calcium \diagup \overset{\displaystyle CaCO_3}{\underset{C\,=\,carbon}{\diagup}} \diagdown O = oxygen$$

Calcium carbonate contains calcium, carbon and oxygen – three different elements.

Notice that sometimes symbols for elements have two letters, for example 'Ca'. You can look up the symbols on the Periodic Table (page 313) or on an element list (page 314).

9 Look at the list of formulae for different substances below.

$$CO_2 \quad H_2SO_4 \quad CaO \quad Na_2CO_3 \quad NH_3 \quad Cl_2$$

(a) Which formulae contain only two different elements?

(b) Which formulae contain three different elements?

(c) Which formula is an element?

(d) List all the elements in Na_2CO_3.

(e) One of these substances is made using sulphur. Which one?

(f) Explain why the formula H_2SO_4 must be a compound.

(g) Which substances can be made from limestone?

How many atoms?

The formula also tells you how many atoms of each type of element there are in a compound.

A molecule of H_2O looks like this:

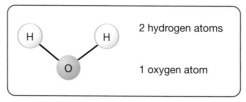

2 hydrogen atoms

1 oxygen atom

The formula shows it contains two hydrogen atoms and one oxygen atom.

10 Look again at the list of formulae in question 9. Write down the NAMES and NUMBER OF ATOMS of each type of element in NH_3 and Cl_2.

11 Look at the list of compounds on page 314. Choose FIVE formulae. Write down the names and number of atoms of each type of element in the formulae you have chosen.

see Elements from the Earth, page 146

3.2 Compounds from the Earth

Apex Cement Works   CASE STUDY

Tim is the manager of Apex Cement Works. He explains:

'We make cement from limestone and clay. We quarry the limestone and clay at Cairnhill Quarry. We built the cement factory next to the quarry. This makes the cement cheaper and is better for the environment.

'At the cement factory, we crush the limestone. We mix it with clay and mill it to a powder. We have a huge kiln to heat the powder to convert it into calcium oxide, the main ingredient in cement. After that, we mill the cement again to make sure it's really fine. We add gypsum, which helps the cement to set, before we put it into bags.

'We are very keen to help the environment. We burn old tyres and waste plastic and paper to heat the kiln. We have made a "bat cave" for wild bats in one of our old mines.'

Cement works are usually built beside limestone quarries.

12 This process uses waste tyres, paper and plastic to heat the kiln.

(a) What fuels do you think most kilns use?

(b) List reasons why using waste as fuel helps the environment.

13 (a) Why is it 'environmentally friendly' to have the cement works near the limestone quarry?

(b) Why does this make the cement cheaper?

14 The 'bat cave' is a big success. What other information would you need to know to decide whether or not the cement works has been good for local wildlife in general?

Key facts

Copy and complete the sentences by choosing the correct word from the key words list. Each word may be used more than once, or not at all.

1 Limestone and marble contain mainly _____ _____ and can be used straight from the ground.

2 Limestone is used to make _____.

3 A _____ contains more than one element combined together.

4 The _____ of a compound shows what elements it contains.

Key words

calcium carbonate

cement

compound

concrete

formula

glass

mortar

3.3 Salt from rock salt

Worth your weight in salt?

If you had been a Roman soldier, you would have got some of your wages as a 'salary' – a payment in salt. (We still use the word 'salary' today.) Salt was very precious because without it you would probably die – with no fridges it was the only way to preserve meat to carry on the long marches. Salt was a treatment for battle wounds. Incredibly, the UK still produces about 100 kg of salt every year for every person living here – this is probably more than you weigh! Most of the salt is used for making other **chemicals**.

Salt mining

Word check ✓

A **mixture** contains more than one substance that can be separated from each other.

The UK mines over five million tonnes of salt every year. In Cheshire, there are two types of salt mine. In rock salt mining, the salt is dug out of the ground using machinery. The mines are about 250 m deep. The roof of the mine stays up because 'pillars' of salt are left to hold it up. This salt is very impure. It is a **mixture** because it has impurities of grit and sand – it would be no use for sprinkling on chips! Rock salt is spread on roads in winter to stop ice forming.

The roof of a salt mine is held up by pillars of salt.

Solution mining is used to get purer salt for food use and chemicals. Hot water goes down pipes into the underground salt. The salt is **separated** from the sand and rock when it **dissolves**. The salty water (brine) is pumped up another pipe. The water **evaporates** to separate the pure salt from the water.

Brine from a solution mine is not usually evaporated just by boiling it. In hot countries, the brine is left in huge shallow pans in the sun. In the UK, brine goes into low-pressure vacuum tanks. The low pressure means that the brine boils at a much lower temperature than usual.

❶ Explain why using each of these methods of evaporating makes salt manufacturing cheaper.

3.3 Salt from rock salt

Salt from rock salt

ACTIVITY

Raji investigated getting salt from rock salt. This is what he did.

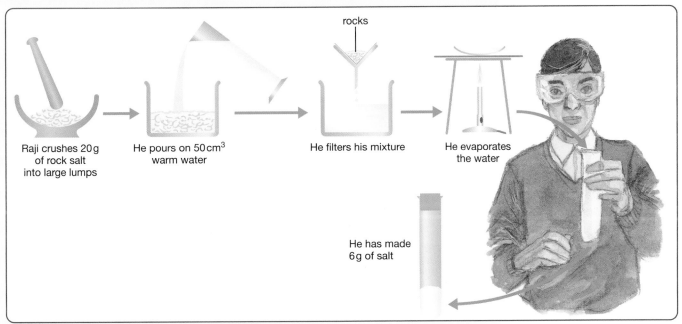

Raji crushes 20g of rock salt into large lumps

He pours on 50cm³ warm water

rocks

He filters his mixture

He evaporates the water

He has made 6g of salt

Raji separated salt from rock salt.

❷ (a)   Work out the percentage of salt Raji made from his rock salt (his yield).

(b)   How could Raji improve his method to increase his yield?

Raji made a plan to show how his process could be scaled up to a factory scale.
This is the first step in his plan.

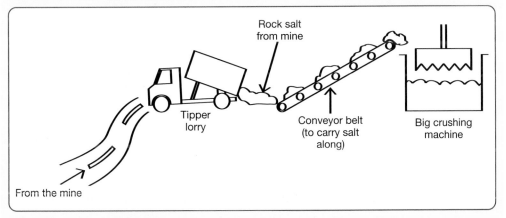

Rock salt from mine

From the mine

Tipper lorry

Conveyor belt (to carry salt along)

Big crushing machine

The start of Raji's plan.

❸ Design your own factory! Make a full drawing of a possible factory that could
use Raji's process. Make a list of the machinery the factory would need
(make up names for the machines). What parts of the process would use the
most energy and fuel?

❹ What would be the main costs in SETTING UP the factory? What costs would
there be in RUNNING the factory?

3.3 Salt from rock salt

How do we use all the salt?

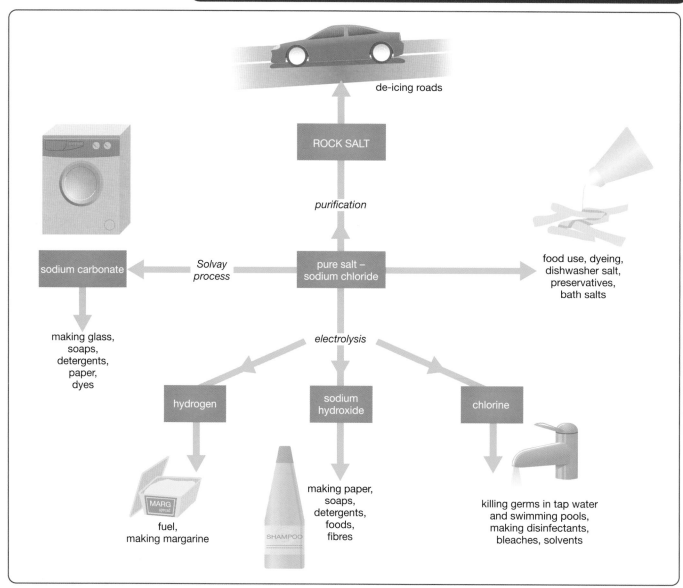

de-icing roads

ROCK SALT

purification

sodium carbonate

Solvay process

pure salt – sodium chloride

food use, dyeing, dishwasher salt, preservatives, bath salts

making glass, soaps, detergents, paper, dyes

electrolysis

hydrogen

sodium hydroxide

chlorine

fuel, making margarine

making paper, soaps, detergents, foods, fibres

killing germs in tap water and swimming pools, making disinfectants, bleaches, solvents

This diagram shows how salt is used.

5 (a) What is pure salt used for?

(b) Name four chemicals made from salt and give a use for each.

6 After a Roman history lesson, a friend says, 'I'm glad my Saturday job doesn't pay me in salt. I only use it on chips!' Write down what you would say to her to show her she was wrong.

7 These formulae are all substances on the diagram.

$$NaCl \qquad Na_2CO_3 \qquad H_2 \qquad Cl_2 \qquad NaOH$$

(a) Match each formula to a substance on the diagram.

(b) Which substances are elements? Which are compounds?

see Elements from the Earth, page 146

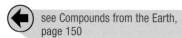
see Compounds from the Earth, page 150

3.3 Salt from rock salt

Gritting the roads

Phil drives a gritting lorry for a Winter Maintenance Team. He talks about his work.

'Whenever snow and ice are forecast I get sent out gritting the main roads with rock salt. The salt lowers the freezing point of the water so it doesn't freeze. The grit in the rock salt helps cars grip the road. We usually try to get our gritting done overnight, so we are not holding up traffic. (Motorists don't like their cars getting sprayed with rock salt as they pass me either!)

Road gritters put rock salt on roads in winter.

'Our team use "precautionary salting". "Precautionary" means "just in case" – we go out when snow or ice is expected. We spread our salt at the rate of 10 g m^{-2}. Some teams only go out after there has been a snowfall. Sometimes, a snow-plough has to go in front of the gritter. You need 40 g m^{-2} of salt on fallen snow.

'Putting salt on the roads can cause problems as well as solve them. It makes cars rust faster. I always wash my car underneath to get the salt off. (You should see the rust on some of the gritters.) Modern cars are designed to have smooth, sealed undercarriages so the salt falls off. Iron parts of bridges go rusty too. The salt can kill the plants alongside the roads.

'I always say, "I might not look like a brave man, but I save a hundred lives a year."'

8 Why do you think gritters use more salt per square metre on fallen snow than for 'precautionary salting'?

9 'Precautionary salting' over the whole winter uses more rock salt, and costs more money, than only gritting after snow falls.

(a) Explain why 'precautionary salting' costs more.

(b) What are the advantages of 'precautionary salting'?

10 Airports use liquid de-icers instead of rock salt on runways. Suggest some reasons why.

Key facts

Copy and complete the sentences by choosing the correct word from the key words list.

1 Rock salt is a _____ of salt and sand.

2 The sand can be easily _____ from the salt because the salt _____ in water.

3 Water _____ to leave clean salt.

4 Salt is used for food and making _____ .

Key words

chemicals

dissolves

evaporates

mixture

separated

3.4 Iron and steel

Making cars

New cars contain about 70 per cent steel. **Steel** is an alloy (a mixture of metals) but contains over 90 per cent iron.

The blast furnace

Iron for making steel for cars is made in a **blast furnace**. The furnace is used to get iron metal from impure iron **ore** called **haematite**. Haematite contains iron (III) oxide, Fe_2O_3, mixed with impurities.

This is what happens in the furnace.

- Iron ore, **limestone** and **coke** go in the top of the furnace.

- Hot air (at 1000°C) is blown in the bottom of the furnace.

- The coke, which is mainly **carbon**, burns.

$$C \quad + \quad O_2 \quad \rightarrow \quad CO_2$$
carbon + oxygen → carbon dioxide

- This reaction gives out a lot of heat, so the furnace gets even hotter.

- The limestone (calcium carbonate) breaks down.

$$CaCO_3 \quad \rightarrow \quad CaO \quad + \quad CO_2$$
calcium carbonate → calcium oxide + carbon dioxide

- The carbon dioxide reacts with more coke to make carbon monoxide.

$$CO_2 \quad + \quad C \quad \rightarrow \quad 2CO$$
carbon dioxide + carbon → carbon monoxide

- The most important reaction of all happens – the carbon monoxide reacts with the iron oxide to make iron.

$$Fe_2O_3 \quad + \quad 3CO \quad \rightarrow 2Fe + \quad 3CO_2$$
iron oxide + carbon monoxide → iron + carbon dioxide

- The main impurity in the haematite is sand, silicon dioxide. This reacts with the calcium oxide (from the limestone) to make 'slag'.

$$SiO_2 \quad + \quad CaO \quad \rightarrow \quad CaSiO_3$$
silicon dioxide + calcium oxide → calcium silicate (slag)

- The molten slag floats on the iron. It can be run out of a hole just above the surface of the iron. The iron flows out of a 'tap hole' in the bottom of the furnace.

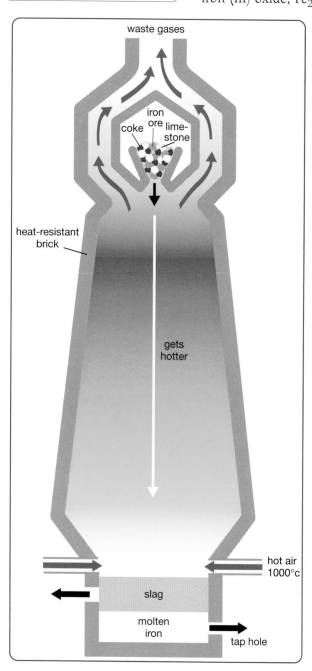

The blast furnace.

3.4 Iron and steel

Thinking about the blast furnace   ACTIVITY

Use the information on the facing page
to answer these questions.

1 'Raw materials' are the starting
materials for a process. Make a list
of the four raw materials used in
the blast furnace.

2 (a) Copy out the equations for the
blast furnace reactions. Put a
ring around the formula of
every gas that is involved in
the reactions.

(b) Gases that have not reacted
are collected and piped away
from the top of the furnace
because they are hazardous to
the workers. What hazards do
these gases have?

3 The melting point of iron is 1540°C.
What do you think is the temperature
inside the furnace? Explain how
you arrived at your estimate.

The blast furnace at Redcar

The biggest blast furnace in Europe is
at Redcar on the coast of north-east
England. The furnace uses coal and
haematite imported from abroad.

4 The blast furnace runs 24 hours a
day. The raw materials are
continuously fed in at the top and
the products come out at the
bottom. Explain why not having to keep stopping, emptying and
refilling the furnace makes the process cheaper to run.

5 The furnace employs many local people. The heavy work is carried out by
machinery, but people control the machinery and make sure that the process
runs smoothly. Make a list of some jobs that would have to be carried out
every day to keep the furnace running.

Molten blast furnace iron is made into steel by taking out impurities and mixing in
other metals. The steel is used for making products like cars, cans and machinery.

6 Write a cartoon strip to show what happens from the point of view of a lump
of iron ore. What happens after you are mined? Where do you end up?

This blast furnace is over
30 m high.

3.4 Iron and steel

Oxidation and reduction

Many metal ores contain compounds of metals with oxygen. For example, we extract tin from tinstone: tin oxide SnO_2. We extract aluminium from bauxite: aluminium oxide, Al_2O_3. To extract the metals we need to remove oxygen from the metal oxide. Removing oxygen is called **reduction**.

In the blast furnace, iron oxide is reduced by carbon monoxide.

$$Fe_2O_3 \quad + \quad 3CO \quad \rightarrow \quad 2Fe \quad + \quad 3CO_2$$
iron oxide + carbon monoxide → iron + carbon dioxide

The carbon monoxide is a reducer because it takes oxygen away from iron oxide. At the same time, carbon monoxide gains oxygen – it has been oxidised. This process is called **oxidation**.

Extracting lead

Lead is used for making car batteries, roofing, solder and underground pipes for cables. Lead ore contains lead sulphide. To get lead metal, the lead sulphide is changed into lead oxide. The lead oxide is then heated with **carbon** to produce pure lead and carbon dioxide.

Lead is used to make solder.

The lead sulphide is *oxidised* to make lead oxide when it is 'roasted' or heated in oxygen. Lead oxide, PbO, is *reduced* when it is heated with powdered carbon.

lead oxide + carbon → lead + carbon dioxide
$$2PbO \quad + \quad \text{........} \quad \rightarrow \quad 2Pb \quad + \quad \text{.............}$$

7 Copy the equations and finish the symbol equations by writing in the formulae for carbon and carbon dioxide.

8 Copy and complete the following sentences. Use these words:

oxidised   reduced   reducer

Lead oxide is ....to form lead. Carbon acts as a .... Carbon has been .... to make carbon dioxide.

Key words

blast furnace

carbon

coke

haematite

limestone

ore

oxidation

reduction

steel

Key facts

Copy and complete the sentences by choosing the correct word from the key words list.

1 Iron is extracted from its ore in a _____ _____.

2 _____, _____ and iron _____ are raw materials used in the blast furnace.

3 The ore of iron that is used in the blast furnace is called _____.

4 Iron is used to make _____ for cars.

5 Lead can be extracted from its oxide by heating it with _____.

6 Gain of oxygen is called _____.

7 Removal of oxygen is called _____.

3.4 Iron and steel

The scrap yard   CASE STUDY

There always seems to be new cars on the roads, but what happens to old ones? When old cars are scrapped, they are recycled so that many of their parts are used again. Almost all the steel parts are recycled and made into new steel.

Cars arriving at a scrap yard are often already 'gutted'. Garages and car parts dealers take out all the reusable parts, such as tyres, batteries, lights and working engine parts. These are often sold to people who want to buy 'reconditioned' car parts.

The cars are crushed so that they can be transported more easily and cheaply. They are put into a processor which shreds them into small pieces. An electromagnet separates out the steel, so it can be sent by rail or road to the steelworks. Other metals can also be sent for recycling. Fluff, plastics and fabric are also collected – these are buried with other rubbish in a landfill site.

The scrap steel is mixed with blast furnace iron and purified in the steelmaking process. The finished steel ends up in food cans, cars, fridges and surgical instruments. About 55 per cent of British steel is made from recycled scrap.

9 Recycling iron uses less energy than making iron in a blast furnace. Explain why recycling is both cheaper and better for the environment.

10 Where do you think the 'fluff, plastics and fabrics' come from in the scrapped cars?

11 One of your classmates says, 'I don't understand the difference between re-using and recycling. They're the same thing to me.' Use ideas from this page to explain the difference.

12 Use a telephone directory to find out how many scrap companies there are in your area. How many car dealers are there? Why do you think the numbers of companies are so different?

Review questions

1 This table shows how much limestone is used for chemical purposes. (Aggregate for roads has been left out.)

(a) Make a bar chart to show the uses of limestone. *[3]*

(b) What percentage of limestone in the table is used for making building materials? *[1]*

Use	Percentage
Cement making	58
Making iron and steel	13
Spreading on fields	8
Powders and fillers	5
Making glass	2
Other chemical uses	14

2 The list below shows the formulae of some chemicals and the raw materials used to make them.

Raw material (not in correct order)	Chemical	Uses of chemical
Sulphur, S	chlorine, Cl_2	
Nitrogen, N_2, from air	octane C_8H_{16}	petrol
Sodium chloride, NaCl, from rock salt	ammonia, NH_3	fertilisers
Hydrocarbons, e.g. $C_{12}H_{26}$, from crude oil	sulphuric acid, H_2SO_4	

(a) Use the formulae to work out which raw material has been used to make which chemical. *[3]*

(b) Write down ONE use for chlorine and ONE use for sulphuric acid. *[2]*

(c) Write down the names and number of atoms of each element in sulphuric acid and octane. *[4]*

3 Here is some information about worldwide iron production for May 2002.

(a) Draw a suitable chart to show how much iron is produced in Europe and the UK compared to the rest of the world. *[4]*

(b) What percentage of the world production of iron is produced in Europe? *[2]*

	Iron produced in May 2002/ thousands of tonnes
World	75 000
Europe	13 700
UK only	1057

(c) The Severn Bridge is made from 4500 tonnes of steel. The Millennium Stadium in Cardiff contains 11 000 tonnes.

The Redcar blast furnace can make 12 000 tonnes of steel per day.

How long would it take to make the steel for each of these structures using the Redcar blast furnace? *[3]*

(d) Many people lost their jobs in Sheffield when the steel works closed. One man said, 'Steel-making in this country is finished. We don't need steel for the big shipbuilding or heavy industries any more.'

What reply would you make to this man? What is modern steel used for? *[3]*

3 Useful chemicals

THE CHEMICAL INDUSTRY

Contents

Assignments and practical activities linked to this section:

Quantitative analysis;

The production of a fertiliser;

The production of an ester.

Setting up a distillation apparatus

Investigating dyes

Investigating rates of reaction

Finding the concentration of an acid

Use the following to check your progress.

Unit 2

You will:

- know the difference between organic and inorganic compounds
 see pages 166–169

- know how crude oil is separated by fractional distillation
 see pages 166–169

- understand that fractional distillation works because of the different boiling points of the liquids
 see pages 166–169

- know some uses of crude oil fractions
 see pages 166–169

- be able to explain why liquids with different sized molecules have different boiling points
 see pages 166–169

- be aware of the importance and scale of the chemical industry
 see pages 170–177

- know why some chemicals are made in bulk and others are made on a small scale
 see pages 170–173

- be able to give examples of bulk and fine chemicals
 see pages 170–173

- be able to balance symbol equations
 see pages 174–177

- know how reactions are made faster in the chemical industry.
 see pages 174–177

Unit 3

You will:

- understand reversible reactions
 see pages 174–177

- be able to calculate theoretical, actual and percentage yields
 see pages 178–181

- be able to explain why actual yields are not 100 per cent
 see pages 178–181

- be aware that industry compromises between yield and rate to make processes profitable.
 see pages 178–181

3.5 Crude oil to petrol

The black stuff

Men working on an oil rig.

Crude oil is a sticky, black liquid. It is found soaked into rocks underground. Oil companies drill into the rocks and pump the oil up. They send the crude oil by pipeline or tanker to an oil refinery.

What happens at an oil refinery?

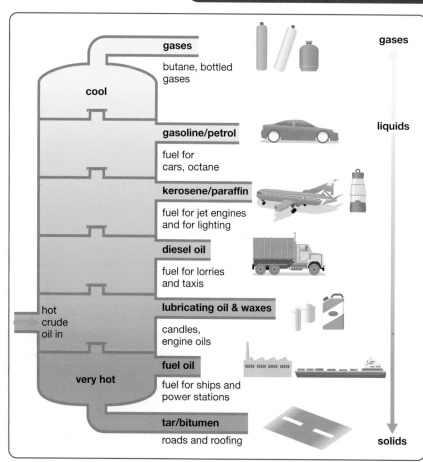

gases
butane, bottled gases

cool

gases

gasoline/petrol
fuel for cars, octane

liquids

kerosene/paraffin
fuel for jet engines and for lighting

diesel oil
fuel for lorries and taxis

hot crude oil in

lubricating oil & waxes
candles, engine oils

fuel oil
fuel for ships and power stations

very hot

tar/bitumen
roads and roofing

solids

The fractionating column in an oil refinery.

Crude oil contains a mixture of **hydrocarbon** molecules. Hydrocarbons are compounds which contain only hydrogen and carbon. The hydrocarbon molecules are all different shapes and sizes and therefore have different **boiling points**.

In an oil refinery, the crude oil is split into **fractions** using **fractional distillation**. Different fractions have different boiling ranges and uses. Hot crude oil goes into the bottom of the **fractionating column**.

The big, heavy molecules have high boiling points. They remain thick liquids and run out of the bottom. Smaller, lighter molecules with lower boiling points rise up the column as gases.

The column is cooler further up, so the different fractions condense at different temperatures and come out of the column. Only the smallest, lightest molecules with very low boiling points are still gases at the cool top part of the tower.

3.5 Crude oil to petrol

Using oil   ACTIVITY

Look at the table about uses of crude oil.

Final use	Percentage of crude oil used
Petrol	30
Central heating	25
Fuel for industry	15
Generating electricity	15
Aviation, rail and ship fuels	6
Making chemicals (detergents, paints, dyes, plastics, medicines and synthetic fibres)	9

1 Make a bar chart to show this information.

2 What percentage of crude oil is burned for fuel?

3 Suppose one of your friends said, 'It doesn't matter about oil running out – we'll have wind and solar power sorted out by then.' What would you say to answer them? Draw a cartoon to show what your life might be like 'after the oil runs out'.

The Fawley refinery

The biggest oil refinery in Europe is the Fawley refinery near Southampton.

Fawley refinery uses crude oil from the Middle East and the North Sea. It is very important that the refinery makes just enough of each fraction to meet demand. If too much of one fraction is made, big stockpiles will build up that nobody wants to buy. The refinery also wants to use as little crude oil as possible because it is expensive to buy, refining uses a lot of energy and oil reserves need to be conserved.

Here is some information about the demand for the different fractions and the contents of two types of crude oil.

Oil fraction	Customer demand (%)	Contents of	
		Arabian heavy oil (%)	North Sea oil (%)
Gasoline/naphtha	30	18	23
Kerosene	8	11	15
Diesel/gas oil	24	18	24
Fuel oil	38	53	38

4 Draw a comparative bar chart to show this information (you could use a spreadsheet for this).

5 Which fractions are in highest demand? Why do you think this is so?

6 Which fractions have a bigger supply than demand?

7 Fawley refinery uses a 'cracking' process to split larger molecules into smaller ones. Explain how this helps to meet demand.

An oil refinery.

3.5 Crude oil to petrol

A closer look at molecules in oil

Organic and inorganic

Crude oil is made from the rotten remains of dead sea creatures which lived millions of years ago. The molecules in oil are sometimes described as **organic**, because they are made from living organisms. All organic molecules contain carbon, usually with hydrogen and sometimes oxygen, sulphur or other elements. **Inorganic** compounds are not made by living things and do not usually contain carbon. Sodium nitrate fertiliser ($NaNO_3$) and water (H_2O) are inorganic compounds.

One of the exceptions is limestone, calcium carbonate, which is an inorganic carbon compound. Chemists can make many organic compounds artificially now, but we still use the term 'organic' for molecules which originally came from living things.

Word check

Organic compounds contain carbon and come from living things.
Inorganic compounds are not made by living things and do not usually contain carbon.

Big and small molecules

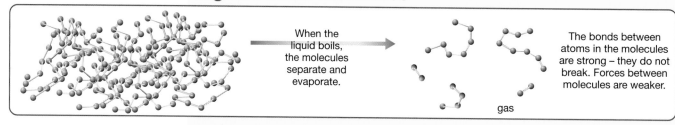

When the liquid boils, the molecules separate and evaporate.

The bonds between atoms in the molecules are strong – they do not break. Forces between molecules are weaker.

gas

What happens when a mixture of hydrocarbons boils?

Bigger hydrocarbon molecules have higher boiling points because they are heavier and have stronger forces between molecules.

8 Look at this information about some hydrocarbons in crude oil.

Name	Number of carbon atoms	Formula	Boiling point/°C
methane	1	CH_4	−161
ethane	2	C_2H_6	−88
propane	3	C_3H_8	
butane	4		−1
pentane	5	C_5H_{12}	36

(a) Draw a line graph with 'Boiling point' (remember to start at a negative number!) up the side and 'Number of carbon atoms' along the bottom.

(b) Use your graph to predict the boiling point of propane.

(c) Use the pattern of formulae to suggest a formula for butane.

(d) Give reasons why these molecules are 'organic'.

(e) Which molecule has the strongest forces between molecules? Which has the weakest? Explain how you can tell.

(f) 'Fuel gas' comes out of the top of the fractionating column at 20°C. Which of these hydrocarbons could NOT be in fuel gas? Explain why.

3.5 Crude oil to petrol

Low sulphur petrol   CASE STUDY

Brian works as manager of a petrol station. He explains:

'Low sulphur unleaded petrol has been available on our forecourt since the end of 2000. Most people don't notice the change, but we have had leaflets of information for people who ask.

'Sulphur compounds in petrol cause problems because when the petrol burns in the car engine, the sulphur burns too. It forms sulphur dioxide, which is a very acidic gas. From the motorist's point of view, that's bad news for metal car parts such as the engine and exhaust. If you're interested in the environment, it's bad news because sulphur dioxide dissolves in rain to make acid rain. Low sulphur petrol has two-thirds less sulphur, so both these problems are reduced.

'The oil company takes the sulphur compounds out of the petrol in desulphurisation plants at the refinery. They sell the sulphur for making sulphuric acid. All the big petrol companies remove sulphur now. It's good news for the UK oil industry too because our North Sea oil naturally contains much less sulphur than Middle Eastern oil. The interest in low sulphur petrol has meant that the oil companies will pay more for crude oil with less sulphur in it.'

9 What gas reacts with sulphur when it burns? Write a word equation for the reaction.

10 Why is it 'bad news for car parts' that sulphur dioxide is acidic?

11 Find out what problems acid rain causes.

12 Design an information board to go up in a petrol station to tell customers about 'low sulphur petrol'. Explain why it is a better choice.

Key facts

Copy and complete the sentences by choosing the correct word from the key words list.

1 Carbon compounds that come from living organisms are known as _____ compounds.

2 _____ compounds do not usually contain carbon.

3 The compounds in crude oil are _____ and can be separated because they have different _____ _____.

4 The separating process is called_____ _____.

5 Different _____ are removed from the _____ _____ at different points.

Key words

boiling points

fractions

fractional distillation

fractionating column

hydrocarbons

inorganic

organic

3.6 Bulk and fine chemicals

We all use chemicals

It says here that every family spends £1300 a year buying chemicals.

Good grief! Nobody in our family ever buys any!

What chemicals do we buy?

The UK chemical industry is one of our most successful industries. It makes huge profits by exporting chemical products. The industry produces five categories of chemicals which we buy and use every day.

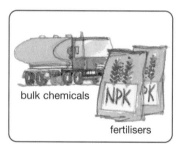

bulk chemicals

fertilisers

Inorganics and fertilisers

These are produced in huge amounts (millions of tonnes) and are sold to industry (to make final products in the other four categories) and agriculture.

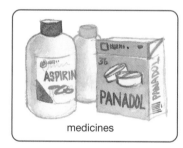

medicines

Dyestuffs, paints and pigments

Research has led to new paints being developed which do not contain harmful solvents. Paintbrushes can be washed in water and the waste does not harm fish.

paints

dyes

Pharmaceuticals

Medicines are made for 'over the counter' sales as well as for prescription by doctors and hospitals. UK pharmaceuticals are exported worldwide.

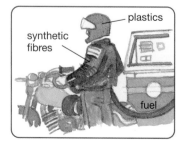

plastics

synthetic fibres

fuel

Petrochemicals and polymers

These include fuels, plastics and synthetic fibres.

liquid crystals

Speciality

This includes a wide range of chemicals with very specific uses, such as perfumes and the liquid crystals used in laptop screens.

❶ Look at the cartoon at the top of the page. What would you say next?

3.6 Bulk and fine chemicals

Why do we make sulphuric acid in bulk?   ACTIVITY

Bulk chemicals are manufactured as cheaply as possible on a very large scale. Inorganics like sulphuric acid and ammonia are bulk chemicals and so are petrochemicals and polymers such as poly(ethene). Chemical products that must be very pure and high quality are known as **fine** (or speciality) chemicals. The manufacturing processes of fine chemicals are small scale. This means that the quality of fine chemicals can be controlled very carefully. Pharmaceuticals, dyes and pigments are made like this.

Sulphuric acid is made in bulk. The UK makes two million tonnes every year: about a bathful for every person! This table shows what the acid is used to make.

> **Word check**
>
> **Bulk** chemicals are made cheaply on a large scale.
> **Fine** chemicals are made on a small scale to ensure purity and quality.

Final product	Percentage of annual production of sulphuric acid used in the process
Steel	1.5
Dyes	5.5
Fibres	6.0
Plastics	3.0
Detergents and soaps	19.0
Paints and pigments	20.0
Fertilisers	2.0
Leather tanning	4.0
General chemicals for industry	21.0
Other uses (for example, photo films)	18.0

❷ Prepare a script for a five-minute video for an audience of Key Stage 3 pupils. The video title is 'Why we use so much sulphuric acid'. You could use other books to help your research. You need to think about:

- What images will you use that will make a strong impact on the pupils?

- How could you present the information in the table to make it meaningful to the pupils? (For example, what kind of graphs could you use?)

If you have access to a camcorder, your group could make the video. If not, present your script as a cartoon strip.

❸ A comment in a book says:

'The chemical industry is its own biggest customer.'

What do you think this means? Explain your answer by talking about how sulphuric acid is used.

❹ Look again at the categories of chemicals on the opposite page.

(a) Which categories can be made in bulk?

(b) Medicines are expensive because they are 'fine' chemicals. List reasons why it is necessary to use small-scale processes to make medicines.

3.6 Bulk and fine chemicals

Making reactions faster

Making a bulk chemical like sulphuric acid usually involves a sequence of chemical reactions. It is very important that the reactions happen as fast as possible. The faster the product is made, the cheaper the process.

In industry, reactions can be made faster by:

- using a higher temperature;
- using a higher pressure for any gases;
- using a higher concentration of solutions;
- using a higher surface area for solids.
- using a **catalyst**.

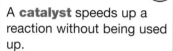

Word check ✓

A **catalyst** speeds up a reaction without being used up.

Why do molecules react faster?

For a reaction to happen, molecules have to bump into each other (collide) before they can react together. However, molecules often bounce off each other – they have to collide with enough energy to react. In industry, a higher temperature is often used to make reactions faster. Look at the diagram below to see why this makes the **rate of reaction** faster.

Word check ✓

Rate of reaction is the speed at which a reaction happens. It increases if particles collide more often, with more energy.

Catalysts work by providing a surface on which molecules meet and react. Catalysts are often used as small pieces. This gives a bigger surface area for reactions to take place. Increasing the surface area of solids in a reaction is another way of increasing the rate.

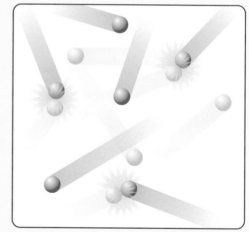

The higher **temperature** makes the molecules move faster so they collide more often and collide with more **energy**.

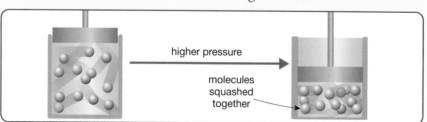

If gases are put under higher pressure, the molecules are closer together so they collide more often.

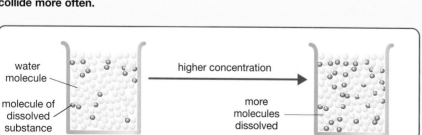

If higher concentrations of solutions are used, the molecules are closer together so they collide more often.

❺ In industry, using a higher temperature is expensive. Using a catalyst is cheap in the long term, although catalysts are expensive to buy. Use ideas from this page to explain this information.

3.6 Bulk and fine chemicals

Sugar-coating tablets

Emma works in Boots' factory in Nottingham. One of the processes puts a sugar coating on tablets like 'Nurofen'.

Emma explains, 'We make Nurofen tablets in batches of about a million tablets. The tablet-making processes are complex and involve many stages. All the equipment has to be kept clean. We test the quality of materials we are using and the tablets at every stage.

'We put a shiny sugar coating on the tablets for several reasons. The coating stops the tablets getting damaged and going dusty. The sugar acts as a seal so that the medicine inside has a longer shelf life. People find the smooth, shiny tablets much easier to swallow and also they don't need to taste the bitter medicine inside. We can print the name on the finished tablets.

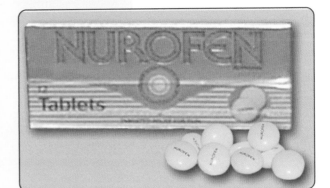

Many tablets have a sugar coating.

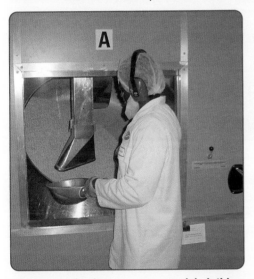

Workers in the factory wear special clothing.

'We seal the tablets. We then pour sugar solution onto them by hand. The tablets move round and round in a huge drum in a blast of hot air (like a giant tumble dryer). When one coat is dried, more sugar solution is poured on. It takes about eight hours to finish a batch. The tablets go to get polished and have their names printed on. We reject any tablets that are not perfect – only perfect tablets go to be packaged.'

6 Tablets without sugar coatings are cheaper. Make an advert for sugar-coated tablets to go in a magazine. In your advert, show your customers why it is worth paying more for sugar-coated tablets.

7 The company needs to make sure the tablets are as pure and high quality as possible. Make a list from the case study to show ways they do this. Use these ideas to explain why medicines are 'fine' chemicals.

8 Why is the energy cost of sugar-coating very high?

Key facts

Copy and complete the sentences by choosing the correct word from the key words list.

1 _____ chemicals are made using small-scale processes.

2 _____ chemicals are made cheaply to meet large demand.

3 A _____ increases the _____ _____ _____ without being used up.

4 Increasing the _____ means molecules move faster with more _____.

Key words

bulk

catalyst

energy

fine

rate of reaction

temperature

3.7 Making ammonia

An essential compound

Word check

Bulk chemicals are made cheaply on a large scale.

About 140 million tonnes of **ammonia** are made worldwide each year. (This is about the same as the total weight of all the cars in the UK!) Ammonia is a **bulk** chemical. Most of the ammonia is used to make fertilisers. Without ammonia-based fertilisers, we would not be able to grow enough food.

The ICI plant in Billingham manufactures ammonia. Fertilisers and nitric acid are made on the same site to save having to transport the ammonia.

The ICI ammonia plant at Billingham in north-east England.

How is ammonia manufactured?

Ammonia is made by reacting nitrogen and hydrogen together.

$$\text{nitrogen} + \text{hydrogen} \rightleftharpoons \text{ammonia}$$
$$N_2 + 3H_2 \rightleftharpoons 2NH_3$$

This reaction looks very simple, but it is difficult to make ammonia profitably on a large scale. Nitrogen is cheap enough – 80 per cent of air is nitrogen – but hydrogen is very expensive to make.

Word check

Reactions that have the symbol $\rightleftharpoons$ are **reversible** – they can go backwards as well as forwards.

The second problem is that the reaction between nitrogen and hydrogen is **reversible** – it goes both ways. So when ammonia has been made, it can react to turn back into nitrogen and hydrogen again.

This means that the yield of ammonia (the amount made from the reaction) never reaches 100 per cent.

1 In the ammonia plant, nitrogen and hydrogen are reacted by being passed over a hot, powdered iron catalyst.

see Bulk and fine chemicals, page 170

(a) Use ideas about rates of reaction to explain:

(i) why the catalyst is used;

(ii) why the catalyst works best when it is powdered and hot.

(b) The mixture passes over the catalyst four times. This makes the yield bigger. Explain why.

3.7 Making ammonia

Getting the best yield

ACTIVITY

Part of a chemical engineer's job is to use chemical understanding to adapt large-scale processes so that they work as well as possible. One example of this is choosing the operating conditions for the ammonia plant. Changing the conditions of temperature and pressure can alter the yield of ammonia (amount produced) and the rate of reaction.

This graph shows the percentage yield of ammonia at different temperatures and pressures.

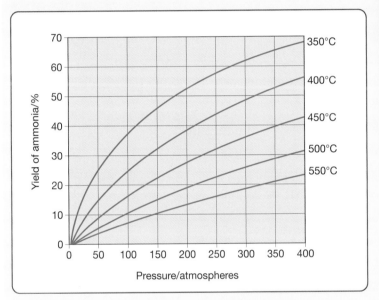

The way the yield of ammonia changes at different temperatures and pressures.

A chemical engineer puts theory into practice.

see Putting numbers into industry, page 178

❷ What happens to the yield of ammonia as the temperature gets higher?

❸ What happens to the yield as the pressure increases?

❹ What conditions would give the best yield?

❺ You are the chemical engineer who needs to decide on the best operating conditions for the ammonia plant. You have considered the following issues:

• You need a good yield.

• The ammonia will be made *faster* at higher temperatures.

• Higher temperatures mean more fuel will need to be bought.

• Equipment that can withstand very high pressures is expensive and breaks down easily. Repairs are costly.

• You need to consider the safest working conditions for your staff.

You have decided to run the process at 150 atmospheres and 400°C. Write a briefing sheet to your boss to explain why these conditions are the best choice in terms of rate of reaction, yield, cost and safety.

3.7 Making ammonia

Balancing equations

Chemical engineers use symbol equations to make decisions about running the chemical processes in chemical plants. For the information to be reliable, the equations need to be **balanced**.

For example:

nitrogen	+	hydrogen	⇌	ammonia
N_2	+	$3H_2$		$2NH_3$

Adding up the numbers of each atom on each side of the equation gives:

Left-hand side

2 atoms of nitrogen

6 atoms of hydrogen

Right-hand side

2 atoms of nitrogen

6 atoms of hydrogen

6 This is the symbol equation to show how hydrogen is made for the ammonia plant. Carbon monoxide, CO, is made at the same time.

$$CH_4 \quad + \quad H_2O \quad \rightleftharpoons \quad CO \quad + \quad H_2$$

(a) Use the list of compounds on page 314 to write a word equation for this reaction.

(b) Count up the number of each type of atom on each side of the equation. What number could you put in front of H_2 to make the equation balance? Write out the balanced equation.

Rules for balancing equations

- Count up the number of each type of atom on each side of the equation.

- Balance the equation by putting numbers in front of the **formulae**.

- You cannot change formulae of individual substances!

7 Eve was visiting a sulphuric acid manufacturing plant. She wrote down the equations for the reactions happening in the plant.

Making Sulphur Dioxide
$S + O_2 \rightarrow SO_2$
Making Sulphur Trioxide
$2SO_2 + O_2 \rightleftharpoons SO_3$
Finally
$SO_3 + H_2O \rightarrow H_2SO_4$

(a) Write word equations for these reactions (you may need to use the element and compound lists on page 314 to help you).

(b) Check whether each equation is balanced. If not, balance it.

(c) Which reaction will not produce 100 per cent yield? Explain why not.

3.7 Making ammonia

Fritz Haber
CASE STUDY

Fritz Haber was the chemist who discovered how to make nitrogen and hydrogen react together to make ammonia. This was world news in 1913, because nobody had ever been able to make synthetic nitrogen compounds for fertilisers before. Countries relied on natural fertilisers – the UK imported seagull droppings from South America to get nitrogen compounds!

Haber used equipment which put the gases under high pressure – this was very new technology in 1913. Chemists were really excited because everyone thought that this meant they could make unlimited supplies of nitrogen compounds for fertilisers. The world could grow enough food for everyone! In 1918, Haber was awarded the Nobel Prize, the greatest honour in science, for his work.

Haber's method worked in the lab, but it was Karl Bosch who scaled up the reaction so it could happen in big chemical works for mass-scale production.

The rest of Haber's life was not quite so happy. He was born in Poland in 1868, his family were Jewish. He worked as a chemist in Germany and it was at Berlin University that he discovered how to make ammonia. He worked for the Germans during the First World War as Chief of the Chemical Warfare Service. He directed chlorine gas attacks, for example at Ypres, where many men died horribly. Most countries have now agreed never to use chemical weapons again.

The ammonia-making process was used not only to make fertilisers, but also to make explosives for use in the Second World War. Haber had to leave Germany in fear of his life in 1933 because he was Jewish. Few chemists were friendly to him after his work on weapons. He died a year later.

Fritz Haber.

8 Fritz Haber was employed as a chemist when he worked out how to make ammonia. Karl Bosch worked as a chemical engineer. Use information from this page to explain the difference between a chemist and a chemical engineer.

9 Look up the properties of chlorine and the hazards of using it, either in a book or using Student Safety Sheets. Find out how its density compares to that of air. Why was chlorine a powerful weapon during the war?

10 Write three diary entries for Fritz Haber's diary. The entries are for 1913, 1918 and 1934 (just before his death). Write about what has been happening and how you are feeling about it.

Key facts

Copy and complete the sentences by choosing the correct word from the key words list.

1 _____ is manufactured as a _____ chemical.

2 _____ equations have the same numbers of atoms on both sides.

3 The _____ of compounds stay the same when equations are balanced.

Key words

ammonia

balanced

bulk

formula

3.8 Putting numbers into industry

Limestone is delivered to the cement works.

How much cement can we make?

A cement works uses limestone to make calcium oxide for cement. The works uses 20 000 tonnes of limestone every week. How does the manager know how much calcium oxide he will make?

The equation for the reaction in the cement works can be used to work this out. Remember that limestone is mainly calcium carbonate. This is the reaction that takes place:

calcium carbonate $\rightarrow$ calcium oxide + carbon dioxide
$$CaCO_3 \rightarrow CaO + CO_2$$

Working out relative masses from formulae

The **relative mass** of an atom tells you how heavy it is.

You can find the relative masses in the Periodic Table (see page 313).

The relative mass of a compound such as calcium carbonate is worked out like this:

Formula:	$CaCO_3$
Relative mass of each atom:	Ca=40 C=12 O=16
Number of each type of atom:	1 Ca atom, 1 C atom, 3 O atoms
Relative mass of $CaCO_3$ =	$40 + 12 + (3 \times 16) = 100$

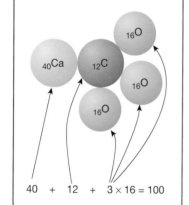

$$40 + 12 + 3 \times 16 = 100$$

The structure of calcium carbonate.

❶ Show that the relative mass of calcium oxide, CaO, is 56.

❷ What is the relative mass of carbon dioxide, CO_2?

Calculations using relative masses

You can use relative masses to work out how much calcium oxide should be made.

	$CaCO_3$	$\rightarrow$	CaO	+	CO_2
Relative masses	100		56		

This shows that 100 tonnes of calcium carbonate should make 56 tonnes of calcium oxide.

❸ How much calcium oxide would be made if 1000 tonnes of calcium carbonate were used?

❹ Look again at the top of the page. How much calcium oxide can the cement works make every week from 20 000 tonnes of limestone?

❺ In a real cement kiln, the **actual yield** is never exactly the same as the **theoretical yield**. Give some reasons why you think this is the case.

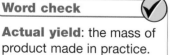

Word check

Actual yield: the mass of product made in practice.
Theoretical yield: the expected mass of product worked out mathematically.

3.8 Putting numbers into industry

Looking at yields

ACTIVITY

Liz and Ben heated some limestone to make calcium oxide. They wanted to compare their theoretical and actual yields. This is a page from Liz's notes.

6 Liz has not finished her working out. Use her notes to work out:

  (a) the mass of limestone lumps she started with;

  (b) the mass of calcium oxide she made (the *actual* yield);

  (c) what her *theoretical* yield should have been.

Liz and Ben were disappointed with their results. They are discussing what went wrong.

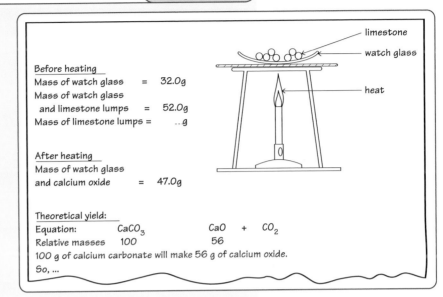

Liz's notes.

7 Why would crushing the limestone improve the experiment?

8 Suggest some other reasons that might explain why the actual yield is different from the theoretical yield.

9 Suggest some improvements to Liz and Ben's experiment.

3.8 Putting numbers into industry

Working out percentage yields

Percentage yield is a way of comparing how much product we expect to get (theoretical yield) with how much we really make when we carry out an experiment (actual yield).

We work out percentage yields like this:

$$\text{percentage yield} = \frac{\text{actual yield}}{\text{theoretical yield}} \times 100 \text{ per cent}$$

Actual yields are often lower than you expect. Some reasons for this are:

- The chemicals you use may have impurities in them.
- The reaction has not had time to finish.
- Reversible reactions never give 100 per cent yields.
- You have lost some of your product when you moved it between containers.

Sometimes, you can adapt your experiments to overcome these problems and improve the percentage yield, but this can be very time consuming. In industry, chemical engineers usually compromise by aiming to get a reasonable yield as fast as possible.

Calculating percentage yield

Yasmine made some copper sulphate using copper oxide and sulphuric acid.

Here are her notes.

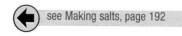
see Making salts, page 192

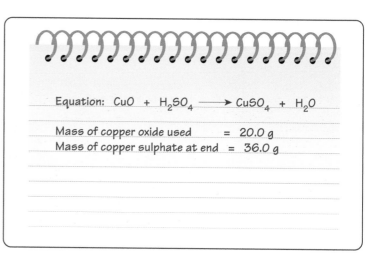

Equation: $CuO + H_2SO_4 \longrightarrow CuSO_4 + H_2O$

Mass of copper oxide used   = 20.0 g
Mass of copper sulphate at end = 36.0 g

❿ Write a word equation for the reaction (you can use the list of formulae on page 314 to help you).

⓫ Work out the relative masses of copper oxide and copper sulphate.

⓬ Work out the theoretical yield of copper sulphate from 20.0 g of copper oxide.

⓭ Work out the percentage yield for Yasmine's experiment.

⓮ Suggest reasons why Yasmine's yield is not 100 per cent.

3.8 Putting numbers into industry

Feeding a blast furnace | CASE STUDY

The Redcar Blast Furnace produces about 11 000 tonnes of iron every day. How does the company make sure that there are enough raw materials on site to keep the furnace running?

Calculating quantities

Remember that the blast furnace uses four raw materials. Haematite (containing iron oxide), limestone and coke must all be transported to the site. Air, the other raw material, is free!

Remember the main reaction happening in the blast furnace is:

iron oxide + carbon monoxide → iron + carbon dioxide

$$Fe_2O_3 \quad + \quad 3CO \quad \rightarrow \quad 2Fe \; + \; 3CO_2$$

Relative masses   160   112

see Iron and steel, page 160

15 Show working to prove that the relative mass of iron oxide in the equation is 160 and the mass of iron made is 112.

16 Use the relative masses to work out how much iron oxide you would need to make 11 200 tonnes of iron.

17 Even the best quality iron ore contains only about 60 per cent iron oxide. What difference will this make to the actual mass of iron ore that needs to be carried to the site?

Getting raw materials to the site

The huge amounts of raw materials are calculated and then must be carried to the blast furnace site. This table shows some information about how raw materials are brought to the Redcar site.

Iron is converted to steel.

Raw material	From:	By:	Notes
Iron ore	Australia	Sea tanker into Teesside	Contains 60 per cent iron oxide compared to 30 per cent in UK iron ore.
Coke	Poland	Sea tanker into Teesside	Higher quality and purity than UK coal.
Limestone	UK	Road and rail	

The finished iron and steel are distributed abroad by sea and go by rail and road to UK works, for example, to Workington for making rails for trains.

18 Use a road atlas to find Redcar.

(a) Why do you think this place is a good site for a blast furnace?

(b) Port Talbot and Scunthorpe are other blast furnace sites. Use the atlas to find out what features the three sites have in common.

(c) Use ideas about yields and disposal of waste to explain why the Redcar furnace imports both iron ore and coal from abroad.

Review questions

1 'Octane' is one of the main hydrocarbons in petrol. Imagine you are a molecule of octane. Draw a cartoon of yourself. Describe what happens to you in a fractionating tower. Use these words to help you.

crude oil	heated	cooled	evaporated
condensed	fraction	liquid	gas

[9]

2 Look at this list of substances.

Inorganic: water (H_2O)   oxygen (O_2)

Organic: octane (C_8H_{18})

(a) Explain why octane is 'organic'. [1]

(b) One of your friends says, 'Water comes out of animals sometimes and plants make oxygen. Water and oxygen must be organic.'

Explain why she is wrong. [2]

3 (a) Classify the following chemicals as 'bulk' or 'fine'.

ammonia   food colourings   aspirin
petrol   fertiliser [2]

(b) Give TWO reasons why perfumes are made as 'fine' chemicals. [2]

4 These equations show reactions that are used in the chemical industry.

Reaction 1: $CaCO_3$ + $NaCl$ → $CaCl_2$ + Na_2CO_3

Reaction 2: PbO + CO → Pb + CO_2

Reaction 3: H_2 + Cl_2 → HCl

(a) $CaCl_2$ is calcium chloride and CO is carbon monoxide.

Use the element and formula list on page 314 to find the names of the other substances. Write word equations for each reaction. [3]

(b) Which reaction uses limestone as a raw material? [1]

(c) Are the equations balanced? Balance any that are not. [2]

(d) Which reaction is a reduction of a metal ore? [1]

5 Use the list on page 314 to name these compounds.

CH_4 PbO $NaOH$ $CuCO_3$ KNO_3 Na_2SO_4

Work out the relative masses of each compound. [12]

6 Tom made some copper by heating copper oxide (CuO) in carbon monoxide (CO).

copper oxide + carbon monoxide   →   copper   +   carbon dioxide

(a) Use the compound list on page 314 to help you write a balanced symbol equation for this reaction. [2]

Tom started with 20 g of copper oxide. His actual yield of copper was 14 g.

(b) Work out the theoretical and percentage yield for Tom's experiment. [4]

(c) Suggest why his yield was not 100 per cent. [2]

3 Useful chemicals

INVESTIGATING CHEMISTRY

Contents

Assignment and practical activities linked to this section:

Qualitative analysis.

Making ammonium sulphate

Setting up a distillation apparatus

Use the following to check your progress.

Unit 1

You will:

- find out about analysing salts.

see pages 196–199

Unit 2

You will:

- know about gels, emulsions, suspensions, foams, aerosols and solutions

see pages 184–187

- know about atomic structure, using the words nucleus, neutron, proton and electron

see pages 188–191

- be able to name elements in compounds by looking at the formula

see pages 188–191

- know that ionic bonding involves transferring electrons between atoms

see pages 188–191

- understand how metals and non-metals lose and gain electrons to make stable, full shells

see pages 188–191

- be able to draw 'dot and cross' diagrams for ionic compounds such as NaCl and MgO

see pages 188–191

- practise using equations

see pages 192–195

- know that covalent bonding involves shared electrons

see pages 200–203

- be able to draw 'dot and cross' diagrams for covalent compounds, e.g. H_2O and HCl

see pages 200–203

- know what is meant by exothermic and endothermic reactions

see pages 204–207

- understand how bond breaking and making involves energy changes.

see pages 204–207

Unit 3

You will:

- find out about making salts and their industrial importance.

see pages 192–195

3.9 Mixtures everywhere

Salad dressings

Rose is training to be a chef. At college, she has been learning about the science behind making a good salad dressing. She explains:

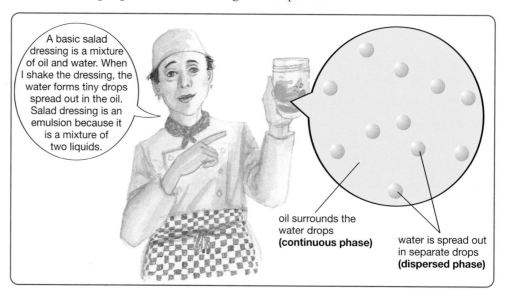

> A basic salad dressing is a mixture of oil and water. When I shake the dressing, the water forms tiny drops spread out in the oil. Salad dressing is an emulsion because it is a mixture of two liquids.

oil surrounds the water drops (**continuous phase**)

water is spread out in separate drops (**dispersed phase**)

Colloids and creams

A **colloid** is a mixture in which one substance (such as salad oil), is mixed as fine drops or bubbles in another substance (such as water). A liquid/liquid colloid, such as oil in water, is called an **emulsion**. What about gases? Or solids?

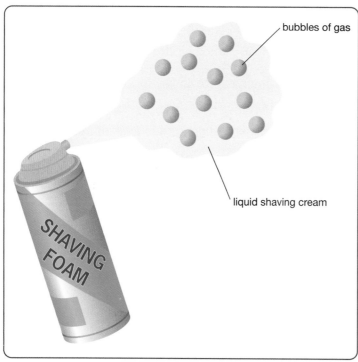

bubbles of gas

liquid shaving cream

SHAVING FOAM

Shaving **foam** is a gas/liquid colloid.

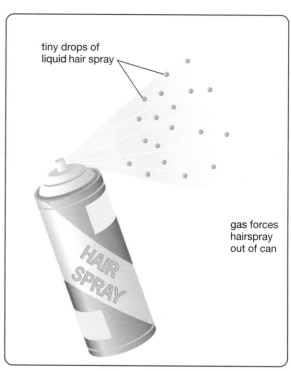

tiny drops of liquid hair spray

gas forces hairspray out of can

HAIR SPRAY

Hairspray is an **aerosol** (a liquid/gas colloid).

3.9 Mixtures everywhere

What makes a good salad dressing? (ACTIVITY)

Rose explains, 'The oil in the salad dressing makes the salad more appetising (like butter on bread). The water spreads the oil out thinly over the salad. Plain water would not taste very nice – salad dressings usually use vinegar or lemon juice. You can add ingredients to stop the oil drops separating out into a layer. Proteins, for example in mustard, flour or eggs, are good for this.'

FRENCH DRESSING

90 ml walnut oil

30 ml herb vinegar or lemon juice

$\frac{1}{2}$ teaspoon sugar

$\frac{1}{2}$ teaspoon mustard

salt and pepper

Place all ingredients in a bowl or jar and shake thoroughly until well mixed

GARLIC MAYONNAISE

4 garlic cloves

$\frac{1}{4}$ level teaspoon salt

2 egg yolks

300 ml olive oil

30 ml lemon juice

Skin the garlic cloves and crush with the salt to form a smooth paste

---

1 Copy the table below and complete it to show what each ingredient in the two salad dressings is for.

Salad dressing	Oil part	Water part	Stops oil from separating	Makes dressing taste better
French dressing		herb vinegar/ lemon juice		
Garlic mayonnaise	olive oil			

2 Rose's friend, Jane, loves garlic but is allergic to eggs and is trying to lose weight (she is eating less fat and sugar). For Jane's birthday, Rose decides to design a special salad dressing for her.

Make up a salad dressing recipe for Jane. Write a letter to explain to Jane how you have adapted the dressing especially for her.

3 Look again at the opposite page to remind yourself about 'dispersed' and 'continuous' phases.

Use the information on these two pages to complete a copy of this table.

Type of colloid	Example	Dispersed phase (drops)	Continuous phase	Colloid contains
Emulsion	salad dressing	oil		liquid/liquid
Foam	shaving foam			
Aerosol	hairspray			

185

3.9 Mixtures everywhere

How do colloids keep babies comfortable?

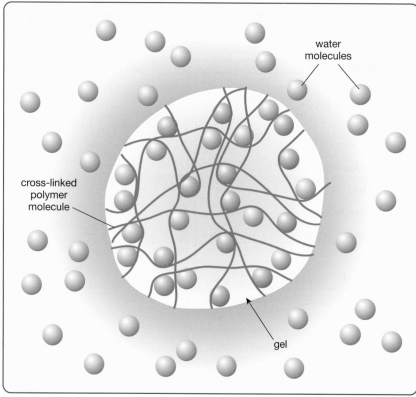

water molecules

cross-linked polymer molecule

gel

A hydrogel keeps babies dry and comfortable.

If you soak a baby's disposable nappy with water and then take it apart, you will see a curious jelly-like substance. This is yet another colloid. It is a **gel** that can absorb about a thousand times its own weight in water!

The solid part of the gel is a network of polymer molecules which absorbs water. A wet gel is a solid/liquid colloid. Gels are used to make hairstyling products, contact lenses and 'artificial soil' because they hold water for plants.

Many other 'baby products' are solid/liquid mixtures. **Suspensions** (like Milk of Magnesia medicine) are a fine powder mixed with water. You would be able to see the fine powder under a microscope. The powder sinks to the bottom, so you have to shake the bottle before you use it. **Solutions**, such as gripe water, are not colloids because a solid is *dissolved* in the water – solutions are all liquid.

4 Make a list of all the colloids you can think of in your bathroom at home. Remember that face creams and body lotions are oil/water emulsions. For each product try to decide what type of colloid it is (emulsion, foam, etc.) and what phases (solid, liquid or gas) it contains. Present your information in a table.

Key words
aerosol
colloid
continuous phase
dispersed phase
emulsion
foam
gel
solution
suspension

Key facts

Copy and complete the sentences by choosing the correct word from the key words list.

1 A mixture of one substance finely dispersed in another substance is called a _____.

2 The substance that is dispersed in tiny drops or particles is called the _____ _____. The other substance is called the _____ _____.

3 Two liquids mixed together are called an _____.

4 A _____ and a _____ are examples of solid/liquid colloids.

5 A gas/liquid colloid is called a _____.

6 A liquid/gas colloid is called an _____.

7 A _____ of salt and water is not a colloid.

3.9 Mixtures everywhere

Pricing hanging baskets   CASE STUDY

Martyn sells plants on a market stall. He makes hanging baskets to sell. Martyn explains, 'My customers sometimes complain that their baskets don't flower very well. I think this is because they don't water them every day. I'm thinking about starting to add hydrogel to my hanging baskets. Hydrogel absorbs a lot of water, so you don't have to water the basket as often, but I'm worried about the cost. I don't want to charge a lot more because my customers will buy their baskets elsewhere.'

Pricing up a hanging basket

5 Work out how much it costs Martyn to make each hanging basket. What other costs does he need to think about before he decides what price to charge? What do you think he should charge per basket?

The instructions on the hydrogel packet say that each hanging basket needs 5 g of hydrogel.

6 How much will using hydrogel add to the cost of each hanging basket? Do you think Martyn should start using hydrogel? Give reasons for your decision.

7 Martyn has decided to try using the hydrogel. He wants to make a poster advertising the baskets to give information about the gel to customers. Design the poster for Martyn. In your poster, explain how the gel works.

The hydrogel costs £1.50 for 75 g.

3.10 Splitting the atom

Everything is made of atoms

John Dalton even invented symbols for the elements.

Over 200 years ago, John Dalton talked about everything being made of tiny atoms. He was born in Cumbria in 1766. He was so clever that he became a schoolteacher when he was only 12!

John believed that atoms were like tiny hard round balls. During the last hundred years, other scientists have managed to 'split the atom' and have found out that atoms are made of even smaller particles. Along the way the 'atom bomb' and 'atomic energy' have been invented.

Inside the atom

Nowadays, we think that atoms have a central **nucleus** (containing **protons** and **neutrons**) with tiny, very light, fast **electrons** whizzing around the outside.

Drawing a helium atom

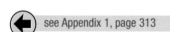
see Appendix 1, page 313

You can draw pictures of atoms by looking at the information on the Periodic Table.

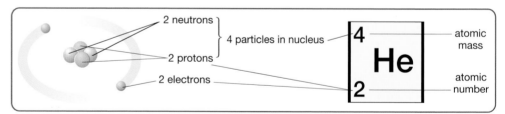

To get the numbers of particles right, follow these rules:

• The atomic number tells you how many protons there are.

• The atomic mass tells you how many protons and neutrons there are altogether in the nucleus.

• An atom always has the same number of protons and electrons.

1 (a) What are the names of the elements in the boxes below?

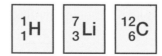

(b) Draw pictures to show an atom of each element.

2 Why do you think that nowadays we find it easier to use letters to represent atoms rather than symbols like the ones Dalton used?

3.10 Splitting the atom

Atom collages

Ben has been making some collages of atoms to display in 'Science Week' at his college. He explains, 'I wanted to make some really eye-catching displays so I used chalk on black paper to show the electron paths. I've used metallic card to represent the protons, neutrons and electrons.

'I wanted the atoms to be as accurate as possible so I did some research about how the electrons move around the atom. I found out that:

- the electrons move in '**shells**';

- the first electron shell is very small and can hold only two electrons;

- atoms with more than two electrons have another, bigger second shell;

- even bigger atoms can have three shells or more;

- the second and third shells can hold eight electrons each;

- the shells always fill up in order.

This is a copy of some rough notes Ben made for another atom poster.

Atom: Beryllium

Symbol:

$^{9}_{4}Be$

Protons: 4
Neutrons: 9 − 4 = 5
Electrons: 4
    Shell 1: 2 electrons (full)
    Shell 2: 2 electrons

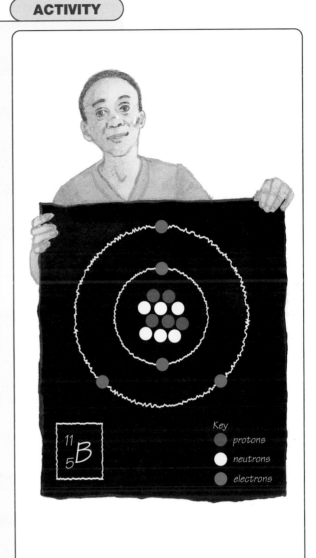

Ben's Science Week atom poster.

❸ Make some collages like Ben's to show what atoms look like. Follow Ben's notes to help you to work out the structure of each atom.

Try these atoms first:

hydrogen   oxygen   sodium   magnesium   fluorine

Make a class display of all the elements with atomic numbers up to 20.

❹ Chlorine has an atomic number of 17. How many electrons are in each shell of a chlorine atom?

❺ Helium, neon and argon are very unreactive gases. Work out how many electrons are in the outer shell of each of these atoms. What do you notice?

3.10 Splitting the atom

Sticking atoms together

Ionic bonds

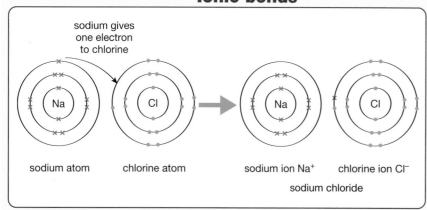

sodium gives
one electron
to chlorine

sodium atom   chlorine atom   sodium ion Na⁺   chlorine ion Cl⁻

sodium chloride

Sodium and chlorine both gain full outer shells.

Atoms use their electrons to combine together to make compounds. They try to gain full outer shells of electrons. An atom with a full outer shell is more stable. One way of doing this is by gaining or losing electrons. Metals usually lose electrons by giving them to non-metals. Non-metals usually gain electrons by taking them from metals. This is how sodium and chlorine make sodium chloride, NaCl, by **transfer** of electrons.

Sodium has only one electron in its outer shell. It can either gain seven electrons to have a full third shell, or lose one electron so it has a full second shell. It is easier to lose one electron.

For the same reason, chlorine gains one electron rather than losing seven.

Electrons are negatively charged. The chlorine atom is now a chloride ion and has a charge of 1⁻ because it has an extra electron. Charged atoms are called **ions**.

Sodium has lost a negatively charged particle and so has become an ion with a charge of 1+ (a sodium ion has one more proton than electrons, so this gives it a charge of 1+). The chlorine and sodium ions 'stick together' because opposite charges attract. This is called an **ionic** bond.

Notice when you draw 'dot and cross' diagrams:

• you use a dot for electrons of one element, a cross for electrons of the other;

• you only show electrons (not the nucleus).

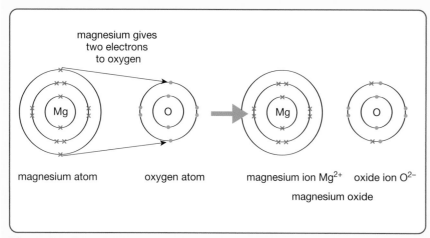

magnesium gives
two electrons
to oxygen

magnesium atom   oxygen atom   magnesium ion Mg²⁺   oxide ion O²⁻

magnesium oxide

Magnesium loses two electrons to oxygen.

❻ Draw a similar diagram to show what happens when lithium and fluorine make lithium fluoride.

❼ Remember that magnesium loses two electrons and oxygen gains two.

(a) What is the charge on a magnesium ion? What is the charge on an oxide ion?

(b) Which two ions are 'stuck together' the most strongly: sodium and chloride or magnesium and oxide? Explain your reasoning.

❽ Draw dot and cross diagrams to show how these compounds are formed:

Na_2O $MgCl_2$

3.10 Splitting the atom

Advising farmers on fertiliser use   CASE STUDY

Molly works as a sales rep for an agricultural chemicals manufacturer. She explains, 'Part of my job is to advise farmers which fertilisers and pesticides to buy. I use chemical formulae to check what elements the fertilisers contain.

'Fertiliser bags often have 'N:P:K' ratings shown on the label. This shows how much nitrogen (N), phosphorus (P) and potassium (K) are in the fertiliser. These are three essential elements that make the crops grow faster and bigger. Different crops and soils need different N:P:K proportions.

'I use formulae to check which elements are in the fertilisers if the N:P:K values are not on the labels.'

Molly uses 'N:P:K' information to choose between fertilisers.

see Intensive farming, page 64, and Minerals, page 60

9 Look at these labels from fertiliser bags.

1. Contains NH_4NO_3 and K_3PO_4

2. Main ingredient: Urea $CO(NH_2)_2$

3. Fertiliser compound: $(NH_4)_3PO_4$

(a) Which fertiliser contains all three essential elements?

(b) Which fertiliser would be good for adding to soil that needed nitrogen and phosphorus but contained plenty of potassium?

(c) Which fertiliser could be labelled 'N:P:K 30:0:0'?

Key facts

Copy and complete the sentences by choosing the correct word from the key words list.

1 These particles are found in the nucleus of an atom: _____ and _____.

2 _____ are very light and very fast and move around the _____ of an atom.

3 Electrons are gained and lost when an _____ bond is made.

4 Atoms try to gain full electron _____ when they make compounds because these are very stable.

5 Ionic bonding involves _____ of electrons between atoms.

6 An atom with an electrical charge is called an _____.

Key words

electron

ion

ionic

neutrons

nucleus

protons

shell

transfer

3.11 Making salts

Fertilisers and fireworks

The salt potassium nitrate has many uses.

Many fertilisers contain potassium nitrate, KNO_3. The potassium in the fertiliser helps the crops to grow bigger and faster. Potassium nitrate can also be used in fireworks to make them 'go with a bang.'

Word check ✓

A **salt** is a compound formed when an acid reacts with an alkali.
Neutralise means to react an alkali with an acid so that they 'cancel out' and make a neutral salt.

Salts from acids

Potassium nitrate is a **salt**. We make a salt whenever we **neutralise** an acid. When potassium hydroxide neutralises nitric acid, potassium nitrate is made.

| potassium hydroxide | + | nitric acid | → | potassium nitrate | + | water |
| KOH | + | HNO_3 | → | KNO_3 | + | H_2O |

Look at the formula of potassium nitrate. You can see that the nitrate in potassium nitrate came from the nitric acid.

Neutralising nitric acid always makes 'nitrate' salts. Other acids make other types of salt.

sulphuric acid, H_2SO_4, makes sulphates.

hydrochloric acid, HCl, makes chlorides.

carbonic acid, H_2CO_3, makes carbonates.

❶ Look at the names of these salts. Which acids have been used to make them?

ammonium nitrate (fertiliser)   copper sulphate (fungicide)

sodium nitrate (fireworks)   potassium chloride (food flavouring)

The names of salts often have a metal part and an acid part.

Sodium benzoate is used in shampoos.

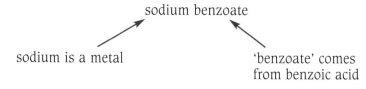

sodium benzoate

sodium is a metal ← → 'benzoate' comes from benzoic acid

BABY SHAMPOO
INFORMATION
Baby Shampoo thoroughly cleans and conditions baby's hair, leaving it healthy. It is also suitable for your hair.
PACKAGING
Cap: (5) PP Bottle: (2) HDPE Labels: (4) LDPE
INGREDIENTS
WATER, POLYSORBATE 20, SODIUM LAURETH SULFATE, SODIUM CHLORIDE, PEG-150 DISTEARATE, COCAMIDOPROPYL BETAINE, CITRIC ACID, PERFUME, TETRASODIUM EDTA, POLYQUATERNIUM-7, FORMALDEHYDE, BENZYL ALCOHOL, SODIUM BENZOATE, MAGNESIUM NITRATE, MAGNESIUM CHLORIDE, METHYLCHLOROISOTHIAZOLINONE, METHYLPARABEN, METHYLISOTHIAZOLINONE, PROPYLPARABEN, COLOURS (CI 15985, CI 16035). salts
sodium benzoate

There are many salts in shampoos.

❷ Which salts on this label can be made using nitric acid? Which can be made from hydrochloric acid?

❸ Do a survey of labels of medicines and cosmetics, for example, toothpastes, shower gels, indigestion remedies and so on. What salts can you find?

3.11 Making salts

Making ammonium sulphate for fertilisers   ACTIVITY

Ammonium sulphate for fertilisers needs to be made accurately so that it is pure. Extra acid or ammonia would kill the crops! Jason is making some fertiliser. This is one way of making sure he mixes exactly the right amounts of ammonia and acid together. It works like this:

- 20 cm³ of sulphuric acid go in the flask with a few drops of litmus (it will look red).

- Jason adds a little ammonia solution at a time, shaking the flask gently.

- When the litmus goes blue he has just neutralised the acid – he stops.

- He makes a note of how much ammonia solution he has used.

- Jason throws this first mixture away.

- He repeats the whole experiment using exactly the same amounts of acid and ammonia but missing the indicator out.

- He has made a pure solution of ammonium sulphate for use as a fertiliser.

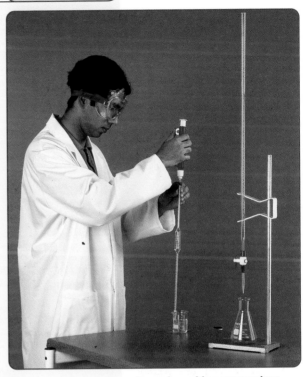

Jason is making ammonium sulphate.

4 Why is Jason's first mixture not pure enough to use as a fertiliser?

5 Jason is working with Becky. They are going to test Jason's fertiliser on some plants for a biology investigation. Becky is annoyed with Jason for taking so long to make the fertiliser.

We haven't got time for all this, Jason. Just mix together some ammonia and some acid in a beaker. That will make enough ammonium sulphate for our plants.

No, Becky, we have to do it like this because . . .

Continue the argument. What will Jason say to Becky?

6 Jason's ammonium sulphate is in solution (dissolved in water). He wants to get some ammonium sulphate crystals to keep in his portfolio. Write a set of instructions to show Jason how to get crystals from his solution.

3.11 Making salts

Films and photos

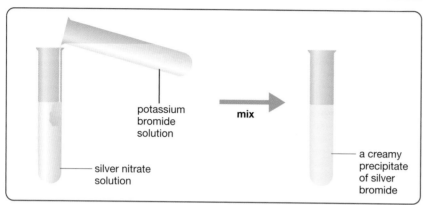

How to make silver bromide.

Another way of making salts, without using an acid, is by **precipitation**. Two compounds react together to make a salt that is **insoluble** (does not dissolve in water). The salt sinks to the bottom of the mixture as a solid **precipitate**.

Silver bromide is used to make photo-film. Tiny crystals of silver bromide are set in jelly on a layer of plastic.

Making silver bromide

Notice that the metal part of the salt comes from the silver nitrate and the non-metal (or 'acid') part comes from the potassium bromide. To get solid silver bromide, you can filter the mixture.

This is the equation for the reaction.

$$AgNO_3 \quad + \quad KBr \quad \rightarrow \quad AgBr \quad + \quad KNO_3$$

7 (a) Write a word equation for the reaction.

(b) Why do film factories produce a lot of nitrates as waste?

8 Silver chloride and silver iodide can be made in a similar way. Suppose you were given these chemicals:

silver nitrate, AgNO3   potassium chloride, KCl   potassium iodide, KI

Write down what you would mix together to make:

(a) silver chloride;   (b) silver iodide.

(c) Write WORD and SYMBOL equations for the reactions.

Taking photos

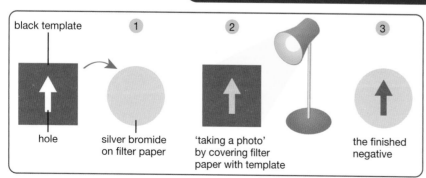

What happens when light shines on silver bromide.

When light shines on silver bromide, it goes dark grey (the grey colour is metallic silver). Notice that the 'photo' is darkest where most light has been shining.

9 The bright areas of a photo appear dark on the negative (look at a negative to see this). Draw diagrams to explain how this happens.

10 Explain why silver bromide for use in photo films is a 'fine chemical' but fertilisers are 'bulk chemicals'.

3.11 Making salts

Road markings

The yellow colour in road markings is due to a salt that is made by precipitation.

The yellow colour is lead chromate. It can be made by mixing solutions of lead nitrate and potassium chromate. This produces a precipitate of bright yellow lead chromate.

What is road marking paint made from?

Road markings are not really paint at all – they are plastic! The plastic melts when it gets hot, so it can be poured on to the road. When it cools down it hardens (this type of plastic is called a thermoplastic).

Road marking paint is a composite material. This table shows what it contains.

Yellow road markings contain lead chromate.

Ingredient	Purpose
Lead chromate	
Thermoplastic beads	
'Filler' – powdered limestone and glass beads	To make the markings hardwearing

see Physical properties, page 222

11 Copy and complete the table to show what the ingredients are for.

12 Sometimes old road markings need to be removed. Suggest how road workers can do this.

13 Look up lead chromate using Student Safety Sheets. Why do you think research is going on to find a replacement for lead chromate?

14 You work for a firm making road markings. A local councillor has complained about the cost of marking out a car park. He says, 'I could have bought some paint and done it myself for next to nothing.' Write a letter to the councillor to explain why road marking is more expensive than using ordinary paint. Explain why road markings will last much longer.

3.12 Chemical analysis

What's in mineral water?

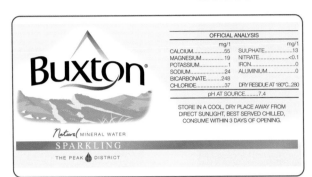

OFFICIAL ANALYSIS	
mg/1	mg/1
CALCIUM..............55	SULPHATE...............13
MAGNESIUM............19	NITRATE................<0.1
POTASSIUM............1	IRON......................0
SODIUM................24	ALUMINIUM...............0
BICARBONATE.........248	
CHLORIDE.............37	DRY RESIDUE AT 180°C...280
	pH AT SOURCE.........7.4

STORE IN A COOL, DRY PLACE AWAY FROM
DIRECT SUNLIGHT. BEST SERVED CHILLED,
CONSUME WITHIN 3 DAYS OF OPENING.

Buxton

Natural MINERAL WATER

SPARKLING

THE PEAK DISTRICT

Water labels show what ions are in the water.

Companies who sell water analyse it to find out exactly what is dissolved in it. Some people drink mineral water because of the health benefits of the metal salts (such as calcium and magnesium) that are dissolved in it. Water companies, such as Severn Trent, test tap water regularly, not only to find out what useful salts the water contains, but also to make sure that the water is free of poisonous salts, such as lead salts or nitrates.

Testing for salts

Water companies use many different methods to identify salts in the water supply. Here are some tests that work in a school lab.

Flame tests

Salts of some metals give different colours if they are heated in a Bunsen flame. To do this **flame test** you need to:

- dip a wire loop in hydrochloric acid;
- use the loop to pick up a tiny salt crystal;
- hold the crystal in a blue Bunsen flame.

Metal in the salt	Flame colour
sodium	yellow
potassium	lilac
calcium	orange-red
copper	blue-green

Flame testing a copper salt.

These tests are not very reliable, because a small amount of sodium can mask the other colours in its bright yellow flame.

Using sodium hydroxide solution

To do this test you need to:

- dissolve the salt in water (or nitric acid) in a test tube;
- add sodium hydroxide (NaOH) solution, drop by drop.

Metal in the salt	Observation after adding NaOH
sodium	no change
potassium	no change
calcium	white precipitate
copper	blue precipitate
lead	white precipitate which dissolves in extra NaOH
iron	brown precipitate

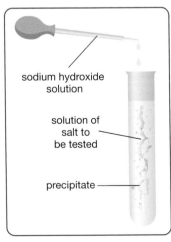

sodium hydroxide solution

solution of salt to be tested

precipitate

Using sodium hydroxide to test for a copper salt.

❶ A salt does not give a precipitate with sodium hydroxide, but gives a lilac colour in a flame test. What metal does the salt contain?

3.12 Chemical analysis

Testing minerals ACTIVITY

Julia and Phil are interested in old mine workings. They have collected three types of rock from around an old mine at Ecton Hill in Derbyshire. Julia has brought the rocks in to her college to test them. She wants to find out what metals were mined there.

Sample 1.

Sample 2.

Sample 3.

Julia and Phil collecting minerals.

Julia ground up the rock samples and then analysed them. Here are her results.

Flame Tests

Sample 1	greeny blue
Sample 2	red-orange
Sample 3	red-orange

I don't think these tests are accurate.

Sodium hydroxide test
(I needed to use nitric acid to dissolve the rocks)

Sample 1	blue precipitate
Sample 2	brown precipitate
Sample 3	white precipitate

I re-did the test for three to make sure it did not dissolve in extra sodium hydroxide.

2 What metals are present in each rock sample?

3 (a) Why does Julia think the flame tests are not accurate? Which result does not agree with the sodium hydroxide test?

Water companies use a 'flame spectrometer' to give a print out of every colour in the flame.

(b) Explain why this is more accurate than using your eyes alone.

4 Why did Julia check to find out if Sample 3 would dissolve in extra sodium hydroxide?

5 Ecton Hill was a lead mine. Julia and Phil collected their rocks from the 'spoil' (waste) heaps. Why do you think they did not find any lead samples?

6 It would not be possible to identify all the metals in bottled water using these tests. This is because bottled water is very dilute and it is a mixture.

(a) Explain why testing dilute mixtures is difficult.

(b) How could you make the bottled water sample more concentrated?

see Mixtures everywhere, page 184

3.12 Chemical analysis

see Making salts, page 192

More tests

It is also possible to test for carbonates, sulphates and chlorides.

Testing for carbonates
To test for a carbonate you need to:

- use a sample of solid salt;
- add hydrochloric acid.

If it fizzes and the gas produced turns lime water milky, it is a carbonate.

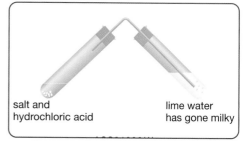

salt and hydrochloric acid

lime water has gone milky

This salt is a carbonate.

Testing for sulphates
To test for a sulphate you need to:

- use a solution of a salt (dissolved in water);
- add a few drops of nitric acid;
- add drops of barium chloride ($BaCl_2$) solution.

A white precipitate shows a sulphate.

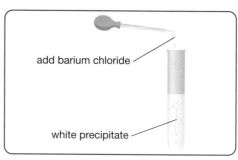

add barium chloride

white precipitate

This salt is a sulphate.

Testing for chlorides
To test for a chloride you need to:

- use a solution of a salt (dissolved in water);
- add a few drops of nitric acid;
- add drops of silver nitrate ($AgNO_3$) solution.

A white precipitate shows a chloride.

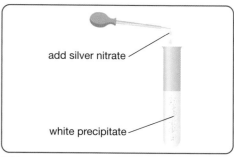

add silver nitrate

white precipitate

This salt is a chloride.

7 A Health and Safety inspector found some bags of white solid near food in a restaurant kitchen. He was concerned because they had no labels. A food analyst was asked to test them. Here are her results (ppt = precipitate).

Sample	NaOH test	Lime water test	BaCl₂ test	AgNO₃ test
A	no change	no change	no change	white ppt
B	white ppt, dissolves in extra NaOH	lime water cloudy	no change	no change
C	permanent white ppt	no change	white ppt	no change

What are the three white solids? What further tests do you need to do to find out for sure? Should the Health and Safety inspector be worried that they are near food? (Use Student Safety Sheets to help you.)

3.12 Chemical analysis

Mining the sea

If you lived near the Dead Sea, you might have a holiday job turning the salt over in the big evaporation pans. The Dead Sea is so rich in salts that they are collected and used to make chemicals. There is a thriving chemicals industry around the Dead Sea.

8 Why does the sea water need to be evaporated?

Salt evaporation pans on the shore of the Dead Sea. The white objects at the left of the picture are 'pillars' of salt that have crystallised out of the sea water.

What salts are in the sea?

Ion	Dead Sea: mass/g dm^{-3}	Atlantic Ocean: mass/g dm^{-3}
sodium	32	11
potassium	7	0.5
magnesium	36	1
calcium	13	0.5
chloride	183	19
bromide	5	0.1
carbonate	almost 0	0.1
sulphate	3	2.5

9 Draw a comparative bar chart (use a spreadsheet if you can) to show the difference in the contents of sea water from the Dead Sea and the Atlantic Ocean.

10 Work out the total mass (in g) of solid that is dissolved in 1 dm^3 of each type of sea water.

11 Use your answers to questions 9 and 10 to explain why it is worth 'mining' the Dead Sea.

The Chemical Industry in Israel exports 230 000 tonnes of bromine every year. It is the largest source of bromine in the world. In the UK, we produce about 40 000 tonnes annually from sea water at a chemical plant in Anglesey in Wales. Bromine is used in huge quantities to make flame-proofing chemicals for fabrics and furniture.

12 Look at the amount of bromine in the two samples of sea water.

(a) Why do you think the Dead Sea is a more important source of bromine than the sea off the coast of Wales?

(b) Which other substances are present in greater concentrations in the Dead Sea water than bromine?

(c) Why do you think extracting bromine from Dead Sea water is more profitable than extracting these other substances?

3.13 More about molecules

Early anaesthetics

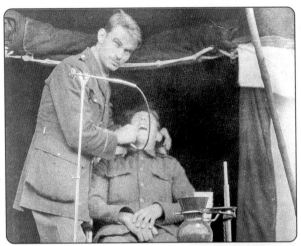

Chloroform was used by dentists 100 years ago.

If you had a tooth taken out a hundred years ago, you might be lucky if you visited a very modern dentist – he *might* give you an anaesthetic! Most dentists still did not use them. One of the first anaesthetics was 'chloroform' (trichloromethane), $CHCl_3$. Even if you found a dentist who used it, you would be lucky to survive the operation – the difference in dose between going to sleep and death was not very much; dentists were always making mistakes...

Nowadays, trichloromethane and similar compounds are used as **solvents** for dissolving grease. Solvents are used in dry cleaning. An unlucky customer once died as a result of driving his car with fresh dry cleaning (still wet with solvents) on the back seat.

Looking at solvent molecules

This is what a single **molecule** of trichloromethane looks like:

Formula: $CHCl_3$

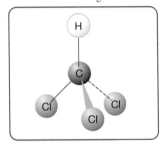

We write the structure like this:

$$Cl - \underset{\underset{Cl}{|}}{\overset{\overset{H}{|}}{C}} - Cl$$

The formula shows...

1 carbon atom

1 hydrogen atom

3 chlorine atoms

Atoms follow rules when they join together to make molecules.

• Carbon, C, always has four bonds around it.

• Hydrogen, H, fluorine, F, and chlorine, Cl, always have one bond.

• Oxygen, O, always has two bonds.

Here are some other examples.

Water, H_2O

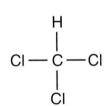

Propanone, C_3H_6O ('nail varnish remover')

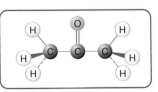

Notice that propanone has two bonds between oxygen and carbon.

Trichloroethane (used as thinner for correction fluid)

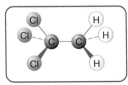

❶ What is the formula for trichloroethane?

❷ Draw 'structures' (you do not have to make them look 3-D) for these molecules:

methane (natural gas), CH_4 halothane (an anaesthetic) F_3C_2HBrCl

3.13 More about molecules

Replacing CFCs ___ACTIVITY___

CFCs (chlorofluorocarbons) were used in massive quantities during the last century. They are non-toxic, they do not burn and they turn easily from a liquid to a gas. These properties meant that they seemed ideal for use in aerosols, in the cooling mechanisms in fridges, in air conditioners and for solvents.

However, in 1985, a British scientist called Joe Farman found that there was a huge hole in the ozone layer. The ozone layer of the atmosphere protects the Earth from dangerous UV light. Without the protection, animals will be damaged (UV causes skin cancers) and crops may fail. CFCs were found to be causing the hole. It became necessary to find other compounds to replace them.

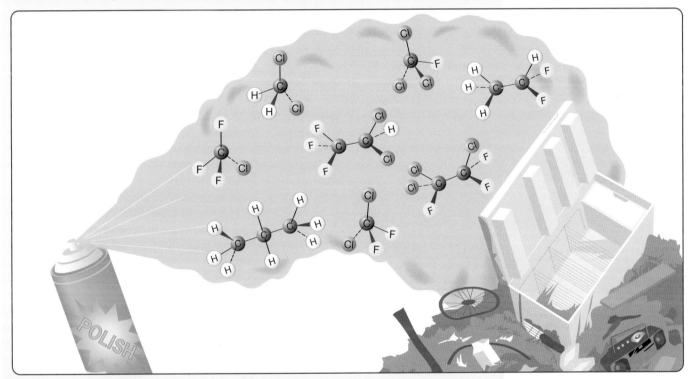

Some CFCs and some possible replacements.

❸ Remember that CFCs contain only chlorine, fluorine and carbon.

Decide in your group which molecules in the diagram are CFCs. Write down:

- the formula of each CFC (for example CCl_3F);

- the names and the number of atoms of each element in each CFC.

❹ Imagine you work for a company that makes aerosols of furniture polish. They used to use a CFC to dissolve the polish and spray it out of the can when the top is pressed down. They now produce an 'ozone friendly' aerosol using another compound instead of the CFC to dissolve the polish.

(a) CFC replacements are often more expensive than CFCs. Discuss in your group the reasons why the company has changed to 'ozone friendly' products.

(b) You are worried about the safety and quality of the new aerosol. What would you look for in an ideal replacement for the CFC?

3.13 More about molecules

Looking at bonds

The molecules in solvents all contain **covalent** bonds. When atoms bond together using covalent bonds, they **share** electrons to gain stable, full outer electron shells.

The dot and cross diagram below shows the formation of water.

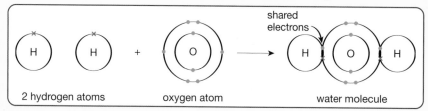

2 hydrogen atoms   oxygen atom   water molecule

Hydrogen and oxygen share electrons in water.

The hydrogen atoms in a water molecule have a share of two electrons – their first shell is full. The outer shell of oxygen has a share of eight electrons – it too has a full outer shell.

The dot and cross diagram for methane is shown below.

The hydrogen atoms in a methane molecule have a share of two electrons – their first shell is full. The outer shell of carbon has a share of eight electrons – it too has a full outer shell.

Dot and cross diagram for methane.

5 Draw dot and cross diagrams for these covalent molecules:

$$HCl \qquad H_2S \qquad CHCl_3$$

6 These compounds are called 'simple' compounds because their molecules are small. This table shows some differences between ionic compounds and simple covalent compounds.

Property	Ionic compounds	Simple covalent compounds
Melting points and boiling points	very high	very low
Solubility in water	usually soluble	usually insoluble
Action on grease	do not mix with grease	can dissolve grease
Conductivity	conduct electricity when dissolved in water	do not conduct

Use the table to explain why:

(a) ionic compounds are used for furnace linings;

(b) simple covalent compounds are good solvents for cleaning circuit boards;

(c) simple covalent compounds are usually gases or liquids, but ionic compounds are always solids at room temperature.

Key words

covalent

molecule

share

solvents

Key facts

Copy and complete the sentences by choosing the correct word from the key words list.

1 When atoms join together they make a _____.

2 Water is an example of a _____ compound.

3 A covalent bond is made when atoms _____ electrons.

4 Covalent compounds are often good _____.

3.13 More about molecules

Going to the cleaners

CASE STUDY

Kim is the manager of Langdons dry cleaners. She explains, 'Dry cleaning means washing clothes in a solvent instead of water. The solvent we use is called "perk".'

7 Look at the photograph. What does the warning cross on the bottle of 'perk' mean?

'We try to re-use as much solvent as we can. We waste very little because the solvent is expensive and chlorinated solvents are very environmentally harmful. This is how our cleaning machines work.'

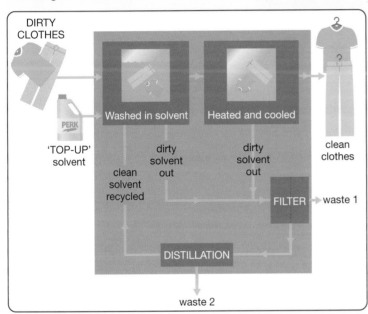

Kim tops up a cleaning machine with 'perk'.

The dry cleaning process.

'At a busy dry cleaners we "top up" our machines with about two bottles (ten litres) of "perk" every week. We lose some in the waste and into the air.'

8 Buttons sometimes fall off clothes during cleaning. Which part of the machine takes buttons and fluff from the dirty solvent?

9 Look up 'distillation' in a dictionary. Explain how this cleans the solvent. Use these words in your answer.

| cool | heat | condenses | evaporates | pure solvent | waste | separates |

10 Old-fashioned machines did not heat the clothes after they were washed. Explain why heating and cooling the clothes helps to recycle as much solvent as possible.

11 An environmental magazine says dry cleaners 'pollute the atmosphere with solvents'.

(a) Identify all the parts of the process where solvents can escape.

(b) Write a letter to the magazine from Langdons explaining how your cleaning process recycles as much solvent as possible.

3.14 Energy and chemical change

Self-heating food and drink

'Self-heating' food packs are used by soldiers, campers and people on expeditions. The packs contain chemicals which give off a lot of heat when they are mixed with water.

Recently, a British university has developed a 'self-heating can' to heat drinks such as coffee.

Soldiers use 'self-heating' packs to heat food.

How does the self-heating can work?

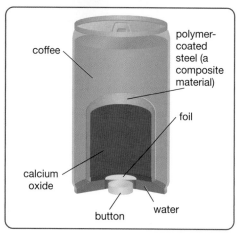

see Physical properties, page 222

A design for a self-heating can of coffee.

Inside the can are two hidden compartments. One is full of water, the other contains calcium oxide. When you push the button at the bottom of the can, a foil seal breaks and the two substances mix.

When water and calcium oxide react together, they form calcium hydroxide. They also give off a lot of heat. The heat warms up the coffee.

This is the equation for the reaction:

$$CaO + H_2O \rightarrow Ca(OH)_2$$

This reaction is **exothermic** because it gives out energy as heat. The heat increases the temperature of the surroundings (in this case, the coffee).

Word check

Exothermic reactions give out energy.

❶ Write a word equation for the reaction.

❷ Use a set of Student Safety Sheets to find out more about calcium oxide and calcium hydroxide. What difficulties do you think the designers had when they were designing a coffee can containing these chemicals?

❸ Calcium oxide is the main ingredient in cement. Write a set of safety instructions to go on a bag of cement. (If you have any cement at home, you can check to see what the bags actually say.)

❹ Which of the following involve exothermic reactions?

    (a)   burning methane

    (b)   filtering sand from salt

    (c)   crushing limestone

    (d)   a firework display

3.14 Energy and chemical change

Designing a cooling can ACTIVITY

Some reactions are **endothermic**. This means they take energy in from the surroundings. The surroundings get colder.

Dave and Sue are experimenting to find out whether it would be possible to design a 'self-cooling can' to give really cold drinks on hot days. They mix various chemicals with water in a polystyrene beaker and measure the temperature change.

Word check ✓

Endothermic reactions take in energy.

Dave and Sue are looking for a 'self-cooling' mixture.

5 (a) What would Dave and Sue have to control (keep the same) in their experiments to make sure the results were reliable?

(b) Write a short set of experimental instructions for them to follow.

see Following standard procedures, page 12

Here are some of Dave and Sue's results.

Chemical	Temperature at start/°C	Temperature at end/°C	Temperature change/°C
calcium chloride	20	23	
ammonium nitrate	20	18	
ammonium chloride	20	17	

6 Work out the temperature change for each of the chemicals tested.

7 Which chemical looks like the best one to choose to investigate further for making a 'cooling can'? Why?

8 Dave says one experiment is not enough to make a definite choice. He thinks they need to do more experiments to make absolutely sure which one to choose. What extra experiments could they do?

9 Use the Student Safety Sheets to look up more information about the chemical you have chosen. What hazards does it have?

10 Use the information you have collected to design a new 'self-cooling can'. Make an advert for your can, showing how it works and what drinks will be sold in it.

3.14 Energy and chemical change

Many exothermic reactions need energy to get them started.

Bangs and bonds

Exothermic reactions often need some energy to 'get them started'. For example, you need to light a firework and a spark from a spark plug is needed to fire a petrol engine.

Bonds and energy

Natural gas is mainly methane. We usually light a gas fire using a match or a 'sparking' device.

When methane burns, energy is given out. This is the equation for the reaction:

$$\text{methane} \quad + \quad \text{oxygen} \quad \rightarrow \quad \text{carbon dioxide} \quad + \quad \text{water}$$
$$CH_4 \quad + \quad 2O_2 \quad \rightarrow \quad CO_2 \quad + \quad 2H_2O$$

During the reaction, two important things must happen:

- all the bonds in the methane and oxygen are broken;

- the atoms bond together again to make carbon dioxide and water.

Breaking bonds uses up energy (energy is taken in). This is why we need to put in some energy to start the reaction off.

Making bonds gives energy out.

For exothermic reactions, like methane burning, the energy given out by making bonds is greater than the energy needed to break bonds. Overall, energy is given out.

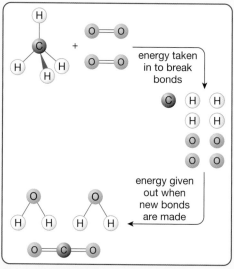

Bonds are broken and made when methane burns.

For endothermic reactions, bond-breaking takes in more energy than bond-making gives out. Overall, energy is taken in.

11 Look again at the explanation of the self-heating coffee can. Use ideas about bond-breaking and making to explain why the reaction heats up the coffee.

Key words

breaking bonds

endothermic

exothermic

making bonds

Key facts

Copy and complete the sentences by choosing the correct word from the key words list.

1 _____ reactions give out energy.

2 Reactions which take in energy are _____.

3 _____ _____ uses energy.

4 _____ _____ gives out energy.

5 If the energy taken in is less than the energy given out, the reaction is _____.

3.14 Energy and chemical change

The hydrogen-powered car

CASE STUDY

Mike works in a car showroom selling cars. He says, 'Some of our customers are starting to ask about the new hydrogen-powered cars that are being developed. I went along to a course to find out about them so that I can give my customers up-to-date information.'

This is an extract from the information Mike was given:

Mike is interested in finding out more about hydrogen-powered cars.

Hydrogen is the real 'fuel for the future'. It has such a <u>very exothermic reaction with oxygen</u> that it is an excellent fuel. In fact, the reaction is so exothermic that in the past it has been difficult to control. Disasters such as the explosions of the *Hindenburg* airship (36 people dead in 1937) and the *Challenger* Space Shuttle (7 dead in 1986) have made many people think it can never be made safe enough for large-scale use!

The beauty of the hydrogen car, though, is that there is no need to <u>ignite</u> or <u>combust</u> the fuel. Advanced fuel cells mean we can tap into the energy of the hydrogen–oxygen reaction with much less risk of explosion.

The fuel cell uses energy from the reaction to make electricity. All this with only water as a waste product – pollution free!

12 Mike has underlined the information he thinks is very important. Explain what the underlined words mean.

13 Why does using fuel cells reduce the risk of explosions?

14 The leaflet glosses over any disadvantages of using hydrogen as a fuel. Find out what disadvantages hydrogen has as a fuel. Find out about:

- How is hydrogen made?
- What energy is used to make it?
- How can it be stored at filling stations and in cars?
- In terms of safety, what are the disadvantages?

Write a leaflet, similar to the one above, to give car salespeople balanced information about hydrogen.

Review questions

1 'Self-freezing' ice packs are used by physiotherapists. They are useful at football games to put on injuries to stop swelling. The packs contain a powdered chemical. When water is added, the pack becomes very cold.

Is the reaction in the pack endothermic or exothermic? Explain your reasoning. *[1]*

2 Around 1800, John Dalton used these symbols for elements.

Look at the table of formulae below.

Name of compound	Modern formula	Dalton's formula
Methane	CH_4	
Ammonia	NH_3	
Water	H_2O	

Dalton's formulae were not exactly right. Look at the elements and numbers of atoms in the formulae in the table.

(a) In what way are Dalton's formulae exactly right? *[1]*

(b) How do our modern formulae show that Dalton was wrong? *[1]*

(c) Draw a 'dot and cross' diagram to show the covalent bonding in NH_3. *[3]*

3 These salts are used in medicines.

   potassium chloride   magnesium sulphate   calcium sulphate

(a) Which acids are used to make each salt? *[3]*

(b) Why are medicines made as fine chemicals? *[2]*

(c) Draw a 'dot and cross' diagram to show the ionic bonding in potassium chloride. *[3]*

4 Laurie is carrying out an investigation into weathering on his local church. He has collected:

- some samples of the building stone; he thinks the stones are made from limestone (calcium carbonate);

- some green powdered corrosion from the copper roof tiles; he thinks the powder might be copper carbonate.

(a) How can Laurie test the samples to make sure he is right? Write a set of experimental instructions for Laurie to follow. *[6]*

(b) What observations will Laurie make? What results will he look for? *[4]*

3 Materials for making things

Contents

Assignments and practicals linked to this section:

Electrical properties

Physical properties

Investigating resistance

Measuring density

Use the following to check your progress.

Unit 1

You will:

- realise that to compare the electrical resistance of different metals, we must use wires of the same length and thickness

see pages 218–221

- use the words density, thermal conductivity and strength to compare materials and relate these properties of materials to their uses

see pages 222–225

- compare thermal conductivities of different materials.

see pages 222–225

Unit 2

You will:

- know what ceramics are used for and what properties they have

see pages 210–213

- know what happens when clay is fired to make bricks

see pages 210–213

- know what 'giant structure' means

see pages 210–213

- be able to explain the properties of silicon dioxide and aluminium oxide by using ideas about their structures

see pages 210–213

- know that polymers are long chain molecules

see pages 214–217

- know the properties of polymers

see pages 214–217

- understand the difference between a thermoplastic and a thermosetting polymer

see pages 214–217

- be able to explain properties of polymers using ideas about chains, side groups and cross links

see pages 214–217

- use the words malleability and hardness to describe materials

see pages 222–225

- understand that metals contain electrons which are free to move, and so metals are good conductors

see pages 222–225

- describe composite materials and their properties.

see pages 216, 222–225

3.15 Bricks

Ceramic materials

Bricks are an ideal building material.

see Electrical behaviour, page 218

Do you live in a brick house? Most people do. Bricks are made by firing clay. They are an ideal building material because they are hard, strong and resist the weather.

Bricks are one of a group of materials known as **ceramics**. You may have come across ceramics in art lessons – pottery is another ceramic, also made from clay. All ceramic materials are hard and have high melting points. They do not dissolve in water or conduct electricity. These properties mean that ceramics have many uses. They are used to line furnaces and to make insulator discs for electricity pylons.

From clay to brick

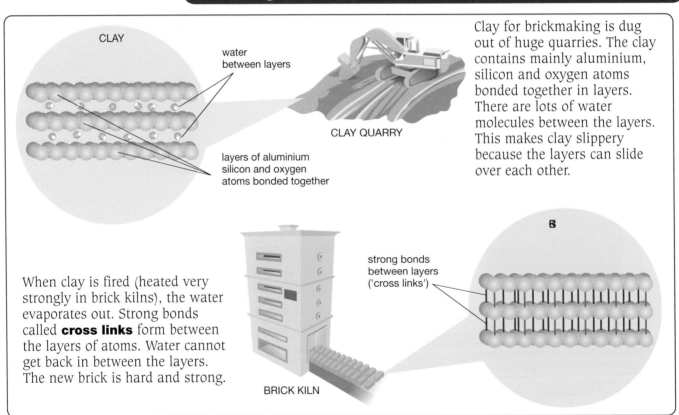

CLAY

water between layers

layers of aluminium silicon and oxygen atoms bonded together

CLAY QUARRY

Clay for brickmaking is dug out of huge quarries. The clay contains mainly aluminium, silicon and oxygen atoms bonded together in layers. There are lots of water molecules between the layers. This makes clay slippery because the layers can slide over each other.

When clay is fired (heated very strongly in brick kilns), the water evaporates out. Strong bonds called **cross links** form between the layers of atoms. Water cannot get back in between the layers. The new brick is hard and strong.

BRICK KILN

strong bonds between layers ('cross links')

❶ Use ideas from the diagram to explain why:

(a) bricks weigh less after firing;

(b) clay can be moulded into different shapes but bricks cannot.

❷ A technical information leaflet explains that, 'Clay contains compounds of both metallic and non-metallic elements.' Explain what this means.

❸ After the Great Fire of London in 1666, the wooden houses were all rebuilt using brick. Give reasons why brick is a better building material than wood.

3.15 Bricks

Comparing clay and brick   ACTIVITY

Bobby is training to be a bricklayer. He goes to college one day each week. At college, he has been investigating the differences between fired and unfired clay.

Bobby cut three brick shapes from clay. He wrapped one in a wet cloth, left one to dry and fired the third brick in a kiln.

He tested each brick a week later.

Bobby's results
This table shows what Bobby found after a week.

Brick	Mass at start/g	Mass after one week/g	Appearance	Hit with hammer	Soaked in water
Wrapped in wet cloth	210	215	no change in colour, soft	flattens	solid disintegrates – water goes brown and cloudy
Left to dry in air	225	185	paler in colour, hard	crumbles	goes soft – looks like fresh clay
Kiln fired	212	170	hard, redder in colour	no effect	goes a slightly darker colour

4 (a) Calculate the change in mass for each brick over the week. Explain why these changes happened.

    (b) Work out the percentage by mass of water in the clay used to make the kiln-fired brick.

5 Drying the bricks in air does not cause the clay to form bonds between the layers of atoms. Use this idea to explain why water can make the air-dried brick soft again.

6 Write a paragraph explaining why bricks need to be fired rather than just dried out. Use these words:

         layers of atoms   water   strong bonds   clay
         reversible change   permanent change   dried   fired

During the winter, wet bricks can be damaged by frost. Houses are designed to keep the bricks as dry as possible. This involves keeping off rain, and preventing ground water from soaking upwards. Bobby is doing a survey of methods of keeping brickwork dry.

7 How is your own house or school building designed to keep the walls dry? How are roofs designed to keep rain off the walls?

Brickwork becomes damaged if it gets too wet.

3.15 Bricks

Giant structures: sand, glass and rubies

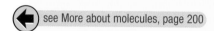
see More about molecules, page 200

Brick is an example of a **giant structure**. A giant structure contains many atoms bonded together in a three-dimensional lattice arrangement. The atoms are held very strongly together so giant structures are very hard with very high melting and boiling points. The bonds can be **covalent** (formed from shared electrons) or **ionic** (the atoms form ions with opposite charges).

Sand and glass

Sand is made of silicon dioxide.

Sand is mainly silicon dioxide, SiO_2. It has a giant structure held together by covalent bonds. Sand is very hard and has a very high melting point because the atoms have very strong bonds in a three-dimensional arrangement. The bonds are so strong that sand has to be heated to a very high temperature before it will melt. The bonds are covalent because they are made by sharing electrons.

Sand is hard enough to be used as an abrasive. Sand blasting cleans dirty stonework on old buildings by firing a jet of sand at the surface.

Silicon dioxide is the main compound in glass. 'Flint' tools from Stone Age times were also mainly silicon dioxide. All of these materials are very hard.

see Splitting the atom, page 188

Rubies

These sapphires, like rubies, are aluminium oxide.

Precious stones are all giant structures. The hardness of the stones mean they will last a very long time. Rubies and sapphires are mainly aluminium oxide. Aluminium oxide is an ionic giant structure – it contains Al^{3+} and O^{2-} ions. The ions are attracted very strongly together because of their opposite charges.

'Emery' is a form of aluminium oxide used to make high-quality sandpaper and 'emery boards' for shaping fingernails.

8 Look at these melting points:

- aluminium oxide 2015°C;

- silicon dioxide 1610°C.

(a) Use ideas about the arrangement and movement of particles to explain what happens when silicon dioxide melts.

(b) Melted aluminium oxide conducts electricity, melted silicon dioxide does not. Use ideas about types of bonding to explain why.

(c) Explain why the melting point of aluminium oxide is evidence that the bonds between its atoms must be very strong.

(d) Which has the strongest bonds, silicon dioxide or aluminium oxide? Explain how you decided.

3.15 Bricks

The Bedford brick kilns   CASE STUDY

Jim works as a 'burner' on the brick kilns in Bedford.

'The bricks come to us after they have been cut from wet clay. We load about 65 000 bricks into one of the 36 chambers of the kiln. We leave them to dry for a few weeks. It is warm in the chamber because there is always firing going on in another chamber nearby.

'We seal the entrance up and direct fire into the chamber. The clay contains about five per cent carbon so the bricks actually catch fire – it gets really hot in there! I'm the burner – it's my job to monitor the fire and top it up with a couple of buckets of coal dust every few hours. After 48 hours we let the fire go out in the chamber. When the bricks are cool they are ready to go to the building site.

'We have had a continuous fire at the Bedford kilns for 50 years!'

The burner's job is to keep the fire burning.

see Bulk and fine chemicals, page 170

9 Coal dust is used instead of lumps of coal because it makes a hotter fire. Use ideas about rates of reaction to explain why.

10 The chambers have chimneys to draw air through them. Why is this needed?

11 The main gases coming out of the chimneys include nitrogen and carbon dioxide. Explain where these gases come from.

12 If wet bricks are fired, they explode.

  (a) What would happen to the water during firing?

  (b) Why does this cause the bricks to explode?

13 The brick company has modernised some of its kilns to use natural gas as a fuel. The fires are monitored by computers instead of by a burner. What advantages do the modernised kilns have?

The finished bricks.

Key facts

Copy and complete the sentences by choosing the correct word from the key words list.

1 Bricks and pottery are examples of _____.

2 Clay does not go soft after firing because it contains _____ _____.

3 Many atoms or ions held together in three dimensions form a _____ _____.

4 Silicon dioxide is _____ because its bonds are made by sharing electrons.

5 When a compound is held together by electrical charges, it is _____.

Key words

ceramics

covalent

cross links

giant structure

ionic

3.16 Polymers

A world of polymers

This woman is wearing and carrying **polymers**! All the fibres in her clothes (nylon, wool, polyester) are polymers. Her carrier bags are made of poly(ethene), or 'polythene', another polymer. Even her hair is made of keratin – yet another polymer!

What are polymers?

Polymers are made of long, chain-like molecules. The molecules are tangled together like a plate of spaghetti.

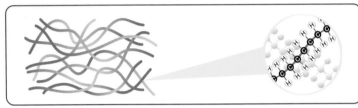

'Polythene' is a polymer.

The properties of a polymer (how the polymer behaves) depends on its structure (how the long chain molecules are arranged). The bonds that join the carbon and hydrogen atoms together are very strong, but there are only weak forces between chains. The chains can move about when the polymer is heated or stretched. This table shows how the structure of poly(ethene) can explain some of its properties.

Property	Structure
Thermoplastic (melts and changes shape when hot)	Polymer chains can move around when they are heated
Flexible/does not shatter easily	Polymer chains slide over each other, so poly(ethene) can stretch
Burns easily	The carbon and hydrogen in the poly(ethene) can burn with oxygen to give carbon dioxide and water
Does not rot (non-biodegradable)	Bacteria cannot use poly(ethene) for food

❶ Poly(ethene) is non-biodegradable. Why is this both an advantage and a disadvantage?

❷ 'Biodegradable' plastics have shorter chain lengths. Carrier bags made from biodegradable plastics are weaker and split easily. Use ideas about structure to explain why.

❸ Explain why poly(ethene) can be easily shaped into products like shampoo bottles.

❹ Poly(ethene) is used to make goods that used to be made of other materials, such as:

* glass milk bottles;

* metal buckets and watering cans;

* paper bags for food.

For each of these uses, explain why poly(ethene) is a better material for the job.

3.16 Polymers

The right polymer for the job (ACTIVITY)

Poly(ethene) was first discovered in 1933. A chemist called Eric Fawcett made some accidentally when he was using ethene gas in a high-pressure experiment. This kind of poly(ethene) is called Low Density Poly(ethene) (LDPE). The polymer chains are all jumbled together.

see Physical properties, page 222

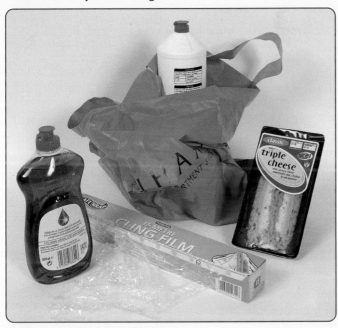

LDPE is used to make packaging.

HDPE is used for higher quality plastic goods.

Over 20 years later, another chemist, Karl Ziegler, used a new type of catalyst. He made the chains line up neatly, very close together. This new arrangement made a harder, denser material – 'High Density Poly(ethene)' or HDPE.

Look at the table of information about LDPE and HDPE.

Property	LDPE	HDPE
Density/g cm^{-3}	0.92	0.96
Strength when pulled /MN m^{-3}	15	29
Stretch before breaking	6 times original length	3 times original length
Effect of heat	softens at 90°C	no change below 200°C
Comparative price	cheaper	more expensive

5 Give reasons why LDPE is used to make 'cheap' food packaging but HDPE is used for higher quality goods.

6 Vending machine coffee cups are made from LDPE but microwave food containers are made from HDPE. Explain why the different plastics are used.

7 Draw diagrams to show how the polymer chains move over each other in a carrier bag handle when it stretches and breaks.

8 Which of the types of poly(ethene) float on water? Explain how you decide.

3.16 Polymers

More about polymers

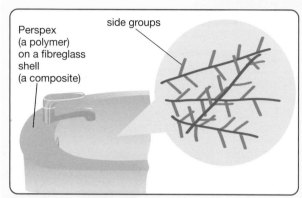

Perspex (a polymer) on a fibreglass shell (a composite)

side groups

Examples of polymers with side groups include polystyrene (car body filler, cups) and Perspex (baths, sinks and plastic windows).

Polymers do not all contain straight chains. Some polymers have differently shaped chains – the shape of the chain will affect the properties of the polymer.

Some polymers have **side groups** which stick out of the chain.

Most plastics are thermoplastic polymers. They melt when they get hot because the chains can slide over each other. Side groups stop the chains sliding over each other so easily because they 'catch'. This means that polymers with side groups are less flexible or stretchy; they are harder and they have higher softening temperatures.

Some polymers have **cross links** that join the chains together. The chains cannot move at all and so these polymers are very hard. They do not melt – if you heat them, they burn rather than melt. They are called **thermosetting** polymers.

9 Pan handles used to be made of metal or wood.

(a) Why is a thermosetting plastic a better material than metal or wood for pan handles?

When pans with plastic handles were first made, people did not want to buy them – they thought the plastic would melt!

(b) Make an advert for a pan with a plastic handle. Convince customers it will not melt. Draw the structure of the polymer to help you to explain what a 'thermosetting' plastic means.

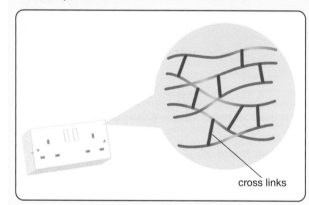

cross links

An example of a thermosetting polymer is melamine (kitchen worktops, laminate flooring, electrical sockets).

 see Physical properties, page 222

Composite plastics

We can change the properties of plastics by adding other materials to make **composite** materials. Adding glass fibres to a polymer makes glass-reinforced plastic (GRP) or fibreglass. This is a very useful, rigid material. Adding compounds called **plasticisers** to PVC makes the plastic more flexible. It can then be used in thin sheets, for example as cling film.

Key words

composite

cross links

plasticiser

polymer

side groups

thermoplastic

thermosetting

Key facts

Copy and complete the sentences by choosing the correct word from the key words list.

1 A long-chain molecule is called a _____ .

2 A _____ goes soft when it gets hot.

3 A polymer with _____ _____ will not melt.

4 Polymers with cross links between the chains are called _____ polymers.

5 _____ _____ make polymers less stretchy and harder.

6 Adding materials such as _____ to polymers makes _____ materials.

3.16 Polymers

Recycling waste plastics   CASE STUDY

Margaret works for her local county council.

She explains, 'Lots of local people ask us about recycling schemes for waste plastics. The trouble is that waste plastics have to be cleaned and sorted before recycling – most people don't wash their bottles out! Our county council spends some of its money paying for recycling schemes.

'Here are some facts and figures:

- It takes 20 000 plastic bottles to make one tonne of plastic.
- Manufacturers buy mixed plastic from us for £40 per tonne.
- PET is the plastic used for making lemonade and cola bottles. Manufacturers buy recycled PET from the council for £150 per tonne.
- It costs us, on average, £250 to collect, sort, clean and bale each tonne of PET.

'Benches like the one I'm sitting on are cheap to make – this one's made out of old black bin bags melted down. It doesn't matter too much if the plastic used isn't very pure. We also sell recycled "mixed plastic" for making lower quality goods like plant pots.

'If we want to sell PET, though, we have to make sure that the bales do not have any other plastics mixed in them. The padding in my anorak is polyester made from recycled PET bottles.'

10 How much does it cost the council to recycle one tonne of PET?

11 Why are recycling schemes that produce mixed plastic less costly?

12 Many county councils run recycling schemes, even though they always make a loss. What benefits to the county council do the schemes have?

13 The company that sells the recycled plastic benches says that they:

- are knot and splinter free;
- never need painting;
- do not rot or rust.

(a) What materials do you think they are comparing their recycled plastic to?

(b) 'Mixed plastic' waste must not contain too much thermosetting plastic or the waste cannot be moulded easily. Explain why.

This bench and the padding in the coat are made from recycled waste plastics.

A plastics recycling bank.

217

3.17 Electrical behaviour

Power connections

The National Grid Company builds and maintains the network of high voltage cables that connects power stations to homes and workplaces.

A lot of the time we just don't notice power cables and pylons. But for some people, like the employees of the National Grid Company, cables for long-distance energy transfer are what their work is all about. They choose the very best materials for the purpose.

Resistance of wires

How do we compare one wire with another? We talk about the electrical resistance of the wire. This is a measure of how much the wire opposes the flow of electrical current when it is connected to a source of voltage.

To work out the resistance of a wire, we compare the voltage with the current. You can make a mathematical comparison by a division calculation:

$$resistance = \frac{voltage}{current}$$

The unit of resistance is called the ohm. We often use Ω as a short way to write ohm.

❶ Draw a table to help you to remember the names of the units of voltage, current and resistance.

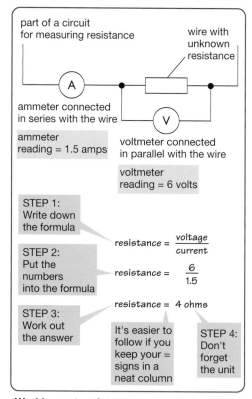

part of a circuit for measuring resistance

wire with unknown resistance

ammeter connected in series with the wire

ammeter reading = 1.5 amps

voltmeter connected in parallel with the wire

voltmeter reading = 6 volts

STEP 1: Write down the formula

$$resistance = \frac{voltage}{current}$$

STEP 2: Put the numbers into the formula

$$resistance = \frac{6}{1.5}$$

STEP 3: Work out the answer

$$resistance = 4 \; ohms$$

It's easier to follow if you keep your = signs in a neat column

STEP 4: Don't forget the unit

Working out resistance.

Good electrical conductors

Metals are good **conductors** of electricity. They have atoms packed closely together with electrons that can move freely inside the metal. The electrons are a bit like fish swimming amongst the fixed atoms (but they are very, very tiny 'fish'). It is a flow of electrons in one direction that makes an electric current.

Some metals are better conductors than others. The National Grid Company needs to use cables that have low resistance, so they must choose the right metals for their cables.

Four factors influence the electrical resistance of a wire:

• what material it is made of;

• its length;

• its thickness or diameter;

• its temperature.

You need to investigate the first three of these influences.

3.17 Electrical behaviour

Installing a high voltage line   CASE STUDY

The National Grid Company looks after the high voltage power lines that connect power stations to homes and workplaces. When a new power station was built near Middlesbrough, the National Grid Company had to plan and install a new high voltage line to connect it to users. They had to balance the cost of the line against profit, need and the environment.

Fields probably look nicer without pylons and cables, but we all want cheap energy supplies. Homes and workplaces have to be connected to power stations.

2 Which of these variables can the National Grid Company control:

- material of cable
- length of cable
- diameter of cable
- temperature of cable?

3 Use Appendix 4 on page 315 to explain why you would NOT use each of these for making cables for distributing energy from power stations:

(a) glass   (b) lead.

4 Would you expect a thick wire to have more or less resistance than a thin wire of the same metal and length? Why?

5 A straight line provides the cheapest route for a new power line.

(a) Why is a straight route cheapest?
(b) Suggest some reasons why the National Grid Company cannot always build long cable routes in straight lines.

6 To protect people from the sight of power lines in the countryside, would you be prepared to:

(a) go without electricity
(b) pay twice as much for electricity?

219

3.17 Electrical behaviour

The insulators on pylons are made of glass or ceramic.

Insulators

Cables that hang from pylon to pylon do not need to have electrical insulator wrapped around them. An electrical insulator is a material that does not conduct electricity well. Contact with the cables kills, but nobody is normally going to touch them.

The cables must not touch the pylons. They hang from the pylons by insulating holders.

7 Use the information on page 315 to sort the materials in Appendix 4 into conductors and insulators.

Investigating wires and other components

A wire has resistance which stays the same as long as the temperature stays the same.

Even though resistance stays the same, you can change voltage by adjusting the power supply in a circuit. When you change the voltage and use a wire at a fixed temperature, then the current changes as in graph A on the right.

Current changes when you do the same with other components, too. Light bulbs, for example, contain wires which do have a big change in temperature when in use. Graphs of voltage and current can help us to compare how a normal cool wire and a wire in a lamp behave.

A diode is another device that you can test. When a diode is connected to a power supply one way round, a current flows, but when you connect it the other way round, there is no current.

In these investigations, voltage is the variable that you control. It is the input variable. Then you see what the current does. Current is the output variable.

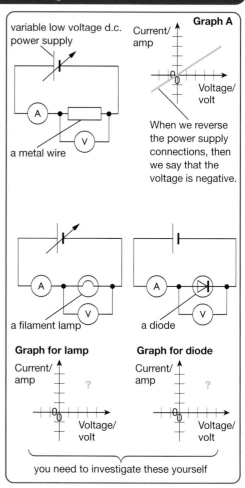

Investigating how current depends on voltage.

8 When you change the voltage that you apply to a cool wire, does the current change by the same amount or by the same proportion? Write a sentence to explain your answer.

3.17 Electrical behaviour

Voltage, current and resistance ACTIVITY

Working out resistance

9 A wire carries a current of two ampere (2 A) when connected to a 12 volt (12 V) battery. Copy the template and replace the zzzz to work out the resistance of the wire:

$$\text{resistance} = \frac{\text{zzzz}}{\text{current}}$$

$$= \frac{12}{\text{zzzz}}$$

$$= 6 \text{ zzzz}$$

How resistance affects current

10 Five wires are connected in turn to a six-volt battery. These are the currents:

Wire	wire 1	wire 2	wire 3	wire 4	wire 5
Current/A	0.6	1.2	2.4	3.0	3.6

(a) Work out the resistance of each wire.

(b) Plot a graph with resistance on the horizontal axis and current on the vertical axis.

(c) Which variable are we treating as the input variable?

(d) Describe the relationship between resistance and current for wires which are connected to the same power supply.

Comparing materials

11 (a) Use the data in Appendix 4 on page 315 to find out the resistance of wires one metre long and one millimetre in diameter made from:

(i) aluminium (ii) constantan (iii) copper (iv) iron (v) lead.

(b) Draw a bar chart to show the information.

(c) Why do we only compare materials by using wires of the same length and diameter?

Working with current–voltage graphs

This is a graph for a 100-watt lamp.

The resistance of the lamp increases as voltage increases.

12 (a) What happens to the filament to make its resistance increase?

(b) How can you tell from the graph that resistance has changed?

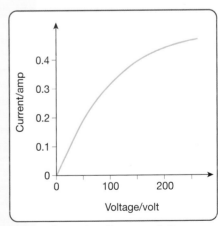

Current–voltage graph for a 100 watt lamp.

3.18 Physical properties

Laying an underground electric cable.

Cables supply us with our electricity. We all want it to be as cheap as possible and as out of sight as possible. So the National Grid Company has to make decisions about what cables to use and whether to put them underground or overhead. The best combinations of materials for underground and overhead cables are not the same.

Density

The density of a metal is an important factor when choosing what to use for overhead power cables. Density is a comparison of the mass and the volume of a substance. Just as for resistance, we make the comparison by dividing:

$$\text{density} = \frac{\text{mass}}{\text{volume}}$$

If cables are made of metal that is very dense, then they could stretch and sag too much under their weight, unless the pylons were very close together.

Aluminium has a low density compared with most other metals. This makes it a good choice for overhead power cables.

1 (a)   Write the formulae for working out resistance and working out density next to each other.

(b)   Discuss and write down the similarities between the formulae.

2 What makes a material expand? What effect does expansion have on density?

Malleability, hardness and strength

The **malleability** of a material describes how easy it is to hammer into shape. Copper, for example, is a malleable metal. Layers of atoms inside it can slide over each other, so that its shape can change.

Hardness is another property of materials. Diamond is very hard. It can scratch other materials, but it is almost impossible to scratch.

You have to be careful about the word **strength**. People use it to mean different things. Here, it means resistance to breaking or snapping when the material is stretched. For a cable, that's obviously important. A cable that snapped and fell from its pylons would be dangerous as well as useless. Steel and rubber are quite strong materials. Glass is not so strong.

3 What are the consequences if a cable breaks:

(a)   overhead   (b)   underground?

3.18 Physical properties

Thermal conductivity

Thermal means 'to do with heat'. Metals have high thermal conductivity – heat can travel through them easily by conduction. The thermal conductivity of a power cable does not normally matter.

Some cables in special applications, such as magnetic brain scanners, need to be kept cool. This means that the circuits have to have thermal insulator around them. A thermal insulator does not let heat travel through it easily.

❹ Cables are heated by the current in them. Why must underground cables NOT be surrounded by thick layers of material with very low thermal conductivity?

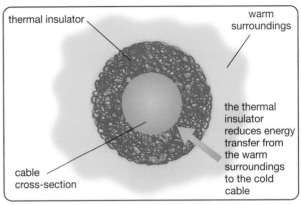

thermal insulator

warm surroundings

the thermal insulator reduces energy transfer from the warm surroundings to the cold cable

cable cross-section

Some cables are surrounded by a thermal insulator.

Other uses of metals

Lead is used as 'flashing' on roofs because it is very malleable to get a waterproof seal.

Copper is used for water tanks and piping because it is easily shaped, corrodes very slowly and is a very good heat conductor.

Composite materials

Some cables have a **composite** structure. They are made of more than one material. By combining two materials to make a composite material, you can often get the benefit of the properties of both. Concrete that is reinforced with steel mesh, for example, does not crack like ordinary concrete. It is not brittle. When it is put together on a building site it can be made into any shape.

Alloys like brass are also composite materials. They are combinations of metals with properties which are different from the properties of the separate metals.

Wood, fibreglass and cling film are other examples of composite materials.

see Polymers, page 214

❺ Do an Internet search on GRP (glass reinforced plastic).

   (a)   Explain why it is a composite material.

   (b)   What individual materials is it made from?

   (c)   What useful properties does the material have and how are these matched to the way we use it?

3.18 Physical properties

It is important to choose the best material for electricity cables.

see Appendix 4, page 315

Choosing the best material ACTIVITY

Working out density

6 Copy the template and replace the **zzzz** to work out the density of water. 1 m³ of water has a mass of 1000 kg.

$$density = \frac{zzzz}{volume}$$

$$density = \frac{1000}{zzzz}$$

$$= zzzz \ zzzz$$

7 Use the same layout to calculate the density of a block of concrete which has volume 2 m³ and mass 5000 kg.

8 The block of concrete is the same all the way through. What is the density of a small piece that breaks off the block?

Comparing copper and aluminium

9 (a) Look up and write down the densities of copper and aluminium.

(b) Look up and write down the resistances of copper wires and aluminium wires, both one metre long and one millimetre in diameter.

(c) Draw bar charts to show the information.

(d) Use the information to explain why copper is better for underground cables and aluminium is better for overhead cables.

Composite structure

Overhead cable has a composite structure. It is made of strands of aluminium and steel.

10 (a) What useful properties does aluminium have for use in electric cables?

(b) Why are the cables not made of aluminium alone?

(c) What useful properties does steel have for use in electric cables?

(d) Why are the cables not made of steel alone?

(e) Why do the cable makers use separate strands of aluminium and steel, rather than melting the materials together to make a new alloy?

Key words

alloy

composites

hardness

malleability

strength

Key facts

Copy and complete the sentences by choosing the correct word from the key words list.

1 The _____ of diamond means it is almost impossible to scratch it.

2 The _____ of copper means that it is easy to bend and shape.

3 Materials made by combining two different materials are called _____. They have different properties from the individual materials they are made from.

4 _____ is a way of describing resistance to breaking.

5 A composite made by mixing two or more metals together is called an _____.

3.18 Physical properties

Planning a new transmission line   **CASE STUDY**

When The National Grid Company installed a new transmission line from Lackenby in Teesside to Shipton in North Yorkshire, they put about six kilometres of the cable under the ground. That was so that it would not spoil views of the countryside. It was an expensive choice, but they would not have been able to obtain planning permission for pylons which could have blocked the view of the Cleveland Hills.

The underground cable has a layered structure. It uses different materials. Each material contributes its useful properties to the composite structure.

11 (a) Why does the National Grid use thick wire?

    (b) Why don't they use even thicker wire?

12 In which case is strength of material more important – for underground cables or overhead cables?

13 Imagine that you have to plan a new transmission line between your home area and a new power station 50 km away.

    (a) Get a map of your region and consider possible routes for the line. What features do you need to avoid? What are the environmental issues?

Underground cable installation costs much more than overhead cable installation.

    (b) Who will want you to make the new line as cheaply as possible? Why?

    (c) Who will want you to make the new line have the lowest possible environmental impact, regardless of cost? Why?

    (d) What route will you decide on? How much will be underground? Produce an illustrated leaflet, using a computer, to explain your decisions.

14 Orange juice cartons have a layered structure, just as underground cables do. They are made of a composite material. The material is mainly cardboard: this is cheap, saves weight, is strong enough for the job and is flexible so it is easily folded into shape. On the inside, there is a layer of poly(ethene) film for water-proofing. Aluminium foil between the cardboard and the poly(ethene) stops oxygen diffusing through and so helps to keep the drink fresh.

    (a) Draw a labelled diagram of the layers of material used for making the cartons. Your labels should say what properties each individual material contributes to the carton.

    (b) Explain why the three layers must be in the right order.

    (c) Compare the carton to underground cable. Which layers have similar roles?

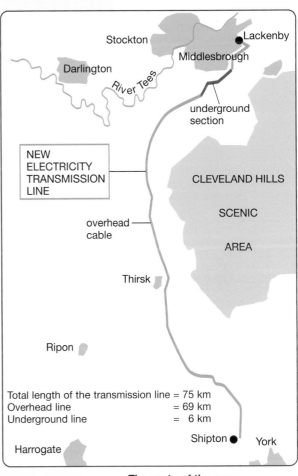

Total length of the transmission line = 75 km
Overhead line = 69 km
Underground line = 6 km

The route of the new transmission line.

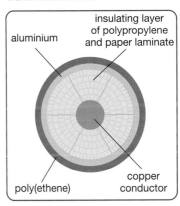

A cross–section of the underground cable.

Review questions

1 Diamonds consist of a *giant structure of covalently bonded* carbon atoms.

   (a) Explain what the words 'giant structure' and 'covalently bonded' mean.   *[3]*

   (b) Use ideas about giant structures to explain why:

      (i) diamonds are very hard;   *[2]*

      (ii) diamonds have a very high melting point.   *[1]*

2 A craft supplier sells clay for making pots. She sells her clay to schools and to people who make small items as a hobby. There is a choice of 'ordinary' clay which must be fired and 'air dry' clay which is designed to harden permanently by drying at room temperature.

Fresh clay (must be fired)	125 kg	£9.99
'Air dry' clay	1 kg	£4.99

   (a) Do a calculation to compare the prices of the types of clay.   *[2]*

   (b) Which type of customer will buy each type? Explain your answer.   *[2]*

   (c) Make an information leaflet for the craft supplier to give to customers. You need to explain to the customers why jugs and bowls made from ordinary clay must be fired before they can be used.   *[3]*

3 (a) Describe a practical situation in which the resistance of wire affects operating costs.   *[2]*

   (b) Copy and complete the template to work out the resistance of a wire that has a current of 4.6 ampere when the voltage is 230 volts:

$$\text{resistance} = \frac{\text{voltage}}{\text{zzzz}}$$

$$= \frac{\text{zzzz}}{4.6}$$

$$= 50 \text{ zzzz} \qquad [3]$$

4 The resistance of a lamp filament is much higher when it is hot than when it is cool.

   (a) Why must the filament be very hot for the lamp to work?   *[1]*

   (b) Sketch a graph of voltage against current, with the input variable on the horizontal axis, to show the effect of the heating of the filament.   *[3]*

   (c) Add a line to show what the graph would look like if the resistance stayed the same.   *[1]*

5 (a) This is a table of measurements for some samples of a metal alloy that is to be used to make a bicycle.

Sample	1	2	3	4
Mass/g	120	480	1000	3600
Volume/cm³	25	100	208	750
Density/g cm⁻³				

Copy and complete the table, using a calculator as necessary. What do you notice about the densities of the samples?   *[6]*

   (b) Name another property of the metal alloy, other than its density, which will be important to the bicycle designers.   *[1]*

4 Energy and devices

Contents

Practical activities linked to this section:

Energy transfers

Investigating electricity generation

Use the following to check your progress.

Unit 2

You will:

- describe the benefits and problems of different energy resources (including fossil fuels, nuclear fuels and renewables)
  see pages 228–233, 238–243 ➡

- explain how energy can be transferred from system to system and how it becomes spread out and less useful
  see pages 228–233, 252 ➡

- calculate efficiency of practical energy transfer processes
  see pages 228–233 ➡

- identify the stages in generating electricity in a power station
  see pages 228–233 ➡

- know the properties of X-rays
  see pages 234–238 ➡

- know the properties of nuclear radiation to include alpha, beta and gamma radiation
  see pages 235–238 ➡

- understand the dangers associated with high energy radiation
  see pages 234–238 ➡

- compare the benefits and costs of different energy resources for different practical uses
  see pages 238–243, 251 ➡

- explain the economic and environmental reasons for limiting use of energy resources and the importance of high efficiency devices
  see pages 238–243 ➡

- observe, investigate and describe the processes of thermal energy transfer (conduction, convection and radiation)
  see pages 248–251 ➡

- describe how heat exchangers are used
  see pages 252–256 ➡

- investigate the desirable properties of coolant materials, including heat capacity
  see pages 252–256 ➡

- calculate the power of an electric appliance from its operating voltage and current
  see pages 244–247 ➡

- use the power rating of an appliance to calculate the energy consumed in a given amount of time
  see pages 244–247 ➡

- compare costs of operating different appliances
  see pages 244–247 ➡

- know what affects breaking distance and thinking distance when a car stops
  see pages 256–260 ➡

- know how to calculate speed and acceleration
  see pages 256–260 ➡

- be able to discuss how tests on cars and drivers improve road safety.
  see pages 256–260 ➡

4.1 Fuels and generators

Keeping warm in Stanhope Street

People on the Stanhope Street estate in Newcastle like warm homes and the convenience of electricity, just like the rest of us. They get electricity from their own Combined Heat and Power unit, which is a small gas-fuelled **generator**.

Just as in bigger power stations, their generator spins at high speed and generates electric current. The difference is that, at Stanhope Street, they make use of the 'waste' heat that the hot gas and spinning generator provide.

Stanhope Street, Newcastle – where efficiency means cheaper warmth.

Word check

A **generator** uses a spinning coil and a magnetic field to generate electricity.

Word check

Fossil fuels are materials from living things which stored energy from sunlight a very long time ago. Now we find them, as coal, oil or gas, underground.

A large conventional power station uses fuel burning in huge boilers to heat water and create hot steam. The steam blasts onto the blades of **turbines** to make the generators turn.

Word check

A **turbine** is a machine that turns when a gas or liquid strikes its blades.

Energy for generating electricity

Most large power stations use jets of very hot steam to produce the spin for generating electricity. **Fossil fuels** – coal, oil and gas – and nuclear fuels are the primary energy resources that most of them use for heating the water.

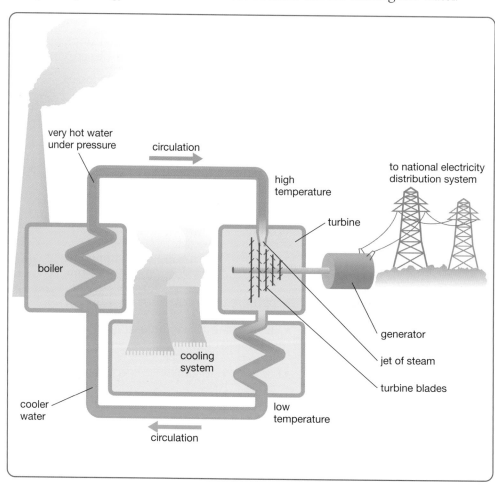

4.1 Fuels and generators

Burning fuels

Fossil fuels burn with the oxygen from air to release their energy. This produces waste products, including carbon dioxide.

fossil fuel + oxygen → carbon dioxide + water

It is a chemical reaction that releases energy.

Some problems with burning fossil fuels are:

- Carbon dioxide is a greenhouse gas. It contributes to global climate change.

- We are bound to run out of fossil fuels sooner or later. When we take them out of the ground, we have no way of replacing them. They are **non-renewable** energy resources.

1 What are the environmental problems of burning fossil fuels?

2 What will happen to the price of oil as the world starts to run out of it?

Drawing the energy inputs and outputs

We can draw Sankey diagrams to help us to compare the energy input of a system, like a power station, with the different forms of energy output it provides. A Sankey diagram is a type of flow diagram. The width of the left-hand side of the diagram represents the energy input. The widths of the arrows at the right-hand side represent the proportions of different forms of energy output.

Energy that is being transferred always tends to heat the surroundings. Energy spreads into the surroundings, but the temperature rise of the surroundings is usually quite small. The energy is then no longer of any use to us. We say that the energy has **dissipated**.

Word check

Energy is **dissipated** when it is transferred into the surroundings of systems, warming the surroundings so that the energy is no longer of practical use to us.

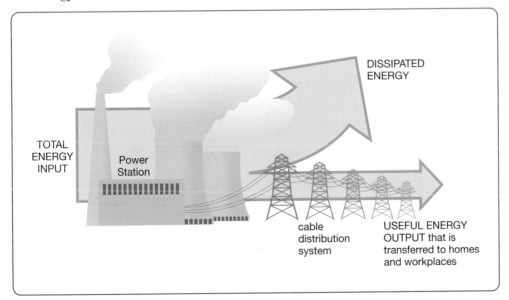

A Sankey diagram for a power station and cable distribution system. Only about a third of the energy input is transferred to useful energy output.

3 What happens to all of the energy you take in each day, stored in your food?

4.1 Fuels and generators

Large and small power stations

Large power stations could be more efficient if we could make more use of their waste energy for heating homes and workplaces. But large power stations are usually a long way from where people live and work. In the process of transferring heat energy from the power station to where it is wanted, the energy would dissipate.

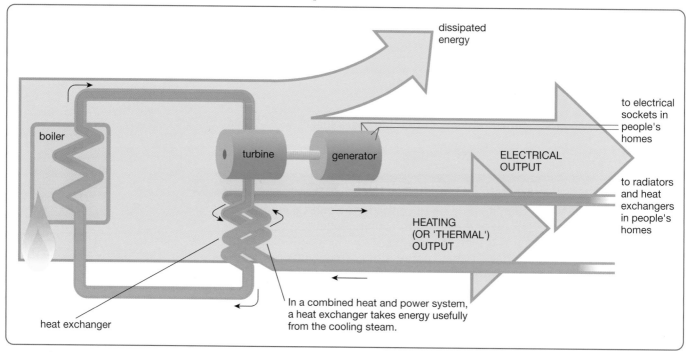

A Sankey diagram for a combined heat and power (CHP) system.

Small power units, like the Stanhope Street system, can be installed right where people are. They make use of their waste heat.

Combined heat and power systems like the one at Stanhope Street transfer a large proportion of the available energy in a useful way. They make use of energy that they take from the steam as it cools. They don't allow that energy to simply dissipate. In other words, they're efficient.

Measuring efficiency

Efficiency is a quantity. It's a way of comparing the energy that's supplied to a system, from fuel or whatever, to the useful energy that we get out of it. We can write it like this:

$$\text{efficiency} = \frac{\text{useful energy transferred by a system}}{\text{total energy supplied to the system}} \times 100 \text{ per cent}$$

...or like this:

$$\text{efficiency} = \frac{\text{useful energy output}}{\text{total energy input}} \times 100 \text{ per cent}$$

If the useful energy that we get out of a system could always be the same as the energy we put in, then we'd all be very happy. Efficiency would be a perfect 100 per cent. Our fuel bills would be much smaller than they are.

4.1 Fuels and generators

4 A working electric motor gets hot.

(a) What happens to the heat energy?

(b) Is the heat energy useful?

(c) Explain why the efficiency of the motor is less than 100 per cent.

5 (a) What provides the energy input of a large power station?

(b) What form does the useful energy output take?

(c) Why is the useful energy output smaller than the energy input?

6 A light bulb might have an energy input of 100 joules in each second. The energy output in the form of light, in the same time, might be only two joules.

(a) Is the efficiency big or small?

(b) Copy this template and replace the zzz to work out the efficiency:

$$\text{efficiency} = \frac{\text{useful energy output}}{\text{zzz}} \times 100 \text{ per cent}$$

$$= \frac{2}{\text{zzz}} \times 100 \text{ per cent}$$

$$= \text{zzz per cent}$$

Key facts

Copy and complete the sentences by choosing the correct word from the key words list. Each word may be used more than once.

1 _____ _____ are the remains of plants and animals that lived a very long time ago. We can find them under the ground but the supply is limited and sooner or later we will run out of them. They are _____ energy resources.

2 Most power stations use _____ _____ as their energy resource. The fuels burn to heat water. Hot steam turns the_____. These are connected to _____ which use spinning coils and magnetic fields to create electric current.

3 Energy spreads out from a power station and _____ so that it is no longer useful. For example, it _____ from the cooling towers and heat is wasted.

4 A combined heat and power system makes use of this waste energy for heating homes and other places. This means that the system has a higher _____ than a large power station.

Key words

dissipates

efficiency

fossil fuels

generators

non-renewables

turbine

4.1 Fuels and generators

Fossil fuels and power stations   ACTIVITY

Fossil fuels on the web

Use 'climate change' as search words and do an Internet search to find out about the link between climate change and fossil fuels. Choose some informative text and images very carefully. Make sure that you understand them. Make sure that the information is useful to you. Print them out and add them to your work.

Add notes on:

• who produced the website and its information;

• why they did it.

Fossil fuel data

Discuss the data and give your own answers to the questions.

The bar chart shows how long the world's known reserves of fossil fuels in the ground will last at the present rate of use.

The graph below shows the rate of oil production between 1930 and 2000.

7 What will happen to known reserves of fossil fuels if we don't find new reserves?

8 Energy companies search the world for fossil fuels under the ground. What effect does this have on known reserves if new sources are found?

9 Use the graph to predict whether we are likely to continue to use fossil fuels at the present rate.

10 What factors could make us increase the rate at which we use fossil fuels?

11 What factors could make us decrease the rate at which we use fossil fuels?

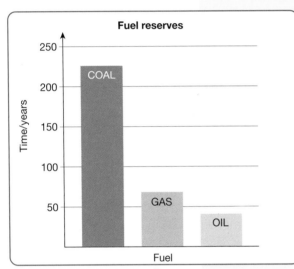

Time is running out for fossil fuel reserves.

Power station efficiency

A large power station releases 5000 megajoules (MJ) of energy from fuel every second. Its output of electrical energy is about 2000 MJ.

12 (a) Write down the formula for working out efficiency.

(b) Write it down again, but substitute the numbers 5000 and 2000 for the correct words.

(c) Do the division calculation to find out the efficiency of the power station and write it down.

(d) How much heat energy is transferred from the power station to its surroundings every second?

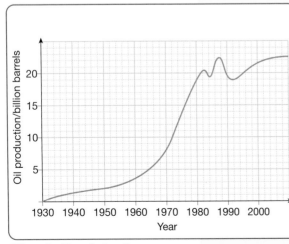

Oil production during the last century.

4.1 Fuels and generators

Stanhope Street gets warmer CASE STUDY

Stanhope Street estate is 30 years old and the energy system in the flats was showing its age. Each flat had electric storage heaters, which heated up overnight using lower price energy. The heaters gave out heat to the rooms during the day. But residents often had to use extra heating, which they struggled to pay for.

So the North British Housing Association, who own and manage the estate, decided to introduce a combined heat and power system. They installed a CHP (Combined Heat and Power) unit powered by gas and capable of generating electricity at a rate of 300 kilojoules each second. Residents get their electrical energy from the CHP unit and not from an outside electricity company. It also supplies 500 kilojoules of heating every second, using a system of hot water pipes. Each flat has radiators that residents can fully control with thermostats and heat exchangers to heat water. Total energy demand on the estate is down by 64 per cent and, as one resident said, 'Our homes are now much more cosy.'

13 Does the Stanhope Street CHP system use fossil fuel or other fuel? Is it renewable or non-renewable? What gas does it produce that contributes to climate change?

14 (a) Make a short list or a table to show how the Stanhope Street CHP system is similar to a large power station.

(b) How is it different?

(c) Explain as fully as you can why a CHP system is more efficient than a large power station.

15 (a) What is a storage heater?

(b) Why is it cheaper than an ordinary electric fire?

(c) Suggest why the storage heaters were unpopular with Stanhope Street residents.

16 Imagine if the Stanhope Street system has a maximum efficiency of 80 per cent. Draw a Sankey diagram to show the energy transfers.

17 (a) Imagine you are carrying out a practical investigation to compare heat loss of 0.5 kg of water in one large container and 0.5 kg of water in several small containers. In which case would you expect the energy to dissipate faster?

(b) How does this investigation relate to big power stations and smaller systems like the one at Stanhope Street?

project profile
COMMUNITY HEATING

Newcastle Stanhope Street

CHP and community heating bring total energy to housing association

Due to its poor energy rating, Stanhope Street became a priority estate and, in 1992, the Association decided to refurbish it.

Adding community heating

The Association received funding from the EU THERMIE programme to demonstrate the reductions in both energy costs and carbon dioxide emissions made possible by adopting a total energy approach.

This involved the use of a total energy design originally developed in Denmark and which called for the

- low energy design takes estate close to self-sufficiency in energy
- 64% reduction in energy use on the estate
- £5,500 total cost per dwelling (homes refurbishment and community heating)

Estate profile

The North British Housing Association's Stanhope Street estate comprises 351 rented flats and maisonettes for people on low incomes in the west end of Newcastle-upon-Tyne.

The mainly five-storey estate was built in 1974. Prior to refurbishment, it was found to have a very low home energy rating of 3.8 out of a range of 1 to 10. The buildings had very poor thermal insulation quality with no wall insulation and single glazed windows which were not air-tight. Residents suffered from cold draughts and condensation.

Homes were fitted with electric storage heating systems which were difficult to control, expensive and unpopular. Many residents supplemented the heating with expensive daytime electricity and struggled to meet their heating costs.

As part of its commitment to the environment and to reducing tenant's fuel costs, the Association developed a policy of improving the energy efficiency of its housing stock.

installation of new low energy windows, extra thermal insulation and new doors to reduce heating demand. The generation and distribution of heat and power on-site could then be optimised by the use of a new community heating system based on combined heat and power (CHP).

Site work began in 1993. The new energy system, designed by consultant Merz Orchard, comprises a gas-fired CHP unit and a condensing boiler to supply a new community heating system. The CHP unit generates 500 kW of heat and 300 kW of electricity.

A 40 cubic metre hot water storage tank allows the CHP unit to run at maximum output during the day to charge the thermal store, avoiding the use of boilers at night. The whole system is controlled by a building energy management system.

The community heating system makes extensive use of pre-insulated polyethylene pipe, both above and below ground, to distribute heat to individual homes with maximum reliability.

4.2 Looking inside the body

X-rays

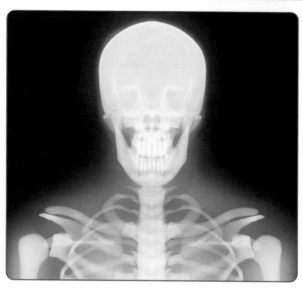

X-rays let us see inside the body without cutting it open.

When we are ill, doctors are sometimes uncertain about what exactly is wrong with us. One way to find out would be to cut us open and have a look at what is going on inside the body. However, this would be a very painful and potentially dangerous experience. Fortunately, there is another way – X-rays.

How do X-rays work?

X-rays pass through soft tissue much more easily than dense tissue such as bone. A sheet of photographic film is placed behind the patient and the X-rays that pass through cause the film to be exposed and turn black. This means that when an X-ray is taken, we get a picture where all the dense tissue shows up as white and the soft tissue as black.

X-rays can be dangerous

Unfortunately, X-rays also transfer a lot of energy. Being exposed to too many X-rays in a short space of time could seriously damage our bodies. When X-rays pass through our body, they cause damage by knocking electrons off atoms. This is called **ionization**.

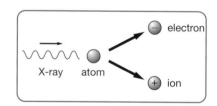

Fortunately, when we are in hospital or at the dentists and have an X-ray taken, the radiographer makes sure that we are exposed to as few X-rays as possible. The machines are also very efficient and can work using very low doses.

1. List one advantage and one disadvantage of using X-rays.

2. Explain why hard tissue, such as bone, shows up white on an X-ray picture.

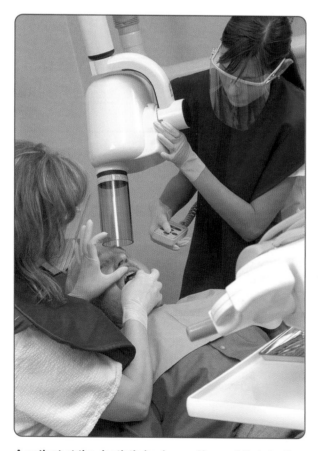

A patient at the dentist's having an X-ray of their teeth.

4.2 Looking inside the body

Radiation is all around us

Where does radiation come from?

Although we may only have two or three medical X-rays taken during our lifetime, we are exposed to background **radiation** all of the time. This background radiation has many different sources.

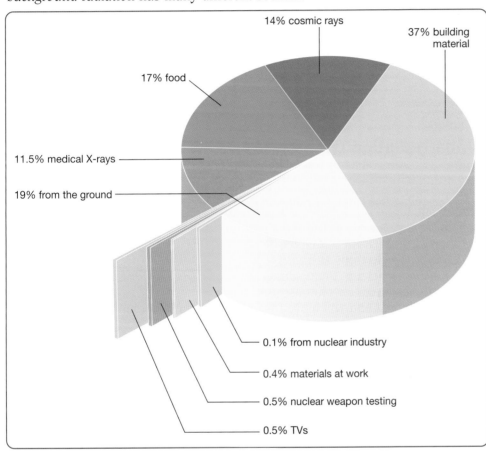

14% cosmic rays

37% building material

17% food

11.5% medical X-rays

19% from the ground

0.1% from nuclear industry

0.4% materials at work

0.5% nuclear weapon testing

0.5% TVs

Background radiation comes from many different sources.

Interesting facts about background radiation

The human body is exposed to:

- 500 000 cosmic rays from space every hour;

- 200 000 000 gamma rays from building materials every hour.

Fortunately, most of these rays pass straight through our bodies without hitting any atoms and doing any harm. The cells of our body are also very good at repairing any damage caused by the rays.

3 Where does most of the background radiation come from?

4 How much more radiation do we get from the nuclear industry compared to the radiation we get from watching our television?

5 Do we get more radiation from our food or from medical X-rays?

6 Explain why we should not be worried about all the background radiation that we receive.

4.2 Looking inside the body

Different types of nuclear radiation

Nuclear radiation is produced by the nucleus of an atom. Some nuclei are unstable and when they break down, they release nuclear radiation. The type of radiation they release depends upon the exact number of different particles in the nucleus.

A nucleus is made up of two types of particle, protons and neutrons.

Key
proton ○
neutron ○

There are three main types of nuclear radiation.

Alpha radiation α

Alpha radiation is made from particles. Each particle consists of two neutrons and two protons. Because it is relatively large, it soon comes to a stop as it crashes into other atoms and ionizes them. It then combines with two of the electrons and turns into an atom of helium. Because the alpha particles have two protons, it is positively charged and will move towards the negative in an electric field.

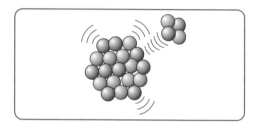

Beta radiation β

Beta radiation is also a particle. This time it is a much smaller particle called an electron. Because it is smaller, it is much less likely to smash into other atoms and therefore it travels further than alpha radiation. When it does hit a nucleus, it also creates ions.

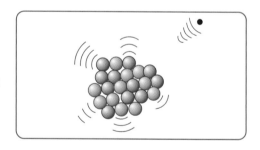

Beta particles are negatively charged and will therefore move towards the positive in an electric field.

Gamma radiation γ

Gamma radiation does not consist of particles at all. It is an electromagnetic wave. It has no charge and can pass straight through many materials. It can cause damage deep inside the body.

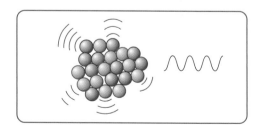

7 Explain why alpha radiation does not travel very far.

8 Explain why gamma radiation can pass straight through many materials.

4.2 Looking inside the body

Radiographer

CASE STUDY

Radiographers work in hospital X-ray departments. They take X-ray pictures of patients.

Because the radiographer takes many X-ray pictures every day, it is important to ensure that they are not exposed to too many X-rays. When the X-ray is being taken, the radiographer stands behind a lead glass screen that will stop any X-rays getting through.

The radiographer also wears a badge that registers any exposure to X-rays. The badge also tells the radiographer if they have received too large a dose of X-rays.

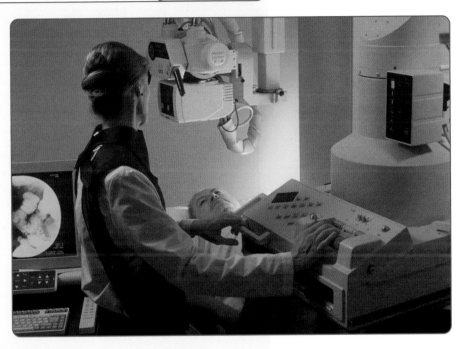

Radiation badges

A simple radiation badge can be used to detect different kinds of radiation. It consists of a plastic case that encloses a piece of photographic film. The film is covered by layers of black paper, aluminium foil and lead sheet. Black paper will stop most alpha particles. Aluminium foil will stop most beta particles. Lead sheet will stop most gamma rays.

When the film is developed, it shows how much radiation the wearer of the badge has received.

9 Which of the materials in front of the film will let through X-rays, beta particles and gamma rays?

10 If the radiographer is exposed to X-rays, which part of the photographic film will turn the darkest colour?

Key facts

Copy and complete the sentences by choosing the correct word from the key words list.

1 _____ can be used to see what is going on inside the body.

2 Alpha, beta and gamma are all types of nuclear _____.

3 Unlike alpha and beta radiation, _____ radiation does not consist of particles.

4 _____ particles consist of two protons and two neutrons.

5 _____ particles consist of an electron.

Key words

alpha

beta

gamma

radiation

X-rays

4.3 Nuclear and renewables

Students saving the planet

Fossil fuels have a limited future. Students of agriculture at Park Lane College in Yorkshire are thinking ahead and working with renewable energy resources.

Why do we need alternatives to fossil fuels?

- The burning of fossil fuels releases carbon dioxide (CO_2) into the atmosphere. This is changing the balance of the atmosphere all around the world ('global warming'). We do not know how much it will affect the climate.

- Burning fossil fuels produces other kinds of pollution, such as sulphur dioxide, which causes acid rain.

- Fossil fuels are non-renewable.

- It is a bad idea to depend on only one sort of energy resource. For example, in times of war or international trading or shipping problems, oil and coal could become hard to import.

The nuclear alternative

Nuclear fuel, uranium, is found under the ground and is also non-renewable. Uranium is a metal. Uranium atoms have very large nuclei and some of them can be made to break into two smaller ones. This splitting of a nucleus is called **fission**. It releases energy.

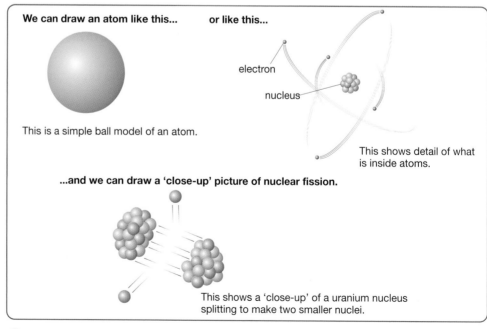

We can draw an atom like this...   or like this...

electron

nucleus

This is a simple ball model of an atom.

This shows detail of what is inside atoms.

...and we can draw a 'close-up' picture of nuclear fission.

This shows a 'close-up' of a uranium nucleus splitting to make two smaller nuclei.

Nuclear fission.

❶ A student writes, 'A nucleus is just one small part of an atom.' Discuss this. Do you agree with the student? What are the other parts of an atom?

4.3 Nuclear and renewables

Radioactive problems

In a nuclear power station, nuclei of uranium split into smaller nuclei of other substances. These new nuclei are almost always unstable. That is, each nucleus can change suddenly. When it does, it emits (gives out) radiation. We say that the new substances and their nuclei are **radioactive**.

We can detect the radioactivity of these substances because their radiation causes **ionisation** of the material it travels through.

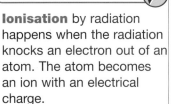

Word check

Ionisation by radiation happens when the radiation knocks an electron out of an atom. The atom becomes an ion with an electrical charge.

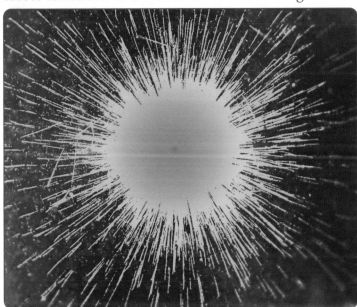

Ionising radiation can be detected by photographic film. The yellow lines show the tracks of radiation emitted by a tiny piece of a radioactive salt. The radiation ionises atoms in the photographic emulsion.

We all have natural radioactive material in our bodies and all around us. Ionisation is happening in your body all the time, but it can be harmful to the chemical reactions in the cells of your body. The more intense the ionising radiation is, the more damage it can do to your body chemistry. So we avoid exposure to it when we can.

2 Imagine that you have to talk to a group of Year 7 students about nuclear power and radiation. Your first job might be to explain the difference between nuclear fission and radioactivity. In a group, decide the points needed to produce a suitable explanation.

High level nuclear waste

The substances made in power stations by fission of uranium are **high level nuclear waste**. This radioactive waste material is hot. It has to be stored in large cooling ponds, so that the energy can dissipate. The intensity of radiation from the waste decreases very slowly. After several years, it no longer has to be stored under water. But that is not the end of the problem.

The waste carries on emitting radiation that is harmful to living things for many thousands of years. One solution might be to put the waste inside glass blocks so that it can't be washed away and then bury the glass blocks deep underground. But so far, nobody has decided what to do with it. It is all sitting in storage, waiting for some future answer.

3 Make a list or a table of the problems of using fossil fuels and using nuclear fuel. Which do you think has the worse problems?

4.3 Nuclear and renewables

Types of renewable

Renewable energy resources don't produce carbon dioxide or radioactive waste. They will never run out. But do they have problems of their own?

Wind

A wind farm.

Most renewable energy resources are created by the heat of the sun. It causes temperature and air pressure differences in the atmosphere which make winds blow. Wind can turn a wind turbine, which then turns a generator to make electricity.

The power output of wind turbines depends on how strong the wind is, so they don't give a continuous energy supply. A single wind generator has a fairly low power output, typically 20 kilowatts (kW). To create a bigger energy resource, they are often built in large numbers on 'wind farms'. Some people object to wind farms because they can spoil beautiful countryside and cause 'noise pollution'.

Waves

Wind blowing across the sea creates waves, which can travel long distances. Waves carry energy and the energy can be taken from them and used to turn turbines.

Conditions at sea are very variable. It can be very calm and then wave generators don't provide much electrical power. It can also be stormy. Storms can destroy wave generators.

Hydroelectric schemes

The sun's energy evaporates water. The water then falls as rain over land. The water flows downhill, back to the sea. We can dam rivers for hydroelectric energy. Water moving from the higher level above the dam to a lower level drives turbines.

A hydroelectric power station can provide a steady electrical supply. Large systems can have high power, but they are expensive to build and the new lakes behind the dams flood large valleys. People may be forced to leave their homes and the habitats of plants and animals can be destroyed.

This array of solar panels is used to generate electricity.

Solar

The direct light of the sun creates electric voltage in solar panels. The energy can be stored by batteries. Small solar panels are portable, so they are useful in places where there is no connection with an electrical mains system.

Solar panels are quite expensive, but they are getting cheaper and being used more and more. They work better in places with reliable sunshine, so they are not as useful in the UK as in many other countries. And, of course, they don't work at night.

4.3 Nuclear and renewables

Biomass

If trees are replanted to replace the ones that are chopped down, then timber is a renewable energy resource. Although it's burned, the new growing trees trap as much carbon dioxide from the air as the burning logs release. Energy resources from living things are called biomass energy resources.

In many parts of the world where there are growing populations, forests have been cut down and not replaced. There is less biomass energy resource available than there used to be.

Tidal

The tidal barrage across the Rance estuary in France. Water flowing through the 24 turbines in the barrier generates enough electricity for 300 000 homes.

Tidal energy is not produced by the heat of the sun, but by gravity. The moon's gravity is strong enough to pull on the Earth's waters to create higher water level in some places than others.

Tidal barrages can be built across estuaries. They can produce high power, though only for about 12 hours each day when the tide is rising or falling fast enough. They have a big impact on coastlines. They change and even destroy the habitats of many plants and animals.

4 Which of the energy resources depend on day-to-day weather conditions?

5 Why don't we make more use of:

(a) wave energy resources?

(b) solar energy resources?

(c) tidal energy resources?

4.3 Nuclear and renewables

Energy decisions   ACTIVITY

Nuclear know-how
Look at the Nirex website (do a UK search on 'Nirex'). What is the job of Nirex? Who pays for them to do their job? What are they doing about high level nuclear waste?

Assessing renewables
You could work in pairs on this to share the work and produce high quality results.

Use information from websites and the text in this topic. Use a full page, or an A3 sheet, to make a table like the one below and fill in the missing information. Illustrate your sheet.

Renewable resource	Reliability	Environmental effects
Wind	Poor – rate of generation depends on strength of wind	Low, but many people think that the generators spoil beautiful views. Can be used at sea where this does not matter so much.
Wave		
Hydroelectric		
Solar		
Biomass		
Tidal		

For your website research, use these search words:

wind energy   wave energy   hydroelectric

solar energy   biomass   tidal energy

Present your views
In small groups or in the class group, discuss the following:

• Should oil and petrol be cheaper as many people claim? Or should we reduce use of fossil fuels as much as possible?

• Could we manage with less energy? Or should we replace existing energy resources with renewables?

• What do politicians say? What do business-people say? What are your own views?

Create a large poster to promote your views about future energy policy.

4.3 Nuclear and renewables

Renewable education

CASE STUDY

Staff and students at Park Lane College in Leeds have installed their own 2.5 kW wind turbine. The students are learning about subjects ranging from Horticulture to Environmental Studies. They use computers to monitor the turbine's output. The electricity they generate heats their greenhouses and other buildings. When they have energy to spare, they sell it to the local electricity company.

Staff and students at Park Lane College have their own wind generator. They can use it to gain direct experience of working with renewable energy.

6 How could your school make more use of renewable energy resources?

7 Create a bullet-point list that you could present to your headteacher to try to persuade her or him to make more use of renewable energy resources.

8 What objections would you expect your headteacher to make to your ideas?

Key facts

Copy and complete the sentences by choosing the correct word from the key words list. Each word may be used more than once.

1 Wind, waves, hydroelectricity, tidal power and solar power are all _____ energy resources.

2 Nuclear energy uses uranium and it is non-renewable. _____ is the splitting of a nucleus, such as a uranium nucleus, to release energy.

3 _____ of a nucleus makes two smaller nuclei. They are usually _____.

4 Radiation from radioactive substances causes _____ in all kinds of other material, including the human body.

5 Used nuclear fuel still contains some uranium. It also contains the radioactive substances that have been made by _____ of the uranium. So far, nobody has solved the problem of what to do with this _____ _____ _____.

Key words

fission

high level nuclear waste

ionisation

radioactive

renewable

4.4 Lighting power

Light work

When the Thorndale Sculpture Centre needed to improve their gallery, one of the first people they spoke to was Jenni Phillips. Lighting engineers like Jenni have to combine art with science and good economics, and make the right choices.

Efficiency and choice of lamp

Filament lamps provide much more heat than light. They can even be a fire hazard in Jenni's work. They waste a lot of energy. They have very low efficiency – only about 2 per cent.

For every **joule** (J) of input energy from the electricity supply, a filament lamp transfers 0.98 J by heating and only 0.02 J in providing light.

Fluorescent lamps don't get as hot as filament lamps. They have higher efficiency – about 20 per cent. For every joule of input energy, they transfer 0.20 J in providing light. For people who want to avoid unwanted heating and save money, they are a better choice even though each one costs more to buy.

> **Word check**
>
> The **joule** is the unit of energy in the international system of units. Its symbol is J.

A fluorescent 'long life' lamp is more efficient than a filament lamp.

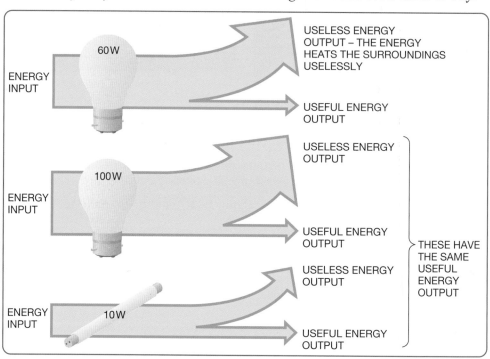

Sankey diagrams for two filament lamps and a fluorescent lamp.

1 What makes filament lamps very inefficient?

2 Use the data above to make a table to compare the performance of filament lamps and fluorescent lamps.

3 Use the Sankey diagrams to identify:

(a) which lamp is least bright;

(b) which lamp wastes energy most quickly;

(c) which lamp is most efficient.

4.4 Lighting power

Power

A 100-**watt** filament lamp is brighter than a 60-watt filament lamp because it transfers energy faster. It has higher **power**.

watt and kilowatt

If power is more than 1000 watts then it's usually easier to measure it in kilowatts. A kilowatt is 1000 watts. If we use W for watt and kW for kilowatt, then:

$$1000\,W = 1\,kW$$
$$1500\,W = 1.5\,kW$$

and so on.

❹ Copy and fill in the gaps:

1 kilowatt	=	_____ watt
2.5 kilowatt	=	_____ watt

Power work-out

There is a formula for working out power from current and voltage:

power   =   voltage × current
(watt)   (volt)   (ampere)

If current is in ampere and voltage in volt then the power will be in watts. These units all work together in an international system.

The electrical supply in your home has a voltage of 230 volts. But not all the appliances and devices use the same current. A kettle has high power and high current. A 60-watt lamp carries just a small current through it.

> **Word check** ✓
>
> **Power** is a measure of the rate of transfer of energy.

> **Word check** ✓
>
> The **watt** (symbol W) is the unit of power in the international system of units. 1 watt is the same as a rate of energy transfer at 1 joule per second.

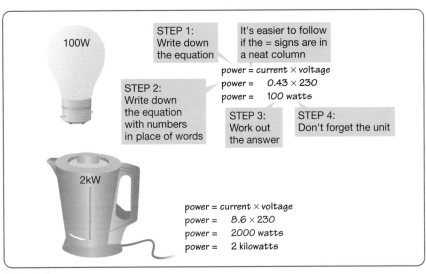

STEP 1: Write down the equation

It's easier to follow if the = signs are in a neat column

STEP 2: Write down the equation with numbers in place of words

power = current × voltage
power =   0.43 × 230
power =   100 watts

STEP 3: Work out the answer

STEP 4: Don't forget the unit

power = current × voltage
power =   8.6 × 230
power =   2000 watts
power =   2 kilowatts

Calculating power.

Counting the costs

Electricity companies charge us for the amount of energy we transfer. They can't use the joule for their unit of energy because one joule is a very small amount of energy. They could use the megajoule, but instead they use their own unit which is easier to work with. It's called the **kilowatt-hour**.

The amount of energy an appliance transfers depends on how long it runs for and its power. We can work out the energy by multiplication:

energy transferred   =   power   ×   time
(kilowatt-hour, kWh)   (kilowatt, kW)   (hour, h)

> **Word check** ✓
>
> The **kilowatt-hour** (kWh) is a unit of energy. It is the amount of energy that a one-kilowatt appliance transfers in one hour.

● How much energy will be transferred by:

(a)   a two-kilowatt appliance in one hour?

(b)   a one-kilowatt appliance in two hours?

(c)   a two-kilowatt appliance in two hours?

4.4 Lighting power

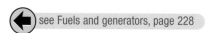
see Fuels and generators, page 228

The cost of lighting
ACTIVITY

Lamp efficiencies

A ten-watt fluorescent lamp is just as bright as a 100-watt filament lamp. It wastes less energy. It is more efficient.

6 Draw a table to sort these into units of energy and units of power:

> joule   watt   kilowatt   kilowatt-hour

7 What is the difference between energy and power? [Hint: Look at the word check box for power on page 245.]

8 Ten-watt (W) is the same as ten joules per second ($J\,s^{-1}$). What is 100 W in $J\,s^{-1}$?

9 The fluorescent lamp provides 10 J of lighting for every 50 J of total energy input from the electricity supply. Replace the zzz to work out the lamp efficiency.

$$\text{efficiency} = \frac{\text{useful energy output}}{zzz} \times 100$$

$$= \frac{zzz}{50} \times 100$$

$$= zzz \text{ per cent}$$

Cost calculations

The price of one kilowatt-hour of electrical energy is about 8p. To work out the actual cost, multiply this price by the number of kilowatt-hours used:

> cost   =   energy in kilowatt-hours × 8p

10 Use data in the diagram on page 245 to work out:

(a)   the energy that the kettle transfers in

(i)   1 hour   (ii)   6 minutes (0.1 hour)   (iii)   10 hours in a week

(Use energy in kilowatt-hours = power in kilowatts × time in hours.)

(b)   the cost of running the kettle for

(i)   1 hour   (ii)   6 minutes (0.1 hour)   (iii)   10 hours in a week

(c)   Repeat the calculations for the lamp.

4.4 Lighting power

Lighting the gallery

'I like talking,' says Jenni Phillips. 'Which is just as well, because every job starts and finishes with discussion with my clients. And every job is different.'

Jenni is a lighting engineer who works with galleries, museums and visitor centres. They are very demanding clients. Jenni has a lot to think about, all at once.

'The most important thing is to make sure that each display fits in with all the others, so that everything is in harmony,' she says. 'Then the lighting needs to be fitted into the display area so that it illuminates the display but doesn't distract the eye. And there are technical questions. Filament lamps can cause too much heating and they can distort how colours look. They're cheap to replace but they cost much more to run. This is because of their low efficiency. Gallery managers are always under pressure to save money, so it's not hard to persuade them that fluorescents are better. Fluorescent lamps come in different sizes and shapes, as well.'

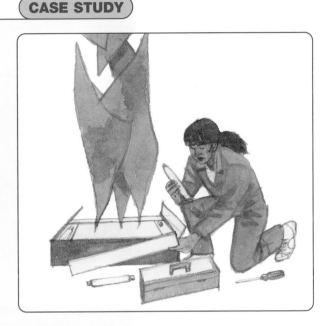

11 Use the text to give TWO reasons why the efficiency of a lamp is important in Jenni's work.

12 What other factors matter a lot when she is choosing lamps?

13 The Thorndale gallery has lighting with a total power input of 4000 W.

(a) How many joules of electrical energy does the system transfer every second?
[Remember, 1 W is the same as 1 J s^{-1}.]

(b) What is the total power input in kilowatt?

(c) How many kilowatt-hours of electrical energy does the system transfer every hour?
[Remember, energy in kilowatt-hours = power in kilowatt × time in hours.]

(d) What is the cost of running the system for one hour if the energy costs 8p per kilowatt-hour?

(e) What is the cost of running the system for a week if the gallery is open for 80 hours?

Key facts

Copy and complete the sentences by choosing the correct word from the key words list.

1 The _____ and the kilowatt-hour are units of energy.

2 The _____ is the amount of energy that a one-kilowatt appliance transfers in one hour.

3 The _____ is a unit of power.

4 To work out the amount of energy transferred by an appliance, we multiply its _____ in kilowatts by the time in hours.

Key words

joule

kilowatt-hour

power

watt

4.5 Heating for profit

Hot potatoes

King Edward potato ovens.

King Edward potato ovens provide tempting views of ready-to-eat potatoes, and they're built to be efficient.

The ovens are designed for stand-alone use in large and small food outlets, so they just plug in to a standard electrical socket. The designers could have decided to use gas. But many places don't have a pipeline connection to the mains supply of natural gas. Bottled gas is bulky to transport.

<table>
<tr><td>

Word check ✓

Thermal radiation transfers heat energy in the same way as light travels. It is invisible, though we can sometimes feel it with our skin.

Convection is transfer of energy by flow of material.

Conduction is thermal energy transfer through material from particle to particle.

</td></tr>
</table>

Useful and not so useful energy transfers

Themal radiation, **convection** and **conduction** all help to cook potatoes. That's useful. But they are also the processes by which heat escapes from the oven, which is not useful.

You can't stop heat escaping from an oven completely, but wasted energy means wasted money. So ovens are designed to reduce loss of energy to the room around them. Materials that we use to reduce wasteful heat losses are called **insulating materials** or **thermal insulators**.

Reducing heat escape by radiation
The outer surface of the oven is quite cool so that it does not radiate energy away too strongly. Shiny surfaces emit less radiation than dull, dark ones, but for a potato oven, appearance also matters. The 'traditional' look is worth the extra cost.

The oven wall is filled with a thermal insulator so that the outer surface is much cooler than the inside of the oven.

Reducing heat escape by convection
Air currents would carry energy away from the oven if its outer surface were hot. The surface is quite cool, so the air is not heated strongly.

Reducing heat escape by conduction
The metal walls can conduct heat rapidly but the fibre between the walls is a good thermal insulator.

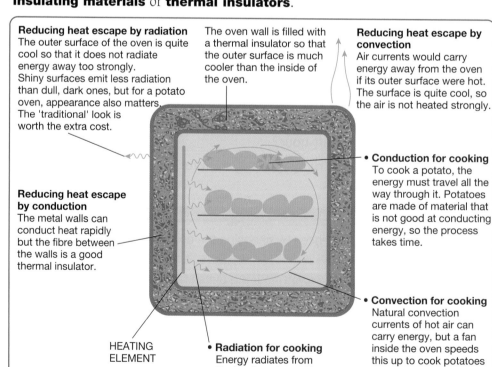

Conduction for cooking
To cook a potato, the energy must travel all the way through it. Potatoes are made of material that is not good at conducting energy, so the process takes time.

Convection for cooking
Natural convection currents of hot air can carry energy, but a fan inside the oven speeds this up to cook potatoes evenly.

HEATING ELEMENT

Radiation for cooking
Energy radiates from the heating element to cook the potatoes.

Thermal energy transfers in the oven.

4.5 Heating for profit

Heat transfer in different kinds of material

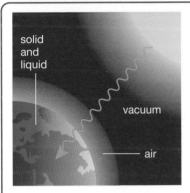

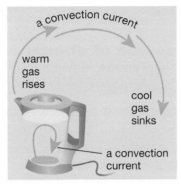

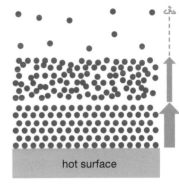

Radiation can transfer energy through air or even through a vacuum. Solids and liquids are not good at letting radiation travel through them. They absorb the energy of the radiation. Radiation from the sun travels through space (a vacuum), through the air (a gas) and is absorbed by the solids and liquids of the Earth's surface.

Convection involves currents of material. If a hot quantity of liquid or gas moves, then it takes its energy with it. Convection is impossible in solids.

In hot material, the particles have more energy so they move faster. In a solid, the particles are close together and there are strong forces between them. So in a solid, energy can pass easily from particle to particle. Gases are bad conductors because the particles are too far apart and the forces between them are weak.

Heat transfer by radiation, convection and conduction.

1 Of radiation, convection and conduction, which one:

(a) is most important in solids?

(b) doesn't need any material at all?

(c) can happen in gases and liquids but not in solids?

2 Explain how clothing and the insulating material used in the King Edward oven are similar.

3 Give some reasons why it's a good idea to keep the outer surface of an oven as cool as possible.

4 Compare the insulation of the oven with insulation of a house. Mention loft insulation, cavity wall and double glazing. A good way to do this would be in a pair of diagrams, one of an oven and one of a house.

5 Use ideas about particles to explain how energy spreads out from an oven.

4.5 Heating for profit

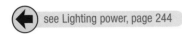 see Lighting power, page 244

Energy sources and energy costs	ACTIVITY

You will find it useful to look back at Topic 4.4 Lighting power, for a reminder about working out energy costs.

Choosing the source of energy

6 What source of energy do King Edward ovens use?

7 What are the reasons for this?

8 What source of energy would you use for each of the following? Give your reasons.

(a) Heating a small quantity of water for staff drinks in a small mobile display unit that travels to country fairs;

(b) Cooking potatoes for a team of 20 working on a road building site;

(c) Heating a liquid in the lab.

9 What sources of energy does your school kitchen use? Find out what the reasons are for this. Find out about the kitchen energy costs.

Power rating

King Edward potato ovens run at a power of 3000 watts. Mains voltage for homes and catering outlets in the UK is 230 volts.

> power =   current × voltage

So if the current is 12 A and the voltage is 230 V:

> power =   12 [A] × 230 [V]
>   =   2760 W

10 Is the current in a 3000-watt King Edward oven more or less than 12 amperes?

11 The same company make a smaller oven which runs with a current of 10 amperes. Copy this template and fill in the zzzz to work out its power.

> power =   zzzz × voltage
>   =   10 × zzzz
>   =   zzzz W

Cost

If you were buying a King Edward oven for your own food outlet, you would want to know about costs. An oven has a power rating of 3000 W, which is the same as 3 kW.

12 Copy the template and fill in the zzzz to work out how much it will cost to run an oven for one hour.

> energy transferred in kilowatt   = power in kilowatt × time in hours

> So for one hour:

> energy transferred in kilowatt-hour = zzzz   ×   1
>   = zzzz kilowatt-hour

> At 8p for each kilowatt-hour, that will cost you:

> 3 × zzzz = zzzz pence

13 Is that a large proportion of the price you could get for your cooked potatoes? Explain.

4.5 Heating for profit

Kate's Kitchen

Kate's Kitchen take-away outlet wanted to smarten up their displays and increase the variety of their foods. So Rob, the manager, started to make some enquiries. On the Internet he found out about King Edward potato ovens.

The potato bakers are ovens designed in 'traditional' style, with a main oven and a top compartment where cooked potatoes keep hot. The top compartment has a glass door so that buyers can be tempted by the sight of the ready-to-eat potatoes.

Before making a commitment to buy a new potato baker oven, Rob had some maths to do. What size of oven would fit the space? How many potatoes might they sell? Most importantly, would they earn money or lose it? There were all sorts of factors involved there: the price of the potatoes and the ingredients for the toppings, the price they could charge for each filled potato, the power rating of the oven and the cost of the electricity.

In the end they couldn't predict exactly how many potatoes they could sell, but they had everything else worked out. They took a calculated risk and bought an oven.

It worked out well. They sell about 400 filled potatoes every week. Business is cooking up nicely.

14 Why is an electric oven more likely than a gas oven to suit Rob's needs?

15 The cost of electrical energy is about 8p per kilowatt-hour. That works out as just over 2p per megajoule. Have a look at a gas bill.

see Lighting power, page 244

   (a) Is the energy more or less expensive on the gas bill?

   (b) Is the cost difference a major or minor consideration for Rob?

16 Explain why the thermal insulator in a potato oven is important in helping Kate's Kitchen to be profitable.

Key facts

Copy and complete the sentences by choosing the correct word from the key words list.

1 Thermal energy transfer involving currents of liquid or gas is called _____.

2 _____ transfers energy from particle to particle.

3 _____ is the only type of thermal energy transfer that doesn't need material to travel through.

4 A _____ _____ or _____ _____ reduces thermal energy transfer by conduction and also by convection and radiation.

Key words

conduction

convection

insulating material

radiation

thermal insulator

4.6 Cooling systems

Energy experts

Laurence is a professional engineer who works for Ford. The engineers work in teams, developing the 'thermal management systems' for new vehicles.

Laurence works on thermal management systems for Ford cars.

Waste energy

Energy must spread out, or dissipate, from an engine or it will overheat. So a vehicle has a cooling system to transfer energy away from the engine out to the surroundings.

Liquid **coolant** flows in a circuit from the engine to the car 'radiator'. The coolant gains energy from the engine and gets hotter. It loses energy in the radiator and cools down again. The radiator transfers the energy to the air around.

Sometimes we can make use of some of the energy to heat the inside of the car, for passenger comfort. When the heater is turned on, a **heat exchanger** transfers energy from the hot coolant to air that warms the people in the car. The heat exchanger is like a small radiator.

When the engine is cool, a thermostat sends the coolant along a pipe that by-passes the radiator. Then the coolant returns to the engine without cooling down so much, which gives the engine a chance to warm up.

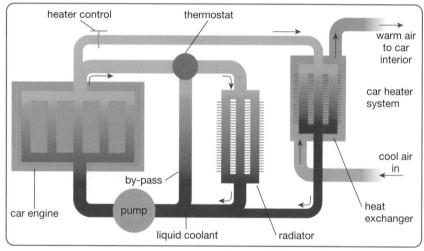

A car cooling system uses a liquid coolant to take energy from the hot engine and transfer it through the radiator to the air around.

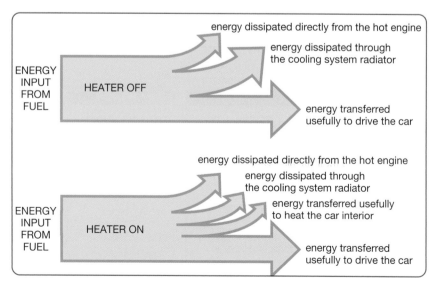

A Sankey diagram of the energy transfer by an engine and cooling system.

❶ What happens to the temperature of the coolant:

(a)   in the engine?

(b)   in the radiator?

 see Fuels and generators, page 228

4.6 Cooling systems

Testing

Laurence and Rebecca work on Ford prototypes. They help to make sure that the design has been thoroughly tested and developed before any vehicles are made to be sold.

Laurence outlines what they do:

'We work with prototype vehicles, so we help to develop the specifications that cars are built to. We test at high altitude in the Austrian Alps, in hot places like Arizona and in the cold in Finland. We also use computers and high-tech test chambers. The design won't go into production until we know we've got everything right, from ensuring the air conditioning works well to making sure your car doesn't overheat and catch fire. It's not just a desk job, but we apply the principles of thermal management to do it.'

A computer image of a Ford prototype in a test chamber.

Rebecca continues, 'My particular work centres on testing new radiators for light commercial vehicles: Transit and Transit Connect. In our wind tunnels and chambers we can create different environments, such as hot climate conditions. Or we can create cold climate conditions, when the outside temperature is below freezing, so heaters are turned on full while other components risk freezing. Every year we go on a number of test trips to hot or cold places, to make sure that data collected in the test chambers is reliable. We make measurements when the engine is working hardest, at maximum velocity or over a steep gradient, when energy is dissipated rapidly as heat. That's when the cooling system must also work hardest.'

2 Use the text to help you to explain the meanings of:

(a) prototype;

(b) specification;

(c) dissipation.

3 Explain why an engine is most likely to overheat when the vehicle is going fast or when it is climbing a steep hill.

4 (a) Why do Laurence and Rebecca use 'test chambers'?

(b) Why don't they do all of their tests in test chambers?

4.6 Cooling systems

Water – a good coolant

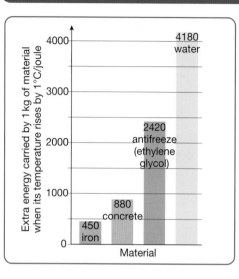

Comparing heat capacities.

Word check

Heat capacity is a measure of the extra energy that can be carried by a particular mass (usually 1 kg) of substance when its temperature rises by 1°C.

In some ways, water is a very good coolant. It is good at absorbing energy and carrying it away.

The bar chart shows the amounts of energy that one kilogram of different materials can carry when the temperature rises by 1°C.

Water can carry more energy than the same mass of almost all other substances when they experience the same temperature rise. We say that the kilogram of water has a high **heat capacity**.

Water – radiator wrecker

When water freezes, its particles move further apart. So they take up more space and the material expands. When most substances freeze, the particles move a little closer together and the material contracts. Water is an unusual substance.

The expansion of water when it turns to ice can split the water container. If the container is a car cooling system, then it can be wrecked.

Antifreeze lowers the melting point and freezing point of water. It prevents the coolant from freezing (unless it is *very* cold). It also reduces the rate of corrosion of the parts of the cooling system. A vehicle cooling system can use a mixture of 50 per cent water and 50 per cent antifreeze. High pressure inside the system prevents the coolant mixture from boiling.

5 What could happen in a car cooling system if:

   (a)   there were no antifreeze?

   (b)   the coolant were not under pressure?

6 Make sketches of particles in ice and the same particles when the ice melts. Show what happens to the arrangement of particles and to the distance between them. How does this affect choice of coolant in a car radiator?

Key words

coolant

heat capacity

heat exchanger

Key facts

Copy and complete the sentences by choosing the correct word from the key words list.

1 A _____ _____ may be part of a cooling system. It transfers energy from a hotter material to a cooler one.

2 The material that flows in a cooling system to carry energy is called a _____.

3 A kilogram of water has a high _____ _____. One kilogram of water can carry a lot of energy, even if its temperature only rises a small amount.

4.6 Cooling systems

Water and antifreeze
ACTIVITY

This table shows the freezing temperature (which is the same as melting point) of mixtures of water and antifreeze.

Proportion of antifreeze in the mixture	40%	50%	60%	66%
Freezing temperature/°C	–20	–32	–72	–94

Plot a graph of proportion of antifreeze (horizontal axis) against temperature (vertical axis). Note that the temperature values are negative.

7 Describe the relationship between the proportion of antifreeze and freezing temperature.

8 What proportion of antifreeze is adequate for a British winter?

Comparing water and antifreeze

9 Copy and complete the table to show the amounts of extra energy that can be stored and carried by water and antifreeze when their temperature increases.

Mass and temperature increase	1 kilogram 1°C	2 kilogram 1°C	1 kilogram 2°C	2 kilogram 2°C
Water				
Antifreeze				

For water:

extra energy stored = $4180 \times$ mass of water $\times$ temperature rise

For antifreeze:

extra energy stored = $2420 \times$ mass of water $\times$ temperature rise

10 What are the units of extra energy stored, mass and temperature rise?

11 Predict the extra energy that is stored in water when 0.6 kg is heated by 70°C.

12 A kettle could provide this energy. Where does the kettle get its energy from?

13 Explain why you wouldn't buy a 100 W kettle.

Refrigerators

A refrigerator transfers energy from the inside to the air outside. Do research to find out how a refrigerator:

(a) uses a coolant;

(b) uses a heat exchanger;

(c) acts as a heat pump.

4.7 Road safety

Road safety

Joe has just passed his driving test. He finds out that 30 000 people are killed or seriously injured on Britain's roads each year. Joe wants to make sure that he drives safely. Part of his test was about how the speed that a car is travelling affects the stopping distance.

Stopping distance

Suppose Joe whilst driving sees a child in the road. When he first sees the child, his brain takes a fraction of a second to react. The car goes on travelling during this 'thinking distance'. Then he puts the brakes on – the car travels while it is braking. So ... **total stopping distance = thinking distance + braking distance**.

The **faster** the car is travelling, the **longer** the stopping distance.

Word check

total stopping distance = thinking distance + braking distance.
Total stopping distance is thinking distance plus braking distance.

❶ (a) Plot a graph of thinking distance against speed. What pattern does your graph show?

  (b) On the same graph, plot braking distance against speed. What pattern does your graph show?

  (c) What is the total stopping distance at 30 mph and 60 mph? Does stopping distance double with speed?

What conditions affect stopping distance apart from speed?

Condition	Example
Weather	Wet or icy roads **reduce friction** between car tyres and the road so stopping distances are longer. In fog, drivers cannot always see very far ahead.
Condition of the car	Worn tyres or worn brakes may make stopping distances longer.
Road surface	Minor roads sometimes have older or damaged surfaces that might not allow the car tyres to grip properly.
Heavy loads	A heavily loaded car or lorry will travel further before stopping.

In areas where cars might have to stop in very short distances, for example, busy towns or outside schools, there are lower speed limits.

❷ Give two reasons why lower speed limits lead to fewer serious accidents.

Speed		Total
20 mph	6 m 6 m	= 12 m or 3
30 mph	9 m 14 m	= 23 m or 6
40 mph	12 m 24 m	= 36 m or 9
50 mph	15 m 38 m	= 53 m or 12
60 mph	18 m 55 m	= 73 m or 18
70 mph	21 m 75 m	= 96 m or 24

Key
Thinking distance
Braking distance
Average car length = 4 m

4.7 Road safety

How fast can you react?   ACTIVITY

Thinking distance relies on a driver's reaction time. Carry out this experiment to find out about your reaction time.

1. Your friend holds a metre ruler just touching the top of your hand.

2. Your friend drops the ruler suddenly.

3. You catch the ruler. Read off the ruler to find out how far it falls before you catch it.

4. Try the same test ten times. Make a table of your results and work out an average.

Try the same test again, but this time deliberately distract yourself. Try saying a times table during the test. Try watching what is going on elsewhere in the room during the test.

3 What differences do distractions make to your average ruler reading? What does this tell you about what happens to your reaction times when you are distracted?

4 Do the results vary within your class? What does this tell you about different people's reaction times?

5 (a) The values for stopping distances are averages – they vary between drivers. Explain why different drivers have different stopping distances.

   (b) Many people think that using hands-free mobile phones can cause accidents. Explain why.

Under the influence

Reaction times are much slower if people have been taking alcohol, drugs or if they are tired. Police campaign against drink driving and can stop and 'breath test' any driver who is driving suspiciously. People who drive for a job, for example, long distance lorry drivers, have to obey laws about taking regular breaks every few hours so that they do not become too tired.

6 What message do you think each advert is making?

4.7 Road safety

Speed and acceleration

Word check

$$speed = \frac{distance\ travelled}{time\ taken}$$

1 m/s = 3.6 km/h

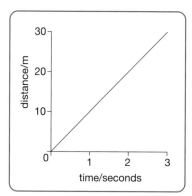

This graph shows the speed of Joe's car as it passes the speed camera.

How do speed cameras work?

Joe passes a speed camera on a straight road on his way to work. Speed cameras time how long it takes a car to travel over some lines on the road. The lines are at a fixed distance apart. The camera calculates the speed of the car and photographs the number plate of cars that are speeding.

For example, a car travels over speed lines in two seconds. The lines are 30 m apart.

So, speed of car $= \dfrac{30}{2} = $ **15 m/s**

or 15 × 3.6 = **54 km/h**

7 Joe travels along the road at a steady speed. It takes him 80 seconds to travel 1.2 km. What is Joe's speed in m/s? (Remember 1 km = 1000 m.)

Speeding up, slowing down

Joe does not drive at the same speed or in the same direction on his way to work. The **velocity** of a car takes into account its speed and its direction. Velocity and speed are the same when the car is travelling in a straight line.

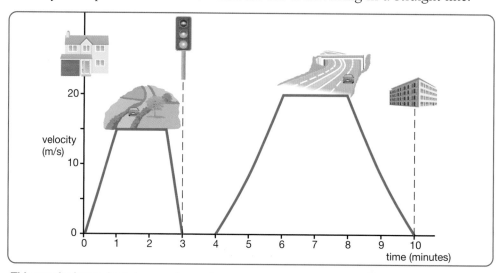

This graph shows Joe's journey to work.

Word check

$$acceleration\ (m/s^2) = \frac{change\ in\ velocity\ (m/s)}{time\ (s)}$$

When Joe leaves home, it takes him one minute (60 seconds) to accelerate from 0 to 15 m/s.

So acceleration $= \dfrac{15}{60}$ m/s²

8 (a) How long does Joe wait at the traffic lights?

    (b) How fast does Joe travel on the dual carriageway?

9 On his journey home, Joe's car overtakes a lorry. He speeds up from 15 m/s to 18 m/s in five seconds. What is his acceleration?

4.7 Road safety

Police speed traps

CASE STUDY

Joe is caught going faster than the speed limit by a policeman. The policeman used a radar gun to show the speed at which Joe's car was travelling. The policeman explains to Joe what will happen. 'You need to go to the police station within seven days to show your driving licence, MOT certificate and insurance. I have already checked that your tax disk is up to date. We need to check these documents because your driving licence proves that you are qualified to drive – we sometimes stop people who have not passed their tests or have been banned from driving because of previous convictions. The MOT certificate proves that the car is safe to drive – as you know, cars over three years old must be checked every year by a qualified mechanic at a garage. Your insurance documents prove that you have insurance so that you can pay for any damage to yourself or others if you have an accident. If you do not bring the documents, you will have to go to court. You will have to pay a fine of £60 and will have three points on your driving licence. You can avoid the fine if you agree to go to a training course about speeding. The course is not a 'soft option' – we usually have a speaker who has had a close member of their family killed by a speeding motorist. The points on your licence show that you have been caught speeding. You must tell your insurance company about this and they may ask you to pay more money for insurance in the future.'

10 (a) Explain what the police do to make it less likely that Joe will speed in the future.

(b) What checks do the police use to make sure that cars and drivers are safe to be on the roads?

Key facts

Copy and complete the sentences by choosing the correct word from the key words list.

1 Stopping distance depends on thinking distance and _____ _____.

2 Thinking distance depends on a driver's _____.

3 Stopping distances are longer when rain or _____ are on the roads because the force of _____ is reduced.

4 The _____ of a car shows its speed and direction.

5 The rate of change of velocity is _____.

Key words

acceleration

braking distance

friction

ice

reaction time

velocity

Review questions

1 Compare a car engine and a coal-fired power station by describing:

(a) where the energy comes from;

(b) the useful energy outputs that they provide;

(c) the type of coolant that is used to carry energy from one part to another;

(d) the harm they do to the atmosphere. [8]

2 (a) Copy and complete the table by writing short explanations of whether radiation, convection and conduction can take place in solids, liquids and gases. [7]

	Solid	Liquid	Gas
Radiation		liquids absorb most radiation so radiation can't travel far	
Convection	can't take place because solids can't flow		
Conduction			takes places very slowly because particles are too far apart to influence each other enough

(b) Does energy travel through the metal of a car engine mostly by radiation, convection or conduction? [1]

(c) A car radiator transfers energy from the hot water inside to the air around it. How are radiation, convection and conduction involved in this process? [3]

3 A typical stage-lighting system works at an average power of five kilowatts.

(a) Complete the calculation to work out the energy that the system transfers during a two-hour performance:

energy in kilowatt-hour = power in _____ × time in hours

= _____ × 2

= _____ kilowatt-hour [3]

(b) If the cost of the energy is 8p per kilowatt-hour, what is the cost for the performance? [1]

4 Look at the diagram of the combined heat and power unit on page 230. How does it make use of a heat exchanger? [1]

5 The law insists that drivers and their cars have documents to prove that they are roadworthy. Make a list of these documents and explain the purpose of each one.

(a) MOT;

(b) Insurance document;

(c) Driving license.

Contents

Assignments and practical activities linked to this section:

The construction of a lifting system.

The design and construction of a nightlight

Constructing an electronic system

Investigating a lever

Use the following to check your progress.

Unit 3

You will:

- draw and use diagrams of electronic systems which monitor and control, showing power source, input components (sensors), processor and output components see pages 262–273

- connect physical components together to monitor and control conditions such as temperature and light level see pages 262–273

- explain that electrical voltage levels in wires and components, and pulses of light in optical fibres, can carry 'data' in systems which monitor and control see pages 270–273

- choose components and build, test and evaluate an electrical or electronic device see pages 270–273

- measure input (applied) and output force for a machine see pages 274–281

- distinguish, with calculations, between machines which are force multipliers and machines which are distance multipliers see pages 274–281

- calculate input and output energy (or work) and efficiency of machines see pages 274–281

- explain the advantages and the disadvantages of friction in machines. see pages 278–281

4.8 Electronic life support

Life support for baby Louise

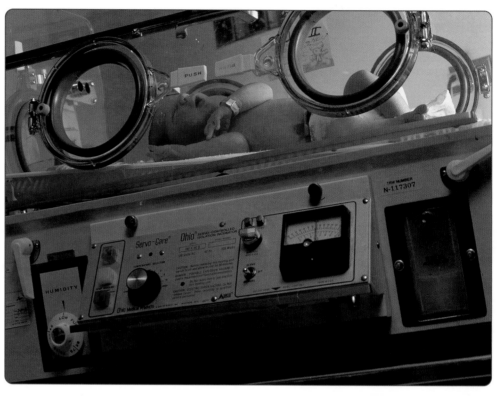

Louise in her incubator.

Louise was born two months premature. At just over one kilogram, her tiny body needed intensive care in a special baby unit. The incubator in which she spent the first days of her life had to be at just the right temperature.

Sensing and monitoring the temperature

Many objects change when their surroundings change. Some expand or contract. Some melt or freeze. Objects which change electrically are especially useful. We can use them as sensors in electronic circuits.

A thermistor is a temperature sensor that can be used in a baby incubator. It has a resistance which changes when its temperature changes. It provides 'information' about temperature to an electronic system. It is an input component of the system.

Controlling the temperature

An incubator must have a heater that is controlled by an electronic system. It may also have a light to show whether the temperature is just right. The light could be from a light emitting diode, or LED. The heater and the LED provide the ways in which the electronic system affects the world around it. They are the system's output components.

The circuitry must be set up so that the heater switches on and off at the right times. The part of the electronic system that controls this switching is called the processor.

4.8 Electronic life support

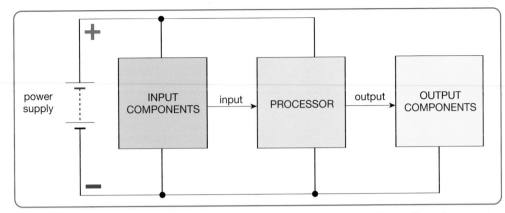

Continuous sensing so that action can be taken is called monitoring. This is the temperature monitoring and control system for the baby incubator.

The temperature monitor and control system in a baby incubator has four main parts: a **power supply**, **input components**, a **processor** and **output components**.

The processor in an electronic system links the input to the output and controls how the output components respond to different inputs.

1 (a) What variable does the system in the diagram monitor and control?

(b) How does it sense the variable?

(c) How does it change the variable?

So how does the thermistor do it?

A thermistor can be connected in series with an ordinary 'fixed value' resistor. They are both input components.

The thermistor and the fixed resistor have different shares of the voltage from the power supply, depending on how big their resistances are. The two of them control the input voltage to the electronic system.

The thermistor and the fixed resistor share the voltage and make a voltage divider system. Understanding voltage dividers is essential for understanding electronic systems.

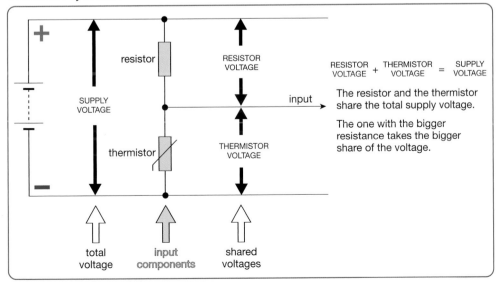

$$\text{RESISTOR VOLTAGE} + \text{THERMISTOR VOLTAGE} = \text{SUPPLY VOLTAGE}$$

The resistor and the thermistor share the total supply voltage.

The one with the bigger resistance takes the bigger share of the voltage.

A voltage divider system.

4.8 Electronic life support

The resistance of the thermistor changes when its temperature changes. So the two resistors have different shares of the supply voltage depending on the temperature. The input voltage to the processor depends on temperature.

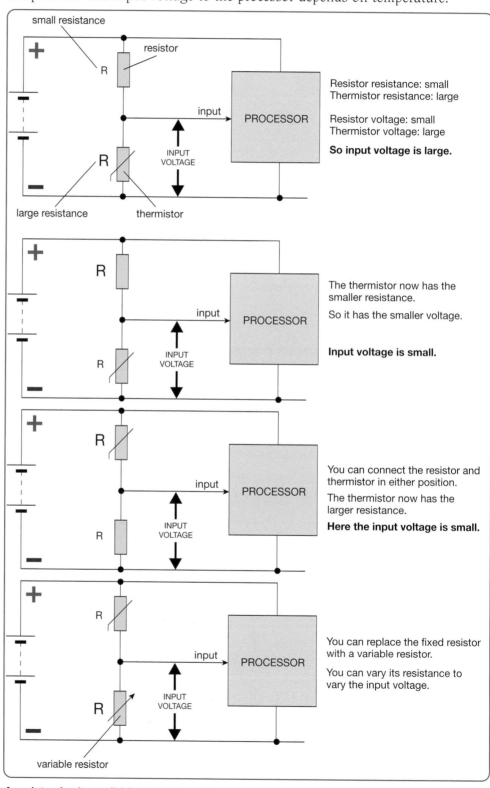

Resistor resistance: small
Thermistor resistance: large

Resistor voltage: small
Thermistor voltage: large

So input voltage is large.

The thermistor now has the smaller resistance.

So it has the smaller voltage.

Input voltage is small.

You can connect the resistor and thermistor in either position.

The thermistor now has the larger resistance.

Here the input voltage is small.

You can replace the fixed resistor with a variable resistor.

You can vary its resistance to vary the input voltage.

A variety of voltage divider arrangements.

4.8 Electronic life support

Inputs and outputs

Voltage divider arrangements

Voltage provided by the power supply is 12 volts. V_1 is the variable resistor's share of the voltage. V_2 is the thermistor's share.

We can use R_t as a quick way to write down the resistance of the thermistor.

We can write the variable resistance as R_v.

Copy the diagram and label the thermistor and the variable resistor.

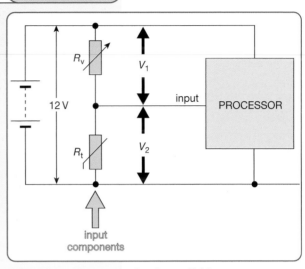

A voltage divider.

❷ Describe how the values of V_1 and V_2 compare when:

(a) $R_t = R_v$;

(b) R_t is bigger than R_v;

(c) R_t is smaller than R_v.

❸ What will happen to V_2 if:

(a) the variable resistor isn't changed and the temperature goes down?

(b) the variable resistor isn't changed and the temperature goes up?

(c) the temperature stays the same and the variable resistance increases?

(d) the temperature stays the same and the variable resistance decreases?

❹ You could swap the positions of the thermistor and the variable resistor. V_2 is then the variable resistor's share of the voltage. Would you expect the answers to question 3 to change or stay the same?

The voltage shares are always in the same proportion as the resistances. For the diagram above, you can write it like this:

$$\frac{V_2}{V_1} = \frac{R_t}{R_v}$$

❺ (a) If V_2 must be eight volts and V_1 must be four volts, what is the ratio of the resistances?

(b) If R_v is 800 ohms, what must R_t be when V_2 is eight volts and V_1 is four volts?

(c) $V_1 + V_2 = 12$ volts. If R_t is 3000 ohms and R_v is 1000 ohms, what are the values of V_1 and V_2?

LEDs as output components

A LED must be connected in series with a resistor. Otherwise a large current could flow and damage the LED.

❻ Explain why current would be bigger without the resistor.

❼ Why are the resistor and the LED not connected directly to the power supply?

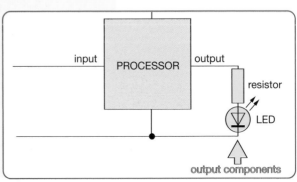

4.8 Electronic life support

Louise's first day   CASE STUDY

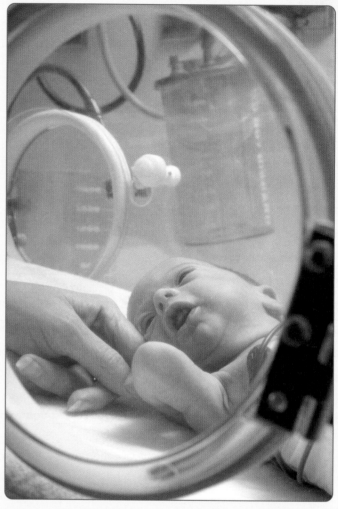

Louise in her incubator.

Thermistors are not the only input components in electronic systems. Louise's baby incubator also has a movement detector, so that her breathing can be monitored. The movement detector is an input component. A buzzer alarm and a LED are output components to attract the attention of nurses so that they can take emergency action if needed.

8 Draw a block diagram similar to the one on page 263 to show the electronic system for monitoring Louise's breathing and providing an alarm signal if breathing stops.

9 What are the input and output components for this system?

10 What input conditions cause the alarm signals to start?

4.9 Movement under control

Windows of opportunity

Opening a window is one effective way to control temperature. But for Steve and Kate's tomato-growing business, there are an awful lot of windows. They grow their tomatoes in greenhouses, under carefully controlled conditions.

It's a high-tech business. As part of the temperature-control system, windows open and close automatically.

The temperature, moisture level and light level have to be just right for the best growing conditions.

Inputs

Input components in a greenhouse include moisture detectors and light sensors called light-dependent resistors or LDRs. Just like thermistors, they are connected in series with other resistors to make voltage divider arrangements.

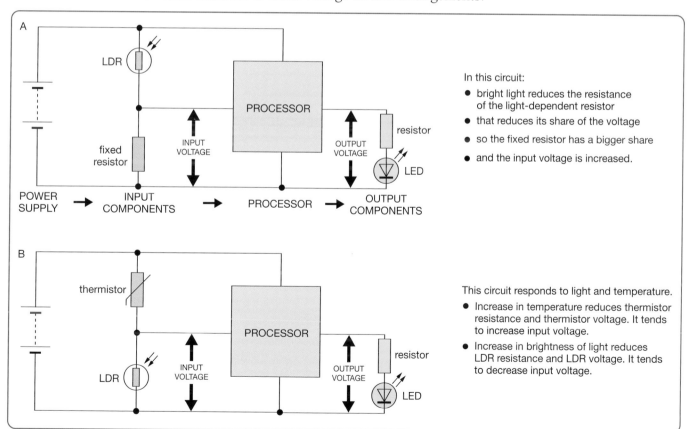

In this circuit:
- bright light reduces the resistance of the light-dependent resistor
- that reduces its share of the voltage
- so the fixed resistor has a bigger share
- and the input voltage is increased.

POWER SUPPLY → INPUT COMPONENTS → PROCESSOR → OUTPUT COMPONENTS

This circuit responds to light and temperature.
- Increase in temperature reduces thermistor resistance and thermistor voltage. It tends to increase input voltage.
- Increase in brightness of light reduces LDR resistance and LDR voltage. It tends to decrease input voltage.

Different input components in voltage divider arrangements.

① Look back at pages 263-4 if you need to and write down explanations of these:

(a) thermistor   (b) in series   (c) voltage divider.

see Electronic life support, page 262

4.9 Movement under control

Transistors as processors

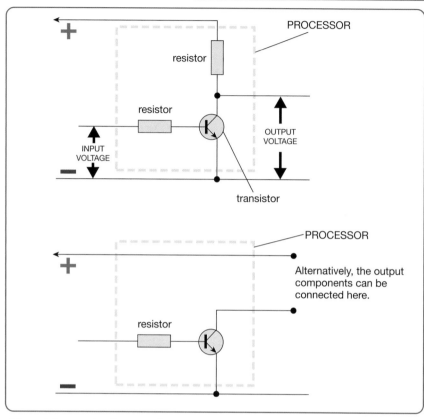

A transistor can be the most important component in some kinds of processor.

A processor can switch output voltage to high value or low value. A transistor is one kind of processor that can switch between providing a low output voltage and a high output voltage. It has three wires to connect it into a circuit. The switching is triggered by changes to the input voltage that is applied to the transistor's third connection.

2 With a six-volt power supply, what are the maximum and minimum values of:

   (a)   input voltage;

   (b)   output voltage?

3 What are the advantages of an electronic switch over a mechanical switch?

Monitoring temperature and controlling motors

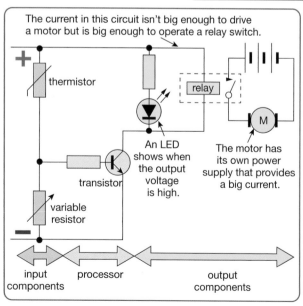

A motor can be an output component, but it needs its own power supply.

Heaters, LEDs and alarm buzzers are all kinds of output component. A motor can be an output component, too.

The transistor circuit can't provide enough current to drive a motor, so the transistor switches on a current in a coil. That makes the coil magnetic. It operates a switch. A magnetic switch like this is called a relay.

That's what happens in Steve and Kate's greenhouses. If the temperature is high, the motors operate to open the windows further. If the temperature is right, the motors stay off. The windows slowly close until the motors operate again.

4 'Input components sense things and output components do things.'

   (a)   Do you agree with this? In general, what do input components sense? What do output components do?

   (b)   Write another sentence to say what the role of processors is.

4.9 Movement under control

Working with transistors ACTIVITY

Copy the circuit diagram and add these labels:

- LDR
- variable resistor
- voltage divider
- input voltage
- transistor
- output voltage
- LED
- resistor to protect the LED

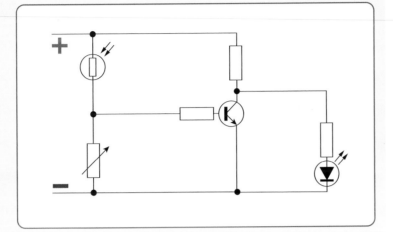

5 Explain whether the LED is on or off when light shining on the LDR is bright.

6 If the LED is replaced by a motor, it won't work.

   (a) Why won't it work?

   (b) Sketch a circuit diagram which can monitor light intensity and work a motor.

7 What similarities and differences are there between a resistor in a voltage divider and a transistor?

The tomato business CASE STUDY

Tomatoes are big business. It's a competitive business. Supermarkets and wholesalers want to buy at the cheapest possible prices. There are other businesses selling the same things. Only growers who use the best technology to keep their costs down will stay in business.

Steve and Kate Jones stay in business with the help of electronic control. Lighting, watering and temperature are all controlled electronically. As Kate says, 'It would take us all week to water the plants if we had to do it manually and we couldn't afford to employ anybody to help us with that. Automatic control is the only answer.'

8 Sketch a voltage divider arrangement that provides a high input voltage for a processor when temperature is low.

9 Sketch a voltage divider arrangement that provides a high input voltage for a processor when light is bright.

10 Explain why a circuit which controls a motor, as in Steve and Kate's greenhouses, uses a relay.

Automatic control systems help to produce a good harvest.

4.10 Digital information

Helping robots to see

Claire Roberts is an expert on optical fibres and robots.

Claire Roberts is a research student working on a project to develop ideas on how optical fibres can be used in robot sensing systems. An optical fibre is a long thread of layered glass that carries digital light signals.

Optical fibres and digital signals

A spoken voice, for example, can't travel down a fibre. Copper wires can carry the information as electrical signals. But they can't carry it as rapidly as optical fibres can. Words and images are sent as codes by very, very rapid flashes of light, along these threads of glass.

The coded pattern of light 'on' and light 'off' is a digital signal. If you use '1' to stand for light on, and '0' to stand for light off, you can write down a digital signal of flickering light as a string of 1s and 0s. Patterns of 1s and 0s carry information in binary code.

A digital signal is a stream of 1s and 0s that carries information.

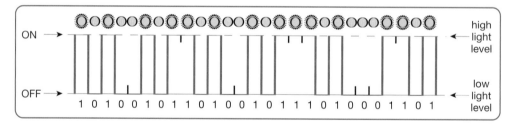

see Lighting power, page 244
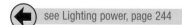

Making digital signals for optical fibres

A light-emitting diode or LED can turn a digital stream of voltages into a digital stream of flashes of light. That's very useful indeed. It can turn electrical signals into light signals.

The light signal doesn't have to be visible to human eyes. Most signals that travel along optical fibres use infra-red light.

How light travels along an optical fibre.

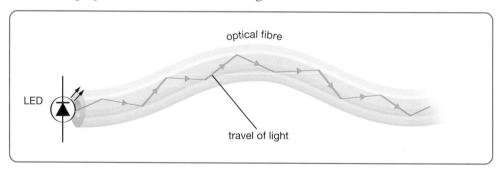

see Movement under control, page 267

❶ What component could you use to turn light signals into electrical signals?

❷ Give one advantage of optical fibres over copper wire.

4.10 Digital information

Logic systems

Optical fibres carry digital signals in patterns of light. Wire and other circuit components can carry digital signals in electrical patterns. High value voltage is called 'on' or 'logic state 1'. Low value voltage is 'off' or 'logic state 0'.

Logic systems are processors that use digital inputs and outputs.

NOT gate

A NOT gate is a processor which provides a high output voltage when the input voltage is low. The output voltage is exactly what the input voltage is not!

We use a truth table to show how different input voltages produce different output voltages.

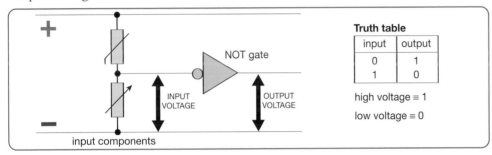

Truth table

input	output
0	1
1	0

high voltage ≡ 1

low voltage ≡ 0

NOT gate.

AND gate

An AND gate has two input connections. It only provides a high output voltage when the input voltage to its input A and its input B are high.

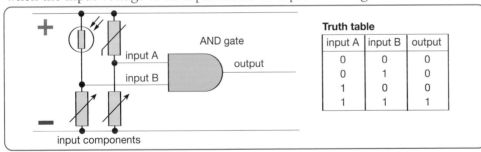

Truth table

input A	input B	output
0	0	0
0	1	0
1	0	0
1	1	1

AND gate.

A system that uses an AND gate as its processor can respond to temperature and brightness of light at the same time. Or it could respond to movement and moisture at the same time. There are a lot of control possibilities.

OR gate

An OR gate will provide a high output voltage when either the voltage applied to its input A or the voltage applied to its input B is high.

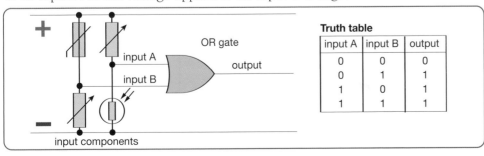

Truth table

input A	input B	output
0	0	0
0	1	1
1	0	1
1	1	1

OR gate.

4.10 Digital information

Optical fibres and logic gates ACTIVITY

The 1s and 0s that travel along optical fibres can provide the 1s and 0s that act as inputs to logic gates.

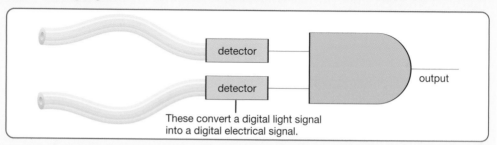

detector

detector

output

These convert a digital light signal into a digital electrical signal.

3 What type of component provides the light for an optical fibre?

4 Give an advantage of using optical fibres and detectors to provide the inputs to logic gates.

5 Devise a use for optical fibres in this way to control systems at home or at school.

6 Do a web search on UK sites using 'optical fibre' as your key term. You'll find a lot of companies selling optical fibres. Try also to find some with:

* general information about optical fibres;

* interesting applications of optical fibres.

Print out one interesting illustration and write your own short caption to explain it.

7

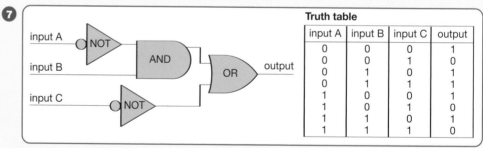

Truth table

input A	input B	input C	output
0	0	0	1
0	0	1	0
0	1	0	1
0	1	1	1
1	0	0	1
1	0	1	0
1	1	0	1
1	1	1	0

What is the output of this system, 0 or 1, when:

(a) input A has logic state 1, input B has logic state 1, input C has logic state 1?

(b) input A is switched to 0 but the others stay the same?

8

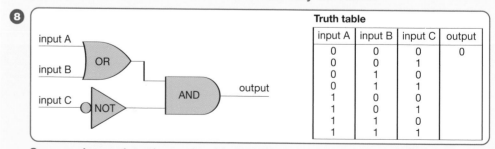

Truth table

input A	input B	input C	output
0	0	0	0
0	0	1	
0	1	0	
0	1	1	
1	0	0	
1	0	1	
1	1	0	
1	1	1	

Copy and complete the truth table for this system.

4.10 Digital information

Claire's robots

LEDs (light-emitting diodes) can flash on and off rapidly. So they can send a lot of information along an optical fibre. The information travels as *digital* codes of flashing light.

LDRs (light-dependent resistors) are light sensors. When light reaches them, their resistance goes down. So they affect voltage when they are connected in *voltage divider* arrangements. They turn digital codes of flashing light into digital patterns of electrical voltage. We can use them as *input components* of electronic systems.

Claire Roberts knows all about digital signals. She builds electronic systems based on optical fibres. She knows that optical fibres are better then electrical wires for sending information over long distances. Wires have quite a lot of electrical *resistance* so that signals become weaker if the wires are very long.

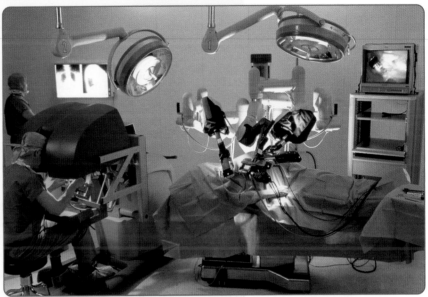

The Da Vinci robot performs heart surgery guided by a surgeon. Optical fibres in one of the robot's arms carry information to produce an image of the operation for the surgeon.

Most of Claire's work, though, is on robots. She uses electronic systems with input–processor–output arrangements to create robots that can respond to their surroundings. It's no problem for her to make a robot that can follow a white line on the floor. She can use LDRs to detect the brightness of light and motors to create movement. The processor provides output voltage that operates *relays* to turn motors on and off.

Claire can build much more sophisticated robots than that. Instead of using single LDRs, she can use arrays of light detectors. So a robot's electronic systems can detect light from different directions, as your eyes can. Her robots have memories, like computers do, so that they can 'learn' about their surroundings. They seem to be able to make their own decisions about which way to move. Clever people can make clever machines.

9 How does Claire use components so that her robots are able to sense their surroundings?

10 What output components does she use to control robot movement?

11 Design a system that uses two LDRs as 'eyes' to control movement of robot wheels. Use block diagrams if you are not sure about the detail of processors.

12 Use the information in this book to write a vocabulary list (words and definitions) for the words in italics.

13 Do a web search on 'artificial intelligence'. Find out more about robot research. Find out what we can use robots for now and what robots might be like in the future.

4.11 Lifting

Using our heads for lifting

We humans can move things around and even build enormous structures like bridges and buildings. Our muscles alone could never do it. It's our brains that succeed.

The Millennium Bridge across the river Tyne is just one example. Here the road is raised up and the balancing arm of the bridge is lowered. Ships can go underneath. You have to know about forces and machines to build something like this.

The Gateshead Millennium Bridge.

You can provide an upwards force to balance your own weight.

Lifting your own weight

Your arms are just about strong enough to lift your body off the ground. They can provide a force that matches your weight, which is the force of gravity that pulls you downwards.

In science, it makes sense to use the same unit for weight as we use for any other kind of force. We measure force, including weight, in newtons (N).

Effort and load

The force that you exert to lift or move or hold an object is your effort (the applied or input force). The force that acts on the object is the load (or output force). We measure effort and load in newtons.

In simple situations, effort and load are the same size but not always in the same direction (see diagram on right). However, we can use machines to lift big loads with small efforts.

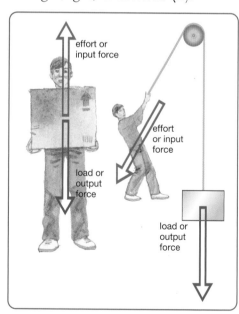

The load is bigger than the effort. This machine gives a good mechanical advantage.

Pulleys provide mechanical advantage

A system of two or more pulleys reduces the effort that is needed to lift or move a load. The pulley system is a machine. It gives us a mechanical advantage.

We measure mechanical advantage by comparing load with effort. The best way to compare them is by a division calculation.

$$\text{mechanical advantage} = \frac{\text{load}}{\text{effort}}$$

A machine that can provide a load that is bigger than the effort is called a force multiplier. For a force multiplier machine, mechanical advantage is more than 1.

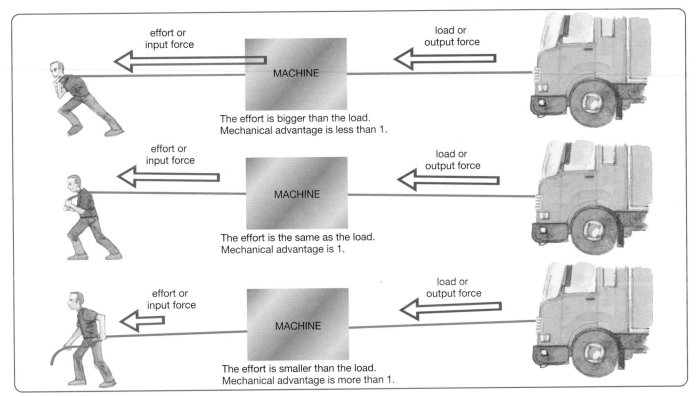

effort or input force — MACHINE — load or output force
The effort is bigger than the load.
Mechanical advantage is less than 1.

effort or input force — MACHINE — load or output force
The effort is the same as the load.
Mechanical advantage is 1.

effort or input force — MACHINE — load or output force
The effort is smaller than the load.
Mechanical advantage is more than 1.

❶ Is mechanical advantage 1, more than 1 or less than 1 when:

(a) effort is smaller than load?   (b) effort = load?

(c) effort is bigger than load?

The price to pay for force multiplication

Machines can multiply force but the energy output can never be bigger than the energy input. We have to pay for the increase in force. We pay by velocity and distance.

For all machines that multiply force, the velocity of the load is smaller than the velocity of the effort. The effort moves faster and further than the load.

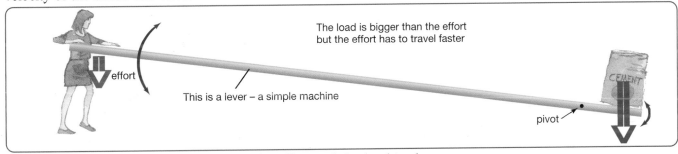

effort

The load is bigger than the effort but the effort has to travel faster

This is a lever – a simple machine

pivot

We can compare the distances moved by the effort and the load in the same time. The comparison is called velocity ratio.

$$\text{velocity ratio} = \frac{\text{distance moved by effort}}{\text{distance moved by load}}$$

❷ What is the velocity ratio if the effort and the load move exactly the same distance in the same time?

4.11 Lifting

Lifts and levers

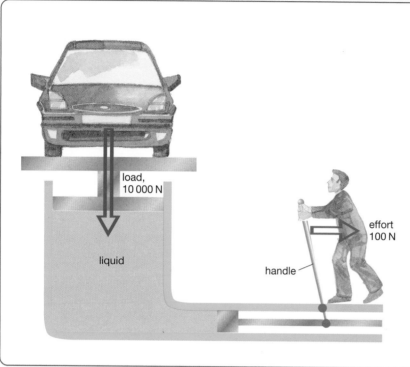

A very simple version of a
hydraulic lift.

Hydraulic lift
The diagram shows a hydraulic lift for raising a car in a garage.

❸ What is the size of the load?

❹ What is the size of the effort?

❺ Is load bigger than effort?

❻ Is mechanical advantage more or less than 1?

❼ Why does the person have to pull the handle a long way but the load only rises a short distance?

Levers

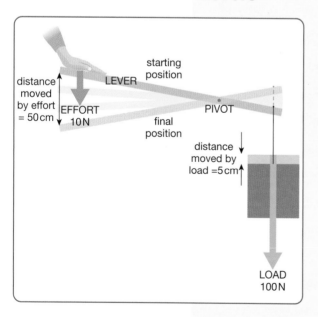

A lever is a simple machine. It has an effort and a load. It also has a pivot that doesn't move.

If the load is closer to the pivot than the effort is, then the load will be bigger than the effort.

❽ Use this template and replace the zzzz to work out the mechanical advantage of the lever:

$$\text{mechanical advantage} = \frac{zzzz}{\text{effort}}$$

$$= \frac{100}{zzzz}$$

$$= zzzz$$

❾ Use this template and replace the zzzz to work out the velocity ratio:

$$\text{velocity ratio} = \frac{\text{distance moved by effort}}{zzzz}$$

$$= \frac{zzzz}{5}$$

$$= zzzz$$

4.11 Lifting

Machines in action

It takes brains to move heavy loads.

Can you lift a car? You can if you know how to use the right machine.

The Gateshead Millennium Bridge across the river Tyne, with the cycle track and walkway in the lowered position. It has pivots at each end, and the force to turn it comes from electric motors with a total power of 440 kilowatts.

🔟 Will the hydraulic car lift have a mechanical advantage that is more than 1? Explain your answer.

⑪ The railway site crane uses pulleys. What is the benefit of using pulleys?

⑫ Explain why the crane motor must turn rapidly, even though the load rises only slowly.

⑬ If you were planning a moving bridge like the Gateshead Millennium Bridge across the river Tyne, would you make use of a machine? What kind of machine? (For example, simple lever, pulley system, gears or hydraulic system.)

4.12 Gears

Bicycle work

Bicycles are machines for travelling further and faster than we can go by walking or running.

Steve O'Brian works in a bike shop where they sell and repair all sorts of bikes.

'They all work basically the same way,' says Steve. 'Your feet go round at a nice steady rate and the bike takes you quickly along the road.'

Driving force and friction

A cycle tyre pushes on the surface of a road. The road can push back thanks to friction. Friction lets surfaces push on each other without sliding. Friction opposes sliding.

Effort and load on bikes

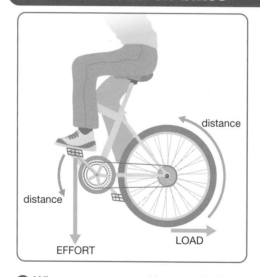

the force of the tyre on the road

the force of the road on the tyre

The tyre pushes on the road and the road pushes back on the tyre.

A bicycle is a distance multiplier – the load travels faster and further than the effort.

 see Lifting, page 274

When you ride a bike, your effort is the force that acts on the pedals as you push down. The load is the force between the tyre and the road.

We usually want machines to multiply force so that we can lift or move a bigger load with a smaller effort. The unusual thing about a bicycle is that the load is smaller than the effort.

But the bicycle gives you a different benefit. You have to push hard on the pedals, but you go a long way. A bike has a bigger output distance than the input distance. A bike is a distance multiplier.

distance

distance

EFFORT

LOAD

❶ Why are some machines called force multipliers?

Using gears on a bike

When you change gear on a bike, the chain moves on to a different cog behind you. The cogs are different sizes.

You choose lower gear (bigger gear cog) when you want the output force of the tyre on the road to be bigger for going uphill or accelerating from slow speed.

You choose high gear (smaller gear cog) when you want to cruise along on flat ground as fast as possible.

4.12 Gears

Remember that:

$$\text{velocity ratio} = \frac{\text{distance travelled by effort}}{\text{distance travelled by load}}$$

Distance travelled by the effort is the same thing as input distance. Distance travelled by the load is the same thing as output distance.

Different gears give you different velocity ratios.

❷ (a) For a bicycle, is input distance or output distance bigger?

(b) Does it have a velocity ratio that is more than one or less than one?

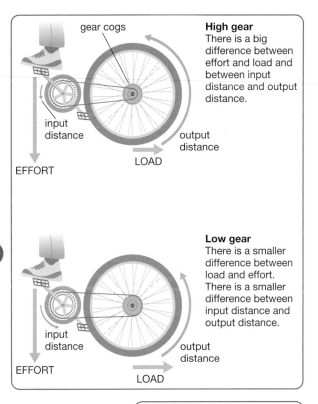

High gear
There is a big difference between effort and load and between input distance and output distance.

Low gear
There is a smaller difference between load and effort. There is a smaller difference between input distance and output distance.

Friction as nuisance

When we need surfaces to slide across each other, like the hub and axle of a wheel, friction is a nuisance. It heats up the surfaces and that wastes energy. It also causes wear.

❸ How do you think we try to:

(a) increase friction between tyre and road?

(b) reduce friction between the axle and hub of a bicycle wheel?

Working out energy inputs and outputs of machines

The energy input of a machine is the work that the effort does. You can calculate this by multiplying the effort by the distance it travels:

energy input = work done by the effort = effort × distance moved by the effort

So if a cyclist exerts an average effort of 50 newtons for one turn of the pedals and the distance moved by either of the pedals is one metre, then:

energy input = work done by the effort = 50 × 1 = 50 joules

You can also work out the useful energy output of the machine:

useful energy output = work done by the load = load × distance moved

If our cyclist travels ten metres for one turn of the pedals and the average load is four newtons, then:

useful energy output = work done by the load = 10 × 4 = 40 joules

You can see that the useful energy output is less than the energy input. Some energy has been lost because of friction in the bike's moving parts.

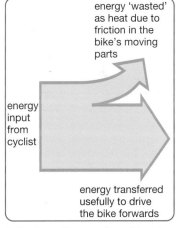

energy 'wasted' as heat due to friction in the bike's moving parts

energy input from cyclist

energy transferred usefully to drive the bike forwards

A Sankey diagram for a bicycle.

Bicycle efficiency

You should remember how to work out efficiency:

$$\text{efficiency} = \frac{\text{useful energy output}}{\text{energy input}} \times 100$$

For the cyclist:

$$\text{efficiency} = \frac{40}{50} \times 100 = 80 \text{ per cent}$$

see Fuels and generators, page 228

4.12 Gears

Gear ratios

ACTIVITY

These are formulae for working out measurements for machines:

$$\text{mechanical advantage} = \frac{\text{load}}{\text{effort}}$$

$$\text{velocity ratio} = \frac{\text{distance moved by effort}}{\text{distance moved by load}}$$

$$\text{energy input} = \text{effort} \times \text{distance moved by effort}$$

$$\text{useful energy output} = \text{load} \times \text{distance moved by load}$$

$$\text{efficiency} = \frac{\text{useful energy output}}{\text{energy input}} \times 100$$

4 Copy the table and use the formulae to help you to complete it.

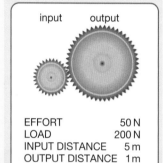

input   output

EFFORT   50 N
LOAD   200 N
INPUT DISTANCE   5 m
OUTPUT DISTANCE   1 m

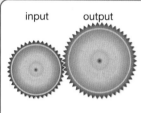

input   output

EFFORT   50 N
LOAD   100 N
INPUT DISTANCE   3 m
OUTPUT DISTANCE   1 m

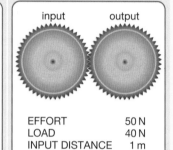

input   output

EFFORT   50 N
LOAD   40 N
INPUT DISTANCE   1 m
OUTPUT DISTANCE   1 m

Effort/newton			
Load/newton			
Mechanical advantage			
Distance moved by effort/ metre			
Distance moved by load/ metre			
Velocity ratio			
Force multiplier or distance multiplier?			
Energy input/joule			
Useful energy output/ joule			
Efficiency			

4.12 Gears

Steve's work

Steve is doing some maintenance work on a bicycle. He says, 'You know that when you are working on a bike like this and you turn the pedals with your hands, you have to push quite hard. The pedal doesn't go very far, but the wheel spins fast. That's the bike being a *distance multiplier*.

'I had to replace some of the cogs on the gears of this bike. They were old and worn. *Friction* had worn them away in places. And that was only making friction worse. The worn surfaces were rubbing more, getting hotter. The gears just weren't as *efficient* as they should be.

'The bearings weren't in a good state, either. They hadn't been oiled for too long and some of the steel "ball bearings" had been worn out of shape.'

5 Write down the meanings of the words in italics.

6 (a) Where does a bicycle get energy for its motion?

(b) Use Steve's words to explain one way in which it wastes energy.

7 What's the purpose of oil and ball bearings in a bicycle?

8 What's the difference between how we use the word work in everyday language and how we use it when we're talking about energy and machines?

9 Imagine an unusual bike that is designed to be a force multiplier.

(a) Sketch the pedals, chain and gear cog for the bike.

(b) What would it feel like to ride it?

Review questions

1 (a) Draw a block diagram for an electronic system that controls the temperature of an office.

(b) Name a sensor and an output device that your system uses. [6]

2 Temperature and lighting control are both important for healthy plant growth in commercial greenhouses.

(a) What device can be used as a light sensor? [1]

(b) Draw a sketch to show such a light sensor in a voltage divider arrangement. [5]

(c) How does the voltage divider provide different voltages to the processor? Use the word 'resistance' or 'resistor' in your answer. [3]

3 Electronic systems can use sensors to monitor:

- light intensity;

- heart rate.

How could each type of sensor be useful in a fitness centre? [2]

4 A lever is a simple machine.

(a) What is a machine? [2]

(b) A screwdriver used to take the top off a tin of paint is acting as a lever. Draw a sketch and show the location of:

(i) the pivot;   (ii) the effort;   (iii) the load. [3]

(c) Which is bigger, the load or the effort? [1]

(d) Is the mechanical advantage more than 1 or less than 1? [1]

(e) Which moves further at the same time, the load or the effort? [1]

(f) Is the lever acting as a force multiplier or a distance multiplier? [1]

5 Why is it impossible to make a machine that is a force multiplier *and* a distance multiplier? [2]

6 For each of these calculations, start by writing the formula you are using.

A pulley system on a crane lifts a load of 1200 N with an effort of 100 N.

(a) Work out the mechanical advantage.

$$\text{mechanical advantage} = \frac{\text{load}}{\text{effort}}$$ [3]

(b) The load moves two metres and the effort moves 30 metres in the same time. Work out the velocity ratio.

$$\text{velocity ratio} = \frac{\text{distance moved by effort}}{\text{distance moved by load}}$$ [3]

(c) Work out the work done by the effort.

$$\text{work done} = \text{force} \times \text{distance}$$

(Don't forget to use the unit of energy, the joule, with your answer.) [4]

(d) Work out the work done on the load.

$$\text{work done} = \text{force} \times \text{distance}$$ [4]

(e) Explain why the previous two answers are not the same. [2]

(f) Work out the efficiency of the system.

$$\text{efficiency} = \frac{\text{work done on load}}{\text{work done by effort}}$$ [4]

5 The Earth and universe

THE EARTH, THE ATMOSPHERE AND THE UNIVERSE

Contents

Use the following to check your progress:

Unit 1
You will:

- be able to discuss the health risks from air pollution and know the hazards of pollutant gases.

see pages 288–294

Unit 2
You will:

- know how the Earth's atmosphere developed over time

see pages 284–288

- know how the use of vehicles affects air quality

see pages 288–294

- know the health and environmental issues for some common gases (carbon dioxide, carbon monoxide) and how scientists work to minimise the problems caused

see pages 288–294

- know about alternative fuels for vehicles

see pages 288–294

- know that the Earth's crust is made of tectonic plates

see pages 294–298

- know how tectonic plates move and how they cause continental drift and formation of mountains

see pages 294–298

- know that earthquakes and volcanoes happen along the edges of tectonic plates.

see pages 294–298

- know how Earth movements are monitored.

see pages 294–298

Unit 3
You will:

- know about the work of scientists in researching the Earth and its atmosphere

see pages 284–288

- know about the work of scientists in developing ways to monitor and improve air quality

see page 291

- know how scientists work to monitor and reduce risk from earthquakes

see pages 294–298

- know that energy is transferred as waves and understand frequency and wavelength

see pages 298–306

- know about the electromagnetic spectrum

see pages 298–306

- know how waves are used for communication

see pages 298–306

- understand the evidence for an expanding universe.

see pages 298–306

5.1 Our atmosphere

Gas	Percentage in air
nitrogen N_2	78%
oxygen O_2	21%
carbon dioxide CO_2	0.03%
other gases	less than 1%

Gases in the atmosphere

If you went back in time 3000 million years, you would see a world covered with volcanoes with molten rock bursting through the surface. You would only survive a few minutes. You would quickly die, choking, as the atmosphere contains no oxygen and is full of toxic gases that pour out of the volcanoes. So where did our atmosphere come from? How does it replace the gases that living things use?

Gases for life

Our atmosphere contains a mixture of gases. Most of our atmosphere is nitrogen. Nitrogen is very unreactive.

Life on Earth depends on **oxygen** and **carbon dioxide** in the air. The amount of these gases in the air has stayed the same for hundreds of millions of years. This is because there is a balance between the way plants and animals make and use them.

see Photosynthesis, page 56

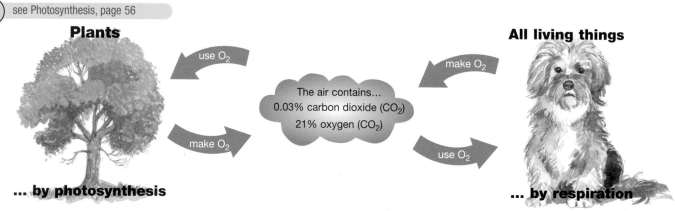

Plants ... by photosynthesis — use O_2 / make O_2

The air contains... 0.03% carbon dioxide (CO_2) 21% oxygen (CO_2)

All living things ... by respiration — make O_2 / use O_2

more CO_2 in the atmosphere
burnt in power stations
250 million year old coal

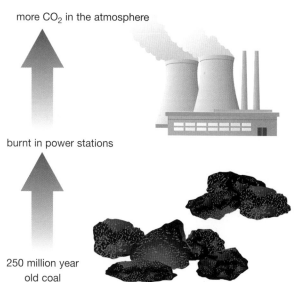

Combustion of fossil fuels

Hundreds of millions of years ago, the atmosphere contained much more carbon dioxide. The Earth was covered in dense forests of tree ferns that used up the carbon dioxide as they grew. These plants became **fossilised** and formed thick layers of coal under the Earth. The carbon that they took from the atmosphere has stayed 'locked up' in the coal for millions of years. Over the last 150 years, we have burnt a lot of this coal and released the carbon dioxide back into the atmosphere.

Many people are worried that this 'extra' carbon dioxide could increase the greenhouse effect and cause **climate change**.

1 Some people have suggested planting more trees to reduce the amount of carbon dioxide in the atmosphere. Explain why this might help.

5.1 Our atmosphere

The greenhouse effect: friend or foe?   (ACTIVITY)

Carbon dioxide causes the **greenhouse effect** – this works a bit like a greenhouse by 'locking' heat into the Earth, just like glass in a greenhouse. The sun warms the Earth and the Earth normally cools down by losing heat back into space. Carbon dioxide absorbs some of the heat and traps it so that it cannot escape and the Earth gets warmer.

Jane and Eve are preparing for a class debate about the greenhouse effect. They have different points of view.

Jane's notes:

- There has been carbon dioxide in the atmosphere <u>ever since the Earth was formed</u>.
- The greenhouse effect is <u>totally natural</u> – it is caused by natural carbon dioxide in the air.
- The moon and the Earth are the <u>same distance from the sun</u>, but the moon has <u>no atmosphere</u>. Here is some data about surface temperatures.

	Distance from sun (millions of km)	Predicted surface temperature (°C)	Actual surface temperature (°C)
Earth	150	–33	17
Moon	150	–33	–33

- Without the greenhouse effect, our Earth would have a surface <u>temperature of – 33 °C</u>. This is <u>far too cold for life</u>. Life would never have evolved on Earth without the greenhouse effect.

Eve's notes:

- <u>Fossil fuels</u>, such as <u>coal, gas and oil</u>, contain very large amounts of carbon.
- We burn <u>millions of tonnes of fossil fuels</u> every year.
- The <u>amount of carbon dioxide</u> in the atmosphere <u>is increasing</u>, causing the <u>greenhouse effect</u>.
- The greenhouse effect could cause the Earth to heat up, <u>melting the ice caps</u>.
- This could lead to <u>sea levels rising, flooding large areas of land and cities</u>.
- Our <u>climate could change</u>, causing <u>severe weather changes, crop failure, famines</u> and <u>extinctions of wildlife</u>.

The greenhouse effect is natural. Without it there would be no life on Earth.

Jane

The greenhouse effect is caused by pollution. It could kill all life on Earth.

Eve

② What do we use 'millions of tonnes of fossil fuels' for?

③ Jane and Eve have very different views. Write a magazine article to give a balanced view of the greenhouse effect using ideas from both Jane and Eve. Your article should give both sides of the story.

④ Make a list of photographs you would choose to help you to make your points in your article.

5.1 Our atmosphere

Where did our atmosphere come from?

When our Earth first formed, it was a very hot planet of molten rock. As the Earth cooled, a crust of solid rock formed on the surface, with volcanoes of molten rock erupting through the thin crust. The Earth's early atmosphere contained gases that came from the molten rock.

Scientists study the gases that come out of active volcanoes today. These gases come from molten rock inside the Earth, so are similar to the gases in our early atmosphere.

Gas	Gases from volcano (Earth's early atmosphere)/per cent	Earth's atmosphere today/per cent
nitrogen	5	78
oxygen	0	21
carbon dioxide	12	0.03
water vapour	74	less than 1
sulphur dioxide	9	trace (almost 0)

Why did our atmosphere change?

1 Over millions of years ... **the Earth cooled**.

→ The **water vapour condensed** to form liquid water, so:
- the seas were formed;
- **soluble gases**, for example, sulphur dioxide and carbon dioxide, **dissolved in the new seas**.

2 About 3000 million years ago, in the sea ... **plants appeared on Earth.**

Plants used up carbon dioxide and started to make oxygen by photosynthesis, so:
- the atmosphere began to contain **oxygen**;
- the amount of **carbon dioxide** began to fall.

3 About 1000 million years ago, in the sea ... **animals appeared on Earth.**

→ The amount of carbon dioxide and oxygen in the atmosphere reached a **balance** and started to stay the same.

5 Look at the table above.

(a) How have the amounts of each gas in the atmosphere changed over time?

(b) Why do you think the amount of nitrogen has risen?

(c) Make a table to show why the amounts of the other gases have changed.

5.1 Our atmosphere

Drilling ice cores
CASE STUDY

How do scientists know so much about what the Earth's atmosphere was like thousands of years ago? Well, every winter, a new layer of ice forms on the permanent ice cap over Antarctica. Bubbles of air get trapped in the ice when it forms.

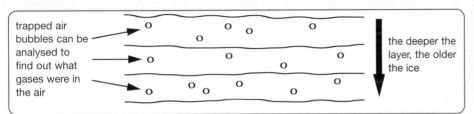

trapped air bubbles can be analysed to find out what gases were in the air

the deeper the layer, the older the ice

The EPICA project drilled over 3km through the ice.

Scientists drill through the ice to find out what gases are trapped in the bubbles. Shallow drills give information about the atmosphere over the last 100 years. In 2004, a group of European scientists (EPICA) drilled the deepest ice core ever – it went down 3270 m (over 3 km or just under two miles!). This gave data about the atmosphere from almost one million years ago. From the samples, they can find out the amount of different gases, for example, carbon dioxide, that were in the atmosphere over that time and also how different the surface temperature of the Earth was compared to today.

The EPICA scientists are very pleased with the data – it shows that there have been many ice ages and 'warm' ages over the last million years. It also shows a clear link between the temperature on Earth and the amount of carbon dioxide in the air – very good evidence that the greenhouse effect really happens!

6 Why does deeper drilling give information about the atmosphere a longer time ago?

7 Read the last paragraph about the EPICA scientists.

(a) Explain why the data shows that there have been ice ages in the past.

(b) Explain why the data shows a link between the Earth's temperature and the amount of carbon dioxide in the air.

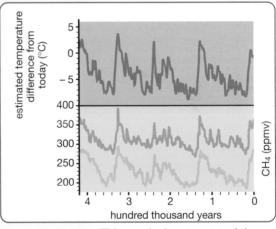

This graph shows some of the data from the ice core drilling.

Key facts

Copy and complete the sentences by choosing the correct word from the key words list.

1 Plants make oxygen by _____.

2 All living things use oxygen during _____.

3 The levels of carbon dioxide in the air are increasing due to _____ of _____.

4 This may cause climate change due to the _____.

Key words

combustion

fossil fuels

greenhouse effect

photosynthesis

respiration

5.2 The Earth and the environment

The air we breathe can affect our health.

The changing environment

The air, water and land that surround us are vital to both our lives and the lives of all other living things. Over the last 150 years, humans have begun to cause harm to the environment and this may threaten the lives of humans, other animals and plants on Earth. What harm are we causing? And what can we do about it?

Natural environmental changes

Many natural processes cause changes to our environment, for example:

Volcanoes give out toxic gases including sulphur dioxide, SO_2, and hydrogen sulphide, H_2S.

Lightning storms make nitrogen oxides, NO and NO_2.

Living things produce and use oxygen, carbon dioxide and other gases.

Living things use nutrients from the soil and water to grow.

Animal waste and dead living things decompose and add chemical compounds to the soil.

Rocks are weathered and add chemical compounds to water.

Until recently, these processes were in a **state of balance**. The overall amounts of gases in the air and compounds in the soil and water stayed roughly constant as they were continually used up and made by natural processes. Over the last 150 years, our air, land and water have begun to change because the population of humans has become very large and because we use industry on a large scale.

❶ (a) Make a list of the types of waste that your street or village produces in a week. Include a rough estimate of the quantity in 'bin bags full' (including toilet waste!).

(b) If the waste was not collected, how could you get rid of it? What problems would it cause?

(c) Explain why getting rid of human waste was not as big a problem hundreds of years ago.

5.2 The Earth and the environment

Humans and the environment

ACTIVITY

For the last 150 years, we have lived in an 'industrial society'. Until recently, all the waste that we produce was released into the air, water and soil. Nowadays, there are strict laws to make sure that we keep environmental pollution to a minimum. The work of scientists has been very important in reducing harm to the environment from our activities.

see Intensive farming, page 64

Burning fossil fuels:
- makes **carbon dioxide** (greenhouse effect);
- makes **sulphur dioxide** (acid rain);
- uses up **finite fossil fuel reserves**.

Scientists help by:
- making processes **more efficient** so less fuel is needed;
- **removing sulphur** from fuels;
- developing 'scrubbing' **processes** to remove sulphur dioxide from power station chimneys.

When food is produced by intensive farming:
- fertilisers cause **eutrophication** of local rivers;
- **pesticides harm wildlife** and can stay in the food we eat;
- **diseases** can spread quickly through farm animals, for example, bird flu.

Scientists help by:
- treating rivers and developing **less harmful fertilisers**;
- developing **less harmful pesticides**;
- developing **organic farming methods**;
- researching new farming methods to keep **farm animals healthy**, for example, vaccination.

Making consumer goods:
- uses up **finite resources of metal ores**;
- uses **energy from fossil fuels**;
- create waste that may enter rivers and cause pollution, for example, by changing water pH;
- creates a lot of **non-biodegradable waste** that has to go into **landfills**;
- uses some **chemicals** that are harmful to the environment, for example, CFCs deplete the ozone layer.

Scientists help by:
- developing **recycling** processes to save waste, energy and metals;
- developing processes to neutralise liquid waste;
- finding **new uses for waste** from industry;
- developing **biodegradable materials** that rot away;
- developing **replacements** for harmful chemicals.

2 Work in a group. Choose one of the boxes above. Carry out some research to find out more information. Make a presentation for the rest of the class. Make sure you tell both sides – what the problems are and what scientists are doing to help.

5.2 The Earth and the environment

Word check ✓

Incomplete combustion happens when there is not enough oxygen for the fuel to burn completely. Toxic carbon monoxide and soot are made.

Transport and the environment

Our society depends on transport, not only to carry people, but to carry food and other goods to shops, raw materials to industry, construction materials – everything we need for our everyday life. Most vehicles use **hydrocarbon** fuels from oil, for example, petrol and diesel. Vehicle emissions (from the exhaust) contain harmful gases.

Smog

Exhaust emissions react together to make smog – this is a thick fog of harmful molecules that can give people very severe breathing problems and even cause death.

120 000 people died in the famous London smog of 1952.

unburnt petrol (hydrocarbons)
carbon dioxide CO_2
carbon monoxide CO
particles of carbon C
nitrogen oxides NO and NO_2
sulphur dioxide SO_2

Acid rain

Nitrogen oxides and sulphur dioxide from exhausts dissolve in rainwater to make acid rain. Acid rain damages trees and wildlife, especially fish and other water animals.

Forests die due to acid rain.

Complete and incomplete combustion of fuel

Hydrocarbons in petrol contain carbon. When carbon burns, it makes very large amounts of carbon dioxide that increase the greenhouse effect and could lead to climate change.

C (in hydrocarbon) + O_2 → CO_2

In vehicle engines, there is not enough oxygen for the fuel to burn completely so carbon monoxide and particles of carbon are made by incomplete combustion of the fuel.

C (in hydrocarbon) + $\frac{1}{2}O_2$ → CO

Notice that this reaction only uses half the amount of oxygen. Carbon monoxide is very toxic when people breathe it in because it stops the blood from being able to transport oxygen. Carbon particles from soot make dirty smoke.

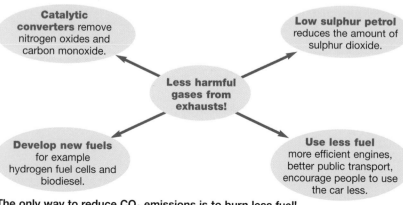

Catalytic converters remove nitrogen oxides and carbon monoxide.

Low sulphur petrol reduces the amount of sulphur dioxide.

Less harmful gases from exhausts!

Develop new fuels for example hydrogen fuel cells and biodiesel.

Use less fuel more efficient engines, better public transport, encourage people to use the car less.

Do something about it!

Over the last 30 years, the laws have become stricter about the amount of harmful gases that vehicles are allowed to give out from their exhausts.

❸ Make a table showing the gases given out by vehicles, the pollution problems they cause and what can be done to solve the problems for each gas.

The only way to reduce CO_2 emissions is to burn less fuel!

5.2 The Earth and the environment

Monitoring air quality

There are 1500 air quality monitoring stations all over the UK. Air quality varies from place to place due to traffic congestion and road layout. Narrow roads between tall buildings usually have poor air quality because the harmful gases become trapped. Cars produce more harmful gases when they are stopped in traffic jams, or when they are slowing down or accelerating, so air quality is often monitored at road junctions and roundabouts. Where air quality is poor, changing road layouts so that traffic moves more smoothly can often help.

Air quality is usually reported by an index using numbers 1–10. 1 means there are low amounts of pollutants and 10 means there are high amounts.

Air quality monitoring station in Leicester city centre.

Banding	Index	Health descriptor
Low	1–3	No noticeable effects, even to people sensitive to pollutants.
Moderate	4–6	Mild effects, unlikely to require action, may be noticed by sensitive people.
High	7–9	Significant effects may be noticed by sensitive people and action may be needed, for example, spending less time in polluted areas outdoors. Asthmatics may need to use inhalers.
Very high	10	The effects on sensitive people's health may worsen.

More detailed tables give the actual amounts of pollutants in the air. The data on the right is from 10 November, 2005. The air pollution index was 1 (low). There are nationally agreed standards for air quality and action must be taken if the quality falls below these standards.

Other types of station monitor the weather. This is important because:

- warm sunshine makes smog form faster;
- rainfall washes pollutants out of the air;
- wind carries pollutants to other areas.

This shows the amount of particles of dust and carbon in the air. ➡

Ozone, O_3, is made in smogs – this shows how much smog is in the air. ➡

Latest Hourly Averaged Data for Leicester Centre
Date: 10/11/05   Time: 10:00am

Pollutant	Measurement (µgm-3)
CO	100
PM_{10}	12
NO	19
NO_2	44
O_3	30
SO_2	0

Air pollution index: 1 (low).

④ Why do you think individual people might be interested in air pollution?

⑤ The data is also used by people who design road layouts.

(a) Explain how this data is useful in designing road layouts.

(b) Road flyovers are sometimes built to replace roundabouts and road junctions. They make cars go faster and also reduce local air pollution. Explain why.

⑥ A new monitoring station is planned for near your school. Use information from this unit to make a short script for a local news item to explain why monitoring stations are needed.

5.2 The Earth and the environment

Choosing the right fuel

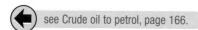
see Crude oil to petrol, page 166.

Petrol, diesel and LPG fuel pumps.

Most petrol stations sell three main types of fuel for cars – **unleaded petrol**, **diesel** and **LPG** (liquid petroleum gas). All these fuels contain hydrocarbons and are made from crude oil. Car companies often sell the same car with a choice of engines so that customers can choose which type of fuel to use.

This data shows some information about the same family car fitted with a petrol, diesel or LPG engine.

Type of fuel	Example of hydrocarbon molecule in fuel	Fuel consumption (litres per 100 km)	CO$_2$ produced g/km	Cost of fuel per litre (Nov 2005)
Unleaded petrol	C_8H_{16}	7.0	167	91
Diesel	$C_{10}H_{22}$	4.8	127	95
LPG	C_3H_8	9.3	151	42

7 (a) Which fuel contains the most energy? How can you tell?

   (b) Read these statements and decide if they are true or false. Explain your reasons.

   1. The higher the carbon content in the fuel, the more energy it contains.
   2. The higher the carbon content, the more carbon dioxide made per km.
   3. The amount of carbon dioxide made depends on the fuel consumption per km.

8 (a) Do calculations to work out how much it costs to travel 100 km using each type of fuel.

   (b) What else would you need to know before you tell which car is cheapest to run?

   (c) Why do you think customers want to know how much carbon dioxide is made per km?

Alternative fuels for cars

Petrol, diesel and LPG all come from **crude oil**. This is a **finite fossil fuel**, so burning crude oil adds carbon dioxide to the atmosphere and the oil will eventually **run out**. Scientists are working to develop alternative fuels for cars. The most likely replacements are **hydrogen**, **biodiesel** and **gasohol**. Biodiesel and gasohol are both made from plants.

Hydrogen:
- produces only water when it burns;
- can be used in a fuel cell to power cars.

But:
- electricity to make hydrogen is expensive and is made using fossil fuels;
- hydrogen is much more difficult to store than petrol.

Biodiesel and gasohol:
- can be made in the UK from crops such as sugar beet or oilseed rape;
- are 'carbon neutral' because when they burn, the same amount of carbon is put back into the air that was used when the crops grew.

But:
- land for growing crops is needed for growing food;
- they cannot be made on a big enough scale yet.

5.2 The Earth and the environment

Joe does a MOT CASE STUDY

In the UK, cars over three years old must have a MOT test every year. The MOT test checks that the cars are safe to drive. One part of the test is testing the exhaust emissions (the amounts of gases coming from the exhaust) when the car is running.

Joe works in a garage. He explains how he carries out the test:

'We run the car to warm the engine to its normal running temperature before we test the exhaust emissions. This makes it a fair test because when cars are cold, they often give out more harmful gases. We fit an exhaust gas analyser to the exhaust to test the amounts of various gases coming out. Two of the gases we test for are unburnt petrol (this shows on the results as 'HC' for 'hydrocarbons') and carbon monoxide. One of the most common reasons that cars fail is when we see smoke coming out of the exhaust – the smoke contains soot (particles of carbon). There are strict limits on how much of each gas the car is allowed to give out, otherwise it will fail its MOT. The limits vary between makes and models – older car engines are not as efficient as newer engines, so the limits are a little higher.

Joe tests exhaust emissions.

'If the car fails, we have to find out the fault that is causing the problem. We can then advise the owner of the car what repairs need to be made so that it will pass. Common faults that cause high exhaust emissions include engine wear, fuel system faults or a damaged catalytic converter. Sometimes the repairs are very expensive, sometimes just putting in clean air filters solves the problem.'

These are the results for the car that Joe tested:

Fast idle test	Limits	Actual value
Engine speed	2500–3000 Rpm	2829 Rpm
CO	less than 0.3%	0.03%
HC	less than 200ppm	28ppm

9 Explain why it is important to find out if a car has too high levels of unburnt petrol or carbon monoxide in its exhaust emissions.

10 (a) Explain why unburnt petrol, carbon monoxide and soot are all caused by incomplete combustion.

(b) Would the car pass the emission test? Explain your reasoning.

Key facts

Copy and complete the sentences by choosing the correct word from the key words list.

1 Some natural processes add harmful gases to the air, for example, from _____.

2 Car exhaust emissions produce _____ and _____ by _____.

3 Examples of replacement fuels for cars include _____ and _____.

Key words

carbon monoxide

gasohol

hydrogen

incomplete combustion

soot (carbon)

volcanoes

5.3 The Earth beneath our feet

The Earth beneath our feet

Most people think that we stand on solid ground. But the rocks that make up our countries and continents are constantly moving. If you lived in an earthquake zone, you might see very fast rock movement. Scientists have shown that even the UK is moving – we are drifting away a few centimetres a year from North America. In 100 years time, aeroplanes may have to fly an extra 100 m to reach America!

Moving plates

The movement happens because the Earth's crust is actually made of plates of solid rock that move around on the hot mantle underneath. These are called **tectonic plates**. The movements are usually very slow.

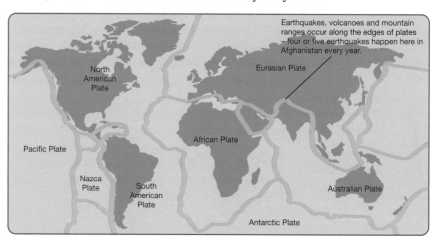

see Waves and communication, page 298

Some plates are moving apart, for example, the African and South American plates. This causes continental drift (continents moving apart). New rock is made as molten rock comes out of the Earth and turns solid. Some plates are moving together, for example, the Eurasian and Australian – this causes the land to fold up and make mountains. When this happens, old rocks get pushed down back into the Earth and re-melt – this forms part of the rock cycle. Sometimes the plates get 'stuck' and pressure builds up until there is a sudden movement – this is what causes an earthquake. Earthquakes under the sea can create very big waves called tsunamis. There are weak spots where the plates join. Molten magma from deep inside the Earth gets forced out through the weak spots causing volcanoes.

❶ Find the UK on the map. We are moving away from North America, but not from Europe. Explain why.

❷ Why do you think the UK does not suffer from volcanoes or earthquakes?

5.3 The Earth beneath our feet

Wegener and continental drift theory   ACTIVITY

Alfred Wegener was the first person to think that the Earth's crust might be made
of moving plates. He published a book about his theory in 1915. He knew that rock
layers on different continents are very similar and he noticed that the continents all
fit together like a jigsaw. He thought that they must all have once been joined
together in a giant continent (called Pangea) and that they had slowly drifted apart
as the plates moved. At first, his theory was not accepted. However, since the
1950s, scientists have learned much more about the Earth's structure and can now
detect even tiny movements in the crust. Since the 1960s, Wegener's theory has
been accepted as being right.

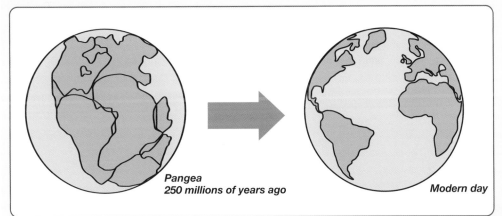

Pangea
250 millions of years ago

Modern day

Continental drift.

Rock layers and fossils

Some rock layers are very similar on land that is
separated by thousands of miles of ocean, for
example, Africa and South America.

Key
mya – millions
of years ago

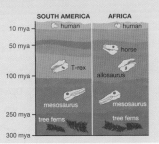

Earthquakes, volcanoes and mountains

If the main areas for earthquakes, volcanoes and mountain
ranges are plotted ona map of the world, they all fall along
the boundaries of the plates.

Earthquakes happen on
plate boundaries.

❸ (a) Look at the evidence shown in the boxes above. Scientists think that
South America broke away from Africa about 120 million years ago. How
do the rock layers support this theory?

(b) Some people used to believe that the Earth's surface was wrinkling and
folding because the Earth was shrinking. What evidence does this theory
explain? What evidence is not explained by this theory?

❹ (a) (Roughly) cut out the continents from a map of the world. Try to fit them
together to form Pangea.

(b) Using an atlas to help you, draw on another map the main locations of
mountains, earthquake zones and volcanoes. Explain how this helps
support Wegener's ideas about continental drift.

5.3 The Earth beneath our feet

How plates move

The Earth's plates that make up the crust rest on a layer of very hot rock called the mantle. The mantle is solid, but in some ways it behaves like a liquid – it moves very slowly. The plates move because there are convection currents in the mantle. Convection currents happen when hotter mantle rock slowly rises and cooler mantle rock slowly sinks. The plates move as the mantle moves.

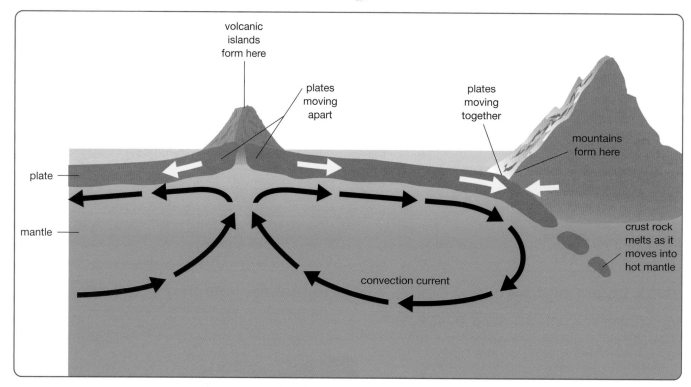

When plates move together, old rock sinks and melts. Mountain ranges form.

When plates move apart, magma rises up and forms new rock. This causes continental drift. Earthquakes and volcanoes happen at both kinds of plate boundaries.

❺ The movement of rocks shown in the diagram is called the rock cycle. Explain what happens to a single piece of rock as it travels through the rock

Key words

continental drift

earthquakes

mountains

tectonic plates

volcanoes

Key facts

Copy and complete the sentences by choosing the correct word from the key words list.

1 The Earth's crust is made up from _____.

2 When plates move apart, it causes _____.

3 When plates move together, _____ are formed.

4 At the edges of plates _____ and _____ happen.

5.3 The Earth beneath our feet

Saving San Francisco
CASE STUDY

The Pacific tectonic plate meets the North American plate under California. The San Andreas fault runs along the boundary between the plates for 650 miles through highly populated, wealthy areas such as San Francisco. Earthquakes are common along the fault. 9000 people were injured in an earthquake in 1994. Another caused 40 billion dollars worth of damage in 1992. Scientists predict 'the Big One' will happen in the next 30 years, but it is very difficult to pinpoint when. Scientists monitor every tiny Earth movement along the fault to try to predict when the next quake might happen.

Monitoring the fault
Scientists are working to predict the next quake by:

- using **seismograms** to monitor Earth movements;
- taking samples from the fault through a three kilometre deep bore hole (the 'SAFOD' hole);
- looking at historical data to try to spot what to look for just before a big quake.

A seismogram makes marks on a roll of paper during Earth tremors. After an earthquake, two types of wave travel through the ground – **p waves** and **s waves**. The waves make the ground shake and cause buildings to collapse and other damage. The p waves travel faster than s waves. By looking at seismographs taken at different places, scientists can work out exactly where the rocks started to move. Most quakes are too small for people to even feel, but all Earth movements give information about where the rocks are under stress.

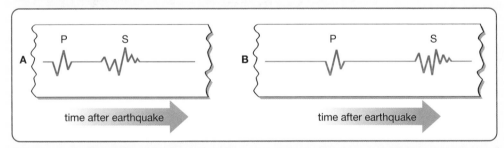

These seismographs are for a small quake recorded at two monitoring stations, A and B. The seismographs show that station A was the nearest to the quake.

6 Look at the seismographs. Why do p waves always reach the monitoring stations before s waves? How can you tell that station A is nearest to the quake?

Early warnings that an earthquake is on the way will save lives because people can be evacuated, but what about the buildings themselves? New, large buildings and bridges in San Francisco are built on shock-absorbing foundations (for example, using rubber posts) and are designed to be flexible so that they don't fall down. No buildings are built on the fault line. There are automatic emergency cut-offs for all the water and gas mains and electricity cables because if any of these were ruptured in an earthquake, they could cause fires.

7 Explain how California is preparing to prevent damage and loss of life in future earthquakes.

The Transamerica Pyramid in San Francisco, built to withstand earthquakes, swayed more than one foot but was not damaged in the 1989 Loma Prieta, California, earthquake.

5.4 Waves and communication

Tsunami

On 26 December 2004, energy from an undersea earthquake caused the tsunami that destroyed coastal towns in South East Asia.

Waves are very good at transferring **energy** from one place to another. The tsunami that destroyed coastal towns in South East Asia was caused by an undersea earthquake. The energy from the earthquake was transferred by waves to the coastal towns where the energy was released to cause massive destruction to life and property.

It is because waves are so good at transferring energy that scientists use waves to communicate over vast distances. The waves are used to transfer a message from one part of the Earth to another. They can even transfer information far out into space so that scientists can communicate with distant spacecraft.

What kind of waves do we use for communication?

Scientists use waves from the **electromagnetic spectrum** for communication. The electromagnetic spectrum consists of waves of different wavelengths. You will have heard of some of these waves before.

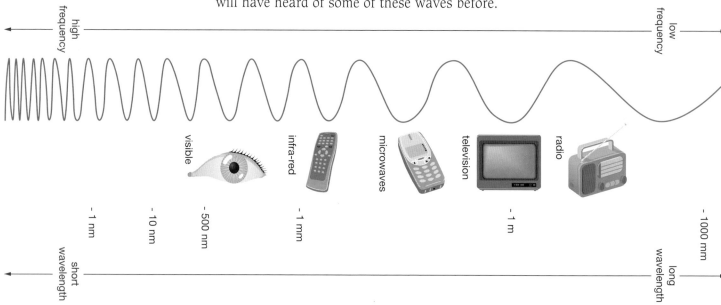

Electromagnetic spectrum.

① Look at the picture of the electromagnetic spectrum. Which of the following has the longest waves and which has the shortest?

Light for eyes to see, microwaves for mobile phones, signal for TV sets and radio waves.

5.4 Waves and communication

The Asian tsunami   ACTIVITY

The Asian earthquake struck deep under the ocean off the island of Sumatra on 26 December, 2004. The map shows how the energy from the earthquake produced waves that spread out over the Indian Ocean. It also shows how long the waves took to reach different countries.

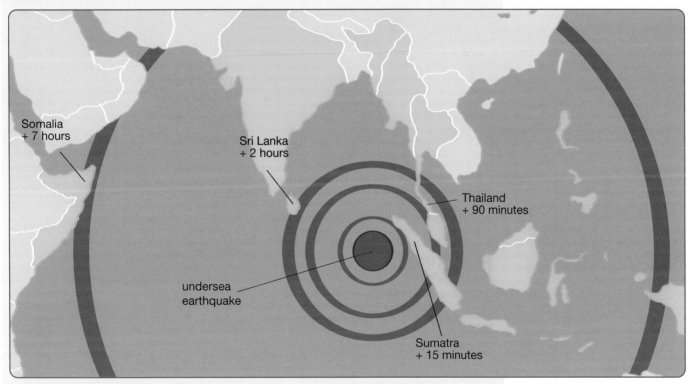

Somalia
+ 7 hours

Sri Lanka
+ 2 hours

Thailand
+ 90 minutes

undersea
earthquake

Sumatra
+ 15 minutes

2 Suggest why the tsunami reached Thailand before it reached Somalia.

3 Suggest why the wave that reached Somalia did less damage than the wave that reached Thailand.

Look at the table of data. It shows the height of the wave as it approached Thailand.

Height of wave/m	Depth of ocean/m
2	more than 20
3	20
5	15
7.5	10
10	5

Plot a graph to show how the height of the wave was affected by the depth of the ocean.

4 Explain the relationship between the height of the wave and the depth of the ocean.

5 Suggest why the wave got higher as it got nearer to the coast.

5.4 Waves and communication

What are waves?

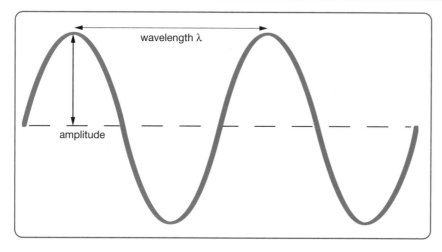

Wavelength

Wavelength is the length of one complete wave. The symbol for wavelength is λ.

Some waves, such as X-rays, can be very short. Other waves, such as radio waves, can be very long.

Frequency

Frequency is the number of waves that pass each second. The symbol for frequency is f. If the frequency is one wave every second, it is called 1 Hz.

100 Hz is one hundred waves every second. More energy is transferred as the frequency of the wave increases.

Amplitude

Amplitude is the height of the wave. More energy is transferred as the amplitude increases. The symbol for amplitude is a.

Waves

Waves can be described by using these three symbols. The speed of a wave can be determined by multiplying the frequency of a wave by its wavelength. The symbol for speed or velocity is v.

$$\text{speed of wave} = \text{frequency} \times \text{wavelength}$$
$$v \quad = \quad f \quad \times \quad \lambda$$

This may seem complicated but is in fact quite simple. If you stand on the beach, you can count how many waves crash on the sand each second (f). It may be less than one and may only be one wave every five seconds. So that would be a frequency 0.2 of one wave every second or 0.2 Hz. If you multiply that by the length of the wave (λ), it will tell you how fast the waves are travelling. This is called the wave equation.

6 If 0.2 waves land on the beach every second and the length of a wave is two metres, calculate the speed of the wave.

5.4 Waves and communication

Working with waves

Steve works at Comet. He sells equipment that people can use to communicate with each other. These are some of the things that Steve sells.

TV and radio waves travel over long distances to our homes. They carry information both as pictures and sound.

Steve works at Comet.

Mobile phones use microwaves. The waves are beamed to and from our phones by transmitter aerials. The signal is then beamed between different transmitters.

TV remotes use infra-red waves. The signal can only travel over a short distance.

Fibre optic cables use light waves to transmit information over long distances. Sometimes the light used is laser light.

7 Which type of device that Steve sells transmits over the shortest distance?

8 Suggest why this device only transmits over a short distance.

9 Which type of device uses light to transmit information?

10 Mobile phone transmitters need to be in line of sight of each other. Suggest why.

11 Which types of device that Steve sells uses the longest wavelength?

Key facts

Copy and complete the sentences by choosing the correct word from the key words list. Each word may be used more than once.

1 Radio waves and microwaves belong to the _____.

2 The symbol f stands for _____. It is a measure of how many _____ pass each second.

3 The height of a wave is called _____.

4 Waves are very good at transferring_____.

5 _____ can be determined by measuring the distance from one point on a wave to the same point on the next wave.

Key words

amplitude

electromagnetic spectrum

energy

frequency

wavelengths

waves

5.4 Waves and communication

Discovering space

Speech bubble 1: See if you can see this beam of light coming towards your eyes.

Speech bubble 2: I can't.

Speech bubble 3: That's because light waves travel so fast.

Space is big

Even though space is big and some of the stars are far away, scientists are still able to discover a lot about space. This is because of waves. When we look into the night sky, we are looking at stars, some of which are so far away that the light waves have taken thousands of years to reach us.

Scientists measure the distance of stars in light years. This is the distance that light can travel in one year. Because light travels so fast, one light year is 9 500 000 000 000 km. Just try to imagine how far away some stars are if they are thousands of light years away.

The solar system – our own backyard

Some objects in space are much closer to us. The sun, our nearest star, is only eight light minutes away. The moon, which orbits the Earth, is only 1.25 light seconds away. The Earth and all the other planets orbit the sun. We can only see them because they reflect some of the sunlight back to our eyes.

Collecting waves

Scientists can use two different kinds of telescope to collect waves from distant stars.

Scientists can even collect infra-red and X-rays from distant stars.

Radio telescopes collect radio waves.

Light telescopes collect light waves.

12 Other than the sun, the nearest star to the Earth is 4.5 light years away. Calculate how far away that is in kilometers.

5.4 Waves and communication

The lumpy universe

Objects such as planets, moon and stars are not scattered evenly through space. They tend to be lumped together. The Earth and the other planets orbit the sun. This is called the solar system. The sun and several other million stars are lumped together in our galaxy. We call our galaxy the Milky Way. All the stars that you can see in the night sky belong to our galaxy. The universe consists of millions and millions of other galaxies. These galaxies are so far away that they can only be clearly seen with a telescope.

13 Look at the photo. It shows some stars in front of four different galaxies. Suggest which galaxy the stars that you can see belong to.

Make your own solar system

Look at the following table of data.

	Represented by a	Distance from sun/ million miles
Sun	giant beach ball	
Mercury	pea	36
Venus	grape	67
Earth	grape	93
Mars	pea	142
Jupiter	cricket ball	484
Saturn	snooker ball	888
Uranus	ping pong ball	1784
Neptune	ping pong ball	2799
Pluto	pin head	3674

Place the beach ball at one end of your playing field. Now place your first pea 23 metres away. On this scale, one million miles is represented by 66 cm.

14 Calculate how far away from the beach ball all the other planets should be.

15 Can you fit your model of the solar system onto your playing field?

16 On this scale, other than the sun, how far away would be the nearest star?

5.4 Waves and communication

The expanding universe

Scientists believe that the universe started from a giant explosion called the big bang.

This means that the early universe must have expanded very quickly. Some years ago, scientists wanted to know if the universe was still expanding. This seemed a hard question to answer. Fortunately, a famous scientist called Edwin Hubble came up with a solution.

Hubble and the Doppler effect

Imagine you are standing next to a race track. As a car approaches you, the pitch of the sound from the engine sounds high. But as the car passes, the pitch drops. This is not because the sound from the car really changes, it is because of the Doppler effect.

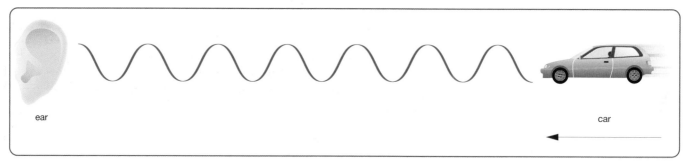

As the car moves towards you, the sound waves get squashed up. They have a shorter wavelength, so the pitch is higher.

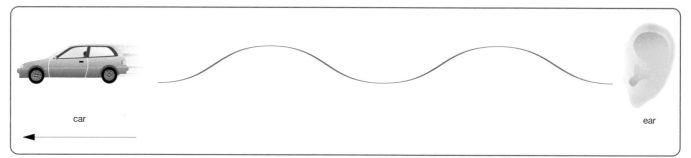

As the car moves away from you, the sound waves get spread out. They have a longer wavelength, so the pitch drops.

Hubble realised the same thing happens with light.

When astronomers examined the light from stars, they discovered that the light was being stretched out. The wavelength of light was longer than it should be and was shifted to the red end of the spectrum. This red shift told astronomers that the universe was still expanding.

Hubble's discovery changed the way that we thought about the universe.

17 Suggest what colour the light would be if the universe was collapsing.

5.4 Waves and communication

Discovering Pluto

Pluto was discovered by Clyde Tombaugh. A famous astronomer called Percival Lowell had predicted the existence of Pluto but had been unable to find it. Tombaugh was hired as a technician at the Lowell Observatory and was asked to find it. He took a series of photographs of where they thought Pluto should be and finally discovered it on the 18 February 1930.

Pluto and its moon Charon.

Pluto – the odd planet

Pluto is an unusual planet. Its discovery changed the way astronomers thought about the solar system.

Pluto's orbit is not in line with the other planets but is tilted at a 19° angle.

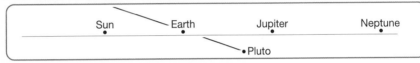

Pluto rotates at exactly the same speed as its moon, Charon, orbits the planet. This means if you stood on Pluto, the moon would always be in the same place.

Pluto's north and south poles almost face east and west when compared to the other planets.

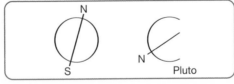

18 What was the name of the person who discovered Pluto?

19 What is the name of Pluto's moon?

20 In what ways is Pluto different from the other planets in the solar system?

21 Pluto is far from the sun. Suggest what it must be like to be on Pluto. Then search the Internet to find out what it is really like on Pluto.

Key facts

Copy and complete the sentences by choosing the correct word from the key words list.

1 The planet that is furthest away from the sun is called _____.

2 All of the planets and the sun belong to the _____ _____.

3 Our _____ is called the Milky Way and includes all the visible stars.

4 Our sun is a type of _____.

5 All of the galaxies are found in the _____.

Key words

galaxy

Pluto

solar system

star

universe

Review questions

1 The table shows how the percentage of oxygen in the atmosphere has changed over time.

Millions of years ago	4000	3000	2000	1000	0
Percentage of oxygen in air	0	1	10	20	21

(a) Plot a graph to show this information. *[3]*

(b) (i) The first plants appeared in the seas on Earth 3000 million years ago. The first sea animals appeared 1000 million years ago. Mark these on your graph. *[1]*

    (ii) Explain why the percentage of oxygen in the atmosphere has changed. *[3]*

2 (a) Draw a box to represent a car engine. Use labelled arrows to show the chemical substances that go in and out. Put a ring around the substances that are harmful to people's health. What risks do these substances cause?

(b) In 2003, the mayor of London introduced a congestion charge for the city of London. All vehicles entering have to pay £8 per day. Many people working in London began to use the tube to get to work instead of using their cars. Write a paragraph to explain the advantages and disadvantages of introducing congestion charges in cities.

3 (a) Three monitoring stations, A, B and C, monitor the same earthquake. A is nearest to the quake, C is furthest away. Draw what the seismographs for p and s waves look like at the three stations. Put labels on the graphs to explain why they are different.

(b) Find out about the Richter and Mercalli scales for earthquakes. Why are two scales used?

4 You are going to do a class talk to explain what changes tectonic plates cause to the Earth's surface.Make a list of photos that you would use to illustrate your talk. Make bullet point notes to go with each photo.

5 Use the formula to answer the following questions:

speed of wave = frequency x wavelength

$$v \quad = \quad f \quad x \quad \lambda$$

(a) A sound wave has a frequency of 500Hz and a wavelength of 0.66 metres. Calculate the speed of sound.

(b) The speed of light is always the same. Suggest what will happen to the frequency (f) as the wavelength (λ) decreases.

6 Science in the workplace

WORKING IN SCIENCE

Contents

Assignments linked to this section:

Using science at work.

Use the following to check your progress:

Unit 3

You will:

- know some names of local, national and international employers who use science see page 308

- know if people employed in science are major, significant or small users of science see page 308

- know companies whose employees use science in different ways see page 308

- be able to discuss why a company chooses its location see page 309

- know about the qualifications and skills needed for various jobs in science see pages 310–311

- know where to look to find out careers information about working in science. see page 311

6.1 Working in science

Colin is a small user of science working locally.

The farrier

Colin is a farrier, which means he shoes horses. He says, 'I left school when I was 16 with five GCSEs. I was lucky to get an apprenticeship with my uncle. He taught me all I know. It took me four years to get qualified.

'I set up my own business then. The job's not just about shoeing horses, though. You've got to be good with people, and strong and fit. My customers often call me, instead of the vet, about their horses' foot injuries and infections.'

Using science in the workplace

Colin works locally – his employer (himself!) lives and works over a small geographical area. His work involves using science – he has to know all about steel and alloys as well as having a good understanding of the medical aspects of caring for horses' feet. He could be considered a small user of science, because it is only one aspect of his job.

Other companies employ people who work nationally (all over the country) or internationally (in several countries). Some employees are major users of science (it is the main thing they do) or significant users of science (it forms a part of their work).

1 Classify these jobs as local, national or international:

    (a) a National Health Service nurse;

    (b) a nurse working for a private residential home;

    (c) a car design engineer working for a company with factories throughout Europe;

    (d) a sales rep selling fertilisers to British farmers for a Dutch firm.

2 What scientific skills and what types of scientific knowledge do these people use in their jobs?

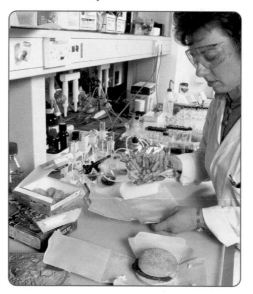

Anita is a food scientist researching new food products for a national company. Anita uses a significant amount of science in her work.

Joe works as a geologist looking into oil field structure for an oil company. He works internationally and is a major user of science at work.

6.1 Working in science

Location and features

Large town/city centre

Good transport links for cars

Parking/traffic problems in some towns

Lots of people (customers and workers)

Other facilities to attract people (cafés, cinemas and so on)

Expensive land and building rents and rates

Difficult access for lorries/heavy vehicles

Town outskirts/industrial estates/smaller villages/beside motorways

Good access for cars and heavy vehicles

Large car parks can be built

Good transport links to where people live

Cheaper land and building rents

Few facilities for people

Some environmental objections to new buildings on fields

Coastal areas

Deep ports can bring in heavy raw materials from overseas

Road/rail access to other areas of the country not always easy

Large, unsightly or hazardous factories sited away from people

Some coastal areas are near lots of people

Land is cheaper than in towns

Some environmental objections to new building on coasts

Why are companies where they are?

> ACTIVITY

If you were starting up your own company, you would have to choose where your new premises were going to be – the best location could make the difference between success and being bankrupt. The table gives information about three types of location.

3 Another type of location for companies is rural areas of the countryside.

    (a)   Make a list of 'features', like the panel on the left, for 'rural areas'.

    (b)   Why do you think it is often difficult for people living in rural areas to find well-paid jobs?

A road map and the Yellow Pages will help you with the next activity.

Employees working for the following companies all use science in their work:

- agricultural chemical manufacturers (make fertilisers and other chemicals for farms);
- beauty salons;
- concrete ready mixed (people who sell ready-to-use concrete);
- dental surgeries (dentists);
- electronic engineering companies (people who manufacture computer systems for businesses);
- livestock breeders and dealers;
- quarries;
- recycling (recyclers of materials like glass, plastics and metals);
- scrap metal merchants (people who collect and sort scrap metal to sell).

4 Choose THREE types of company from this list. Produce a 'wish list' for what each company would want in their ideal location. Share your views with other groups.

5 Look up companies in the Yellow Pages or using www.yell.com on the Internet. Choose one company in your area and explain the advantages of its location.

6.1 Working in science

Different jobs need different levels of qualifications. You can apply for some jobs after leaving school with GCSEs. There are a number of routes you can take after GCSEs. For example, some people study for Advanced level qualifications and some then go to university for three or four years to gain a degree. Some jobs need you to do post-graduate courses after finishing a degree.

However, all jobs need you to continue training and gaining experience as you work. For example, you can get a job working as a car mechanic with GCSEs, but you would not be given responsibility for mending people's cars until you had been fully trained. Only very experienced mechanics could apply for a job as a manager of a car repair garage.

The following pages show some people talking about their work.

Dental nurse

Rosie is a dental nurse.

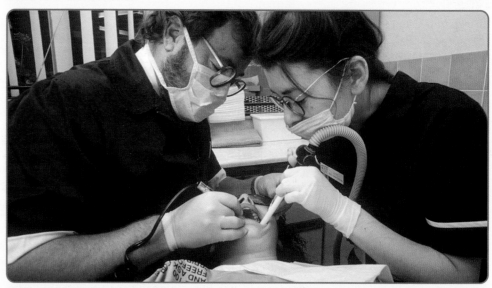

'When I started working here, I used to answer the phone, make appointments and do the filing. After about six months, I started to help in the surgery. We have three surgery rooms. The dentist finishes with a patient in one room and then moves next-door to the next patient. It's my job to tidy the surgery after each patient and get everything ready for the next one. I have to sterilise all the instruments every time they are used. Recently, I have started to help the dentist working on the patients. I hold the suction instruments and record information on the patient's records as the dentist works. I've also been learning to mix fillings and materials for impressions. I'm going to start helping with X-rays next.

'I started working here after I left school with my GCSEs and I studied at our local FE college for my NCDN (National Certificate of Dental Nursing). Most of what I've learned, though, has been by being shown how to do things at work.

'I really enjoy what I do. The dentist said he knew I'd make a good dental nurse when he interviewed me because I was so neat and tidy! I think it's really important to be good with people, too. I try to be as friendly and cheerful as possible. I persuaded the dentist to brighten up the waiting room – the patients seem to take a lot of interest in the new fish tank!'

6.1 Working in science

Science at work (continued)   **CASE STUDY**

Woodland officer

Craig enjoys working outside.

Craig works as a Woodland Officer for the Woodland Trust.

'I left school after doing my A levels and spent three years doing hard physical work pruning and cutting down trees for a local forestry company. I got very strong and fit!

'I decided to study so that I could apply for management work in forestry. I studied for an HND in forestry and then worked for a degree. I was studying part-time while I continued to work, so that I had experience as well as qualifications to offer.

'I look after the woods owned by the Woodland Trust in my area, which cover four counties. Woods need a lot of maintenance. It's my job to organise cutting down trees if they become too overcrowded. We sometimes plant new woods too. We sometimes use chemical pesticides on newly planted trees.

'I need to keep my scientific knowledge up to date to make sure that I am making the best decisions for my woods. The Woodland Trust are keen on protecting the environment. Sometimes I need to ask advice from other people. For example, ecologists give me advice about protecting the animals and plants in our woods.

'If a lot of trees have to be taken down in a wood, we use very big machinery and a lot of people will be involved in the operation. We sometimes even have to build roads into the wood to get the trees out. Measuring and estimating how much timber is in a wood is a specialised skill that I learnt when I was studying. We sell the timber to mills. It goes to make paper and chipboard for the building trade.

'The Woodland Trust is very keen to encourage people to use and take an interest in woods. I make sure the footpaths and facilities are kept in good condition and I go to local shows, do talks and take groups around our woods. The woods provide a good place for walks and leisure.

'I wish I spent all my time in the woods, but I spend about half my time doing paperwork. Working for a big company involves a lot of reading of information, meetings and keeping in contact with other people. I have to keep accounts of all the money spent on maintaining the woods and I also have to work out how much we will need for future work.'

You can find out about other jobs that use science in the *Occupations* book or at www.connexions.gov.uk/occupations/.

Review questions

Note: These activities will help you to gain a wider understanding of science in the workplace before doing your assignment for Unit 3.

1 Look at the case studies in this theme.

'Services' means how a person's work helps the public.

'Products' are what a company makes to sell.

Make a copy of the table below and fill it in for each person.

Case study	Qualifications and training	Science skills used at work	Services given	Products made
Dental nurse				
Woodland officer				

2 Use a copy of the *Occupations* book to find out about the following jobs:

- dental hygienist
- electrician (working in maintenance and servicing)
- sound technician
- veterinary surgeon (a 'vet').

(a) Fill in a copy of this table to show information about the jobs.

Name of job	Qualifications needed to start	Do you need experience/ further training?	Example of daily task that uses science

(b) Which of these jobs can you start to do as soon as you have the necessary qualifications? Which jobs do people need experience or further training to do?

(c) What advice would you give Rosie (the dental nurse in the case study) if she wanted to be a dental hygienist?

(d) Choose ONE of these jobs (or you could choose a job you are interested in doing yourself).

   (i) What science is involved in the work?

   (ii) Make a 'diary' for a Day in the Life article for a magazine about a person doing the job.

3 Look back through the case studies throughout the whole textbook. Find some examples of people at work.

Put yourself in the position of ONE person from the case studies. Think about what your CV must have looked like when you applied for your job. Write a short CV showing your qualifications, training and experience. (The *Occupations* book might help here.) Write a paragraph explaining what skills you have to fit the job.

4 Interview a member of your family or a friend who works in a job using science, for example, anyone handling food, hairdressing, mechanics or engineering and so on. Find out:

(a) about the science they use in their work;

(b) how health and safety affects their work;

(c) why their company is located where it is;

(d) if their employer is local, national or international.

1 The periodic table

Group								
I	II		III	IV	V	VI	VII	0

Key

atomic number — 3
Li
Lithium
relative atomic mass — 7

metals

non-metals

APPENDIX 2/3

2 Some elements and their symbols

You need to know the chemical symbols for the following elements and be able to classify them as metals or non-metals:

Metals		Non-metals	
Element	Chemical symbol	Element	Chemical symbol
Aluminium	Al	Bromine	Br
Barium	Ba	Carbon	C
Calcium	Ca	Chlorine	Cl
Iron	Fe	Fluorine	F
Lead	Pb	Hydrogen	H
Magnesium	Mg	Nitrogen	N
Potassium	K	Oxygen	O
Silver	Ag	Phosphorus	P
Sodium	Na	Silicon	Si
Zinc	Zn	Sulphur	S

3 Some compounds and their formulae

You need to know the names and formulae of the following chemical compounds:

Compound	Formula	Compound	Formula
Ammonia	NH_3	Barium chloride	$BaCl_2$
Carbon dioxide	CO_2	Sodium chloride	$NaCl$
Methane	CH_4	Calcium carbonate	$CaCO_3$
Water	H_2O	Copper carbonate	$CuCO_3$
Hydrochloric acid	HCl	Sodium carbonate	Na_2CO_3
Sulphuric acid	H_2SO_4	Potassium nitrate	KNO_3
Calcium oxide	CaO	Silver nitrate	$AgNO_3$
Iron oxide	Fe_2O_3	Barium sulphate	$BaSO_4$
Lead oxide	PbO	Copper sulphate	$CuSO_4$
Sodium hydroxide	$NaOH$	Sodium sulphate	Na_2SO_4

4 Properties of materials

Material	Resistance of a 1 metre wire with 1mm diameter, in ohm (Ω)	Thermal conductivity, in watt per metre per degree Celsius (W m^{-1} °C^{-1})	Density in kilogram per cubic metre (kg m^{-3})
aluminium	0.031	238	2700
constantan	0.576	22	8900
copper	0.020	385	8940
iron	0.113	80	7860
lead	0.242	38	11350
mild steel	0.216	60	7700
tin	0.146	64	7280
concrete	very high	1.45	2300
sheet glass	very high		2460
nylon	very high	0.25	1130
poly(ethene) (low density)	very high	0.33	920
poly(ethene) (high density)	very high	0.5	960
water		0.6	1000

5 Units of the international system

Quantity	Unit	Abbreviation
chemical quantity	mole	mol
current	ampere	amp or A
density	kilogram per cubic metre	kg m^{-3}
distance and length	metre	m
energy and work	joule	J
force	newton	N
power	watt	W
resistance	ohm	Ω
temperature	degree Celsius*	°C
time	second	s
voltage	volt	V
volume	cubic metre	m^3

* The international unit is the kelvin (K), but °C is an acceptable alternative for everyday use.

Index

Page numbers in blue show the page on which the word is explained.

The Advertising Archives p.136

Alamy pp.244 (Arcaid Ed), 277 (bottom) (Brian Crossley)

Alan Thomas pp.1, 4 (top), 6, 14, 34, 46, 68, 96, 169, 196, 207, 209, 214, 215, 217 (bottom), 277 (top right), 278, 281

Andrew Whitehead pp.238, 243

Ann Tiernan p.217 (top)

Boots PLC p.173

Bureau Veritas p.291

Byron Dawson pp.7, 8 (top), 9, 12, 16, 17, 82 (top), 86 (top), 94, 97, 98, 115, 118, 119, 134, 135, 137, 143, 301 (top right), 302 (right)

Colin Bell pp.40 (top), 41 (top), 42, 52, 54, 55

Combined Heating & Power Association pp.228, 233

Corbis pp.29 (William Taufic), 30 (Kelly-Mooney Photography), 93 (Dave Bartruff), 141 (Jeffrey L.Rotman), 146 (left) (Bettmann), 153 (Ariel Skelley), 156 (Philippe Eranian), 162 (Ed Young), 195 (Owen Franken), 199 (Richard T. Nowitz), 206 (Paul A Souders), 210 (Charles E. Rotkin), 212 (Sotheby's), 234 (bottom) (Royalty Free), 237 (Gabe Palmer), 266 (Chuck Savage), 286 (Kevin Schafer), 288 (Roy Morsch), 290 (right) (Will & Deni McIntyre), 295 (Tom Wagner), 297 (Craig Lovell), 301 (bottom right) (Masahiro Morsch), 305 (left) (Bettmann), 307 (Tom Stewart), 308 (top) (Kit Houghton),

Corel pp.39, 51, 63, 72, 73 (right), 145, 218

Department of Transport p.257

DIY Photolibrary p.223 (left)

Ford pp.252 (John Moffat), 253

Getty Images pp.73 (left) (Brian Brown), 132 (Adam Smith), 150 (Janet Gill), 163 (Harry Sieplinga/HMS Images), 293 (Royalty Free), 301 (top left) (Royalty Free), 301 (bottom middle) (Mark Harwood)

Joanne Mitchell p.292 (top)

John Birdsall Social Issues Photo Library p.128

King Edward pp.248, 251

Marcus Harper p.75

Masterfile pp.244 (Robert George Young), 267 (R. Ian Lloyd), 274 (Mike Dobel)

Oxford Scientific Film pp.60, 64, 70

Patterdale Mountain Rescue Team p.131

Philip Harris Photography p.37

Photodisc pp.107, 122, 124

Photofusion pp.149 (Paul Baldesare), 155 (Dorothy Burrows), 159 (Trevor Perry), 174 (Leslie Garland), 178 (Stan Gamester)